new 17.50
S0-AVQ-732
CASTLE DOWNS

MINERALS AND GEMS:

A Color Treasury for Collectors
and Guide to Hunting Locations

A COLOR TREASURY
FOR COLLECTORS
AND GUIDE TO
HUNTING LOCATIONS

MINERALS AND GEMS

Russell P. MacFall

THOMAS Y. CROWELL COMPANY
New York / Established 1834

Copyright © 1975 by Thomas Y. Crowell Company, Inc.
Part III copyright © 1975 by Russell P. MacFall
Photographs and line drawings copyright © 1973 by Fratelli Fabbri Editori
Maps copyright © 1975 by Russell P. MacFall
All rights reserved. Except for use in a review, the reproduction or utilization of this work in any form or by any electronic, mechanical, or other means, now known or hereafter invented, including xerography, photocopying, and recording, and in any information storage and retrieval system is forbidden without the written permission of the publisher. Published simultaneously in Canada by Fitzhenry & Whiteside Limited, Toronto.

Designed by S. S. Drate

Manufactured in the United States of America

Library of Congress Cataloging in Publication Data
Main entry under title:

Minerals and gems.

Bibliography: p.
Includes index.
1. Mineralogy. 2. Mineralogy—Collectors and collecting—U.S. I. MacFall, Russell P., ed.
II. Title.
QE363.2.G8313 549 74-28082
ISBN 0-690-00687-X
1 2 3 4 5 6 7 8 9 10

Photo credits appear on page 233.
Pages 1–128 of this edition are based on *Guida ai Minerali* by Ambrogio Del Caldo, Cesarina Moro, Carlo Maria Gramaccioli, Matteo Boscardin, published in Italy in 1973 by Fratelli Fabbri Editori.

New material has been added for this American edition.

Preface

Love of beautiful gems and minerals knows no boundaries of nation or continent. Collectors of these aristocrats of the mineral kingdom are numbered in the tens of thousands in the United States, and they have their counterparts in Europe and the other continents. Such a global interest is reflected in the book which you are about to read and use. First published with its superb color illustrations in Italy in the language of that country, it proved to be so well related to the needs and interests of American collectors that it has been translated and adapted with American examples to a new audience.

In his preface to the Italian edition, Vincenzo de Michele, curator of mineralogy at the City Museum of Natural History in Milan, wrote:

"In the last few years, mineral collecting has become widespread here in Italy, as well as in the rest of Europe and America. Whether this is due to the heightened awareness of natural beauties, the improvement in standard of living, or an increase in leisure time we can leave to the sociologists to decide.

"Not everyone takes up rock hunting because of an interest in mineralogy. There's the opportunity to travel, to be outdoors in places . . . away from ribbons of concrete. There's the triumph that comes when, after hours of hammering, a resistant rock splits just the way you want it to. And in the end there's the intellectual stimulation that comes from studying your specimens . . . and from discussions with other collectors."

Certainly Curator de Michele's words apply as well to those who read this book in English as they do to the audience he was addressing in his own country.

The first section of the book, which discusses field trips and preparation of specimens, is the work of Ambrogio Del Caldo, a graduate engineer, and Professor Cesarina Moro, with adaptations for American conditions and with American examples. Professor Carlo Maria Gramaccioli, a crystallographer, prepared the section on identification of gems and minerals. Other important people who helped bring this book to its American public are Edwin Greene, the translator, who ably mastered the problems presented by an often technical text, and Don Pitcher, who meticulously provided the cartography.

The third part of the Italian work, on collecting locations, has been replaced by a fresh and up-to-the-minute description of how to reach hundreds of gem collecting locations in the United States, Canada, and Mexico. It is the work of Russell P. MacFall, author of the *Gem Hunter's Guide,* who is the editor and adapter of this translation.

The American publishers echo Curator de Michele's expressed hope that "this manual will be an invaluable tool for turning out well-grounded, competent collectors," and that readers will also enjoy the beauty of the illustrations while finding them useful in identification of the gems and minerals they seek.

Contents

PART I

FIELD TRIPS AND PREPARATION OF SPECIMENS

PART II
HOW TO RECOGNIZE MINERALS

Part I

FIELD TRIPS AND PREPARING SPECIMENS

The search for minerals often leads the collector to delightful spots where he can enjoy exercise and his hobby in the open air. This shows the entrance to an old shaft of the ferromanganese lode at Praborna, Saint Marcel (Val d'Aosta), southeast of Aosta in the extreme northwest part of Italy.

1

EQUIPMENT AND PREPARATION FOR THE HUNT

It is impossible to enjoy all the pleasures of mineralogy, even at the amateur or hobby level, without having a collection of minerals.

Splendid collections can be found in museums of natural history and in the research laboratories of chemical and mineral companies. But those collections aren't accessible to everyone, and even when they are, the curators generally don't permit specimens to be touched and examined closely without special permission. It is therefore a great satisfaction to have a collection of one's own, built up by one's own efforts, piece by piece. The pursuit is always interesting, and it can be truly rewarding whether you hunt minerals only occasionally or build up a collection systematically.

The first step is to obtain the necessary equipment, and then learn how to choose itineraries, how minerals are sought, how specimens are prepared, and how to organize a personal collection.

INDISPENSABLE EQUIPMENT FOR THE SEARCH

Equipment for hunting and collecting minerals should be simple, light, and not bulky. This will make the trip easier and more fun. The tools you will need are:

A crack hammer, like a small sledge, weighing about two pounds, with a handle about a foot long. This is used for working on solid rock.

A prospector's pick with a point on one end and a square hammerhead on the other. It is useful for raking gravel, poking about in rubble, and working on brittle rock. The handle, about a foot long, allows this tool to be used also as a pickax.

Two chisels, one with a four-sided point, and the other with a flat cutting edge as thick as your thumb and about eight inches long. These are needed to split layers of rock, remove crystal cavities from cliffs, and trim specimens to the desired shape.

A strong pocketknife, for freeing specimens from mud or soft incrustations, for testing hardness, for locating nodules embedded in rocks, and for many other purposes.

A little magnet is useful for identifying magnetic material and for removing it from sand. Get the now-common ALNICO kind, or something similar, such as is used in toys, auto accessories, and many industrial applications.

A lens of 4 or 5 power is often needed. With a little practice you'll be able to make out details that escape the naked eye. There is no need to buy a costly or powerful one. A satisfactory lens can be bought in an optical shop or department store.

Be sure to wear *safety glasses or goggles;* they are indispensable to protect the eyes when working on rocks. Such glasses are available in many shapes, but the ordinary clear welders' glasses are inexpensive and they also shield the corners of the eyes from flying chips.

SUPPLIES EASY TO OBTAIN

Hammers, chisels, picks, and magnets can be bought in any large hardware store or from mail order company catalogs. Take the advice of experienced friends. Buying cheap things that won't last is no economy. Sometimes it's worth spending a little extra. For example, dealers in minerals and mineralogical supplies offer chisels covered with nylon. They are safer and more comfortable to use, which warrants the additional price.

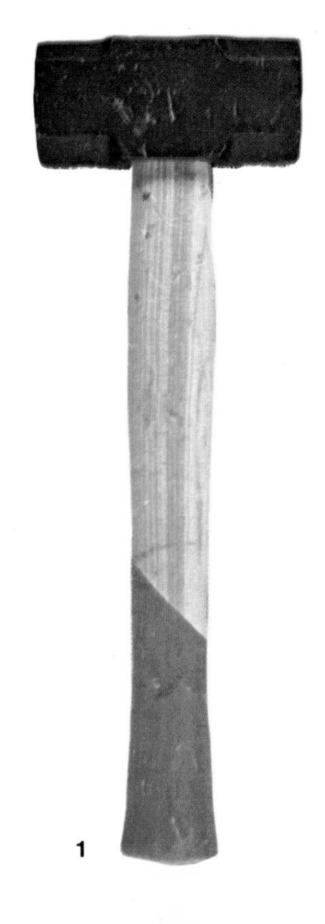

1

EQUIPMENT LESS FREQUENTLY USED

Hammers that weigh more than five pounds, pickaxes, long chisels, and crowbars are needed only for big excavations, smashing operations, and breaking down banks. A small shovel, much like the army trenching tool, or spade is often needed to remove soil or gravel, and a sieve is called for when examining gravel in stream beds.

EQUIPMENT FOR EXPERTS ONLY

It's best to leave the use of climbing ropes and other mountaineering equipment to experts. Better to forget a specimen embedded in a high bank rather than to risk one's neck. The experienced collector knows that in picking around carefully among debris fallen from the same bank, he may come across an excellent specimen of the same material.

A safety helmet is unnecessary in open fieldwork. But both the law and common sense dictate that one be worn in quarries or when collecting near unstable rock walls, where deadly boulders

In your kit these implements should not be lacking: **1** A small sledge weighing about two pounds; **2** a prospector's pick; **3** chisels: one with a flat tip and one with a pointed tip; **4** a lens with a flashlight attachment; **5** a pair of goggles to protect the eyes from flying splinters.

2

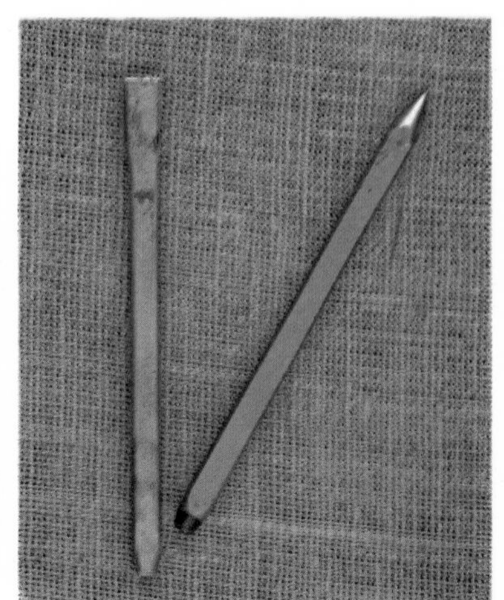

3

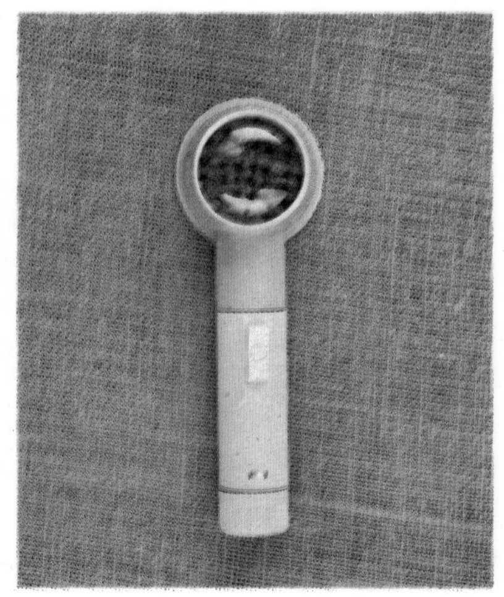

4

5

could come hurtling down without warning. Beware of shafts and tunnels, especially in abandoned mines; they present mortal dangers. If you get permission to visit such a place, it is advisable to hire a guide who will provide lights and other needed equipment.

CLOTHING, KNAPSACK, ACCESSORIES

Ordinary mountaineering garb is good: cotton slacks, wool socks, flannel shirt, light vest, pullover or windbreaker, boots or shoes with thick rubber soles, and old leather gloves. For a knapsack you can use a mountaineering bag or a military bag; it should be equipped with a frame to make it hug the back.

Put into the automobile a piece of soap, and fresh socks and extra shoes, so that you can change into dry ones if those you're wearing get soaked and muddied during the expedition. Also put some cardboard boxes and wooden fruit crates into the car, to be used in packing delicate specimens. Plastic bags, like those sold in the supermarket, can come in handy for carrying small amounts of material. Include some bright-colored scraps of paper or plastic. You will find them remarkably helpful in identifying and locating the many small piles of materials that you'll collect. These markers will make it less troublesome to select and pack your specimens properly.

A Thermos bottle, some string, and a roll of adhesive tape complete the list of indispensables. The only other thing needed is a keen desire for a long tramp.

THE MOST FAVORABLE CONDITIONS

The best time for hunting minerals is spring or fall. Summer is recommended for trips to the high mountains, when the heat makes collecting in caves and rock beds on the lower hillsides decidedly uncomfortable in some parts of the land. In winter, when days are short and cold, snow and mud rule out collecting in many areas. Use common sense, logic, and friendly advice in deciding on time and place. Finally, don't undertake a strenuous field trip unless you're in excellent physical condition.

PRELIMINARY PREPARATIONS

A collecting trip should be preceded by adequate preparation to insure the best results. Plan your trip with the friends who will make up the party. Among them, there may be one who is familiar with the area you're planning to visit and who can give sound advice as to the best trails, the requisite equipment, and the best techniques to be used. Lacking such guidance, you can prepare for the trip by studying the route planned and by visiting a museum or private collection to examine specimens of minerals you hope to come across. This will make recognition of minerals in the field easier for you. If you plan to visit an operating quarry or mine where a permit is required, make the necessary arrangements in advance. This will spare you disappointment and disagreeable arguments with company personnel, bound by regulations.

AIDS FOR HUNTING AND COLLECTING

Itineraries are essential; they provide indispensable help on every field trip. The back of this book can be used as a source for making up itineraries for prospecting in the United States, Canada, and Mexico. However, since there's a little of the pioneer spirit left in most of us, stray a bit from the route now and then and perhaps discover something that's been overlooked. Your experiences and those of your friends may well bring important new data to light.

Unfortunately, the appearance of a place can change rapidly, especially when it comes to quarries and road construction. To avoid disappointment, go over your route plan carefully, verifying locations where possible. It's a good idea to jot down your itinerary on small file cards and keep them in your pocket for convenient reference during the trip. Topographic maps are the most useful source of information. Those for the United States are published by the U.S. Geological Survey and for areas east of the Mississippi river can be ordered from the U.S. Geological Survey's Distribution Branch, 1200 S. Eads Street, Arlington, Virginia 22202. Those for areas west of the Mississippi river can be ordered from the Distribution Center, Geological Survey, Federal Center, Denver, Colorado 80225. Index sheets from which the precise maps needed can be chosen are provided

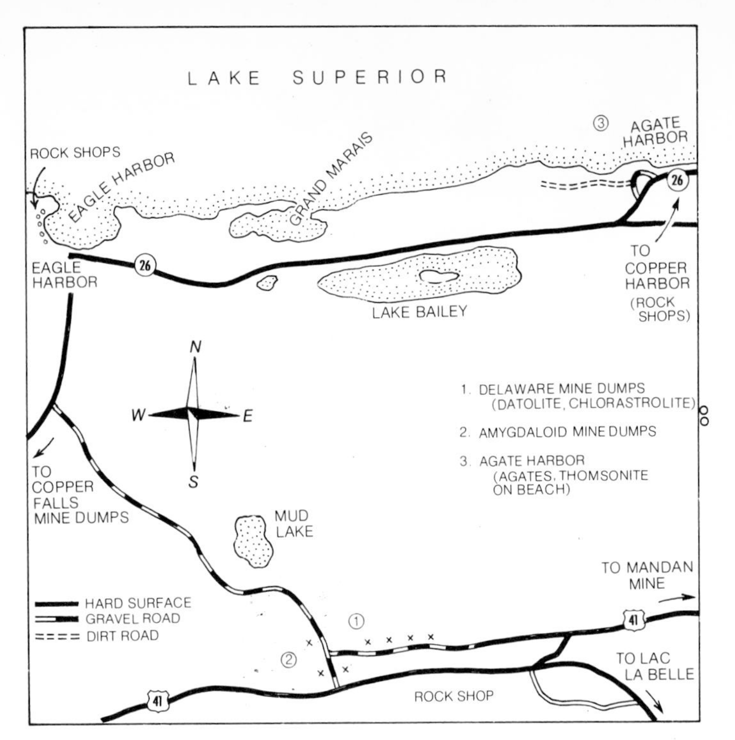

Field drawing to locate a collecting area, describe the condition of the roads, and mark out three locations where material has been found. It is based on the accompanying topographic map, road maps, and collecting experience. For those who have poor collecting luck, it also shows where they may be able to buy specimens.

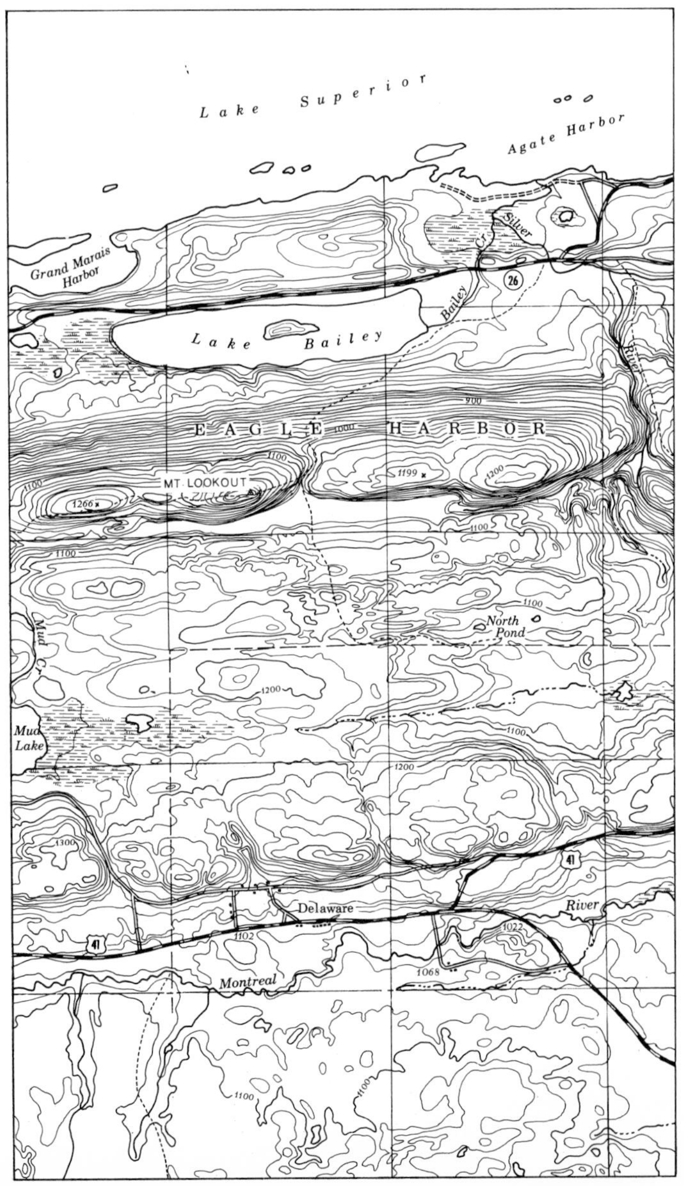

Part of the U.S. Geological Survey topographic map of the Delaware quadrangle of Keweenaw County, Michigan. This is an example of the more picturesque of two types of these maps in that it is drawn to give a three-dimensional effect. Such maps are too large to carry into the field conveniently, so that a field map, such as the accompanying one, is made to embody the essential information.

free on inquiry. The sheets also list map dealers in some major cities who stock topographic maps. Maps of national forests can be obtained from the U.S. Forest Service, Washington, D.C. 20415. Maps for Canada are obtainable from the Geological Survey of Canada, Ottawa, Ontario. This agency also publishes a series of paperback books describing collecting localities in detail.

Road maps issued by gasoline companies are also indispensable guides, because they not only record existing roads but also describe their condition. They are of a convenient size to carry in the pocket. Use these for routings, and the topographic maps for detailed information.

FIRST AID

While serious accidents don't often occur on field trips, mishaps such as scratches and bruises are all part of the day's work. One of the party should carry a first aid kit to patch up small cuts that are bound to be incurred in working around rocks.

Snakes are a different matter: take every possible precaution to avoid them. Move rocks or boulders with a pick or a long stick, not with the hands. Wear long trousers, stout shoes or boots, wool socks, and leather gloves. It's a good idea to add snakebite antivenom and adhesive strips to the first aid kit. Finally, antitetanus shots are recommended. They will provide effective immunity for several years.

ORGANIZING THE BACKPACK

Even though you take along only essentials, your pack can become burdensome if your gear isn't properly stowed in it. If the pack hasn't a frame to make it hug your back, be sure to line it with corrugated cardboard where it hits your ribs; then stuff in a layer of newspaper, covered with a sheet of plastic. In packing, wrap small objects and knives in cloth and stow them in the side pockets. Wrap the head of your hammer in a cloth and place it in the pack head down. The handle should stick out of the opening so that you can tie it in place with the cord that closes the bag. Tuck a sweater and a windbreaker (both indispensable) under the flap closure. Be sure to take along a stout cord; before descending a steep incline, use it to tie your backpack snugly around your waist to avoid having your ribs bruised and bumped when the going gets rough.

KEEP YOUR EYES OPEN

The beginner often is greatly impressed by the ease and speed with which his friend or guide spots tiny bits of minerals (even when they're quite far off) that he doesn't see at all. There's no magic in this. The ability to find minerals grows with training, experience, and careful observation of the rocks and formations associated with the presence of the mineral or gem being sought. A list of clues that might lead to a discovery would be too extensive to give here, but a few examples can be cited.

Beds of limestone and dolomite, the principal constituents of the exposed rocks of the midwestern United States, often contain pockets of calcite or other carbonate minerals. These must be discovered by locating the porous layers in a quarry or other exposure and following them along the rock wall. Likewise, streams in limestone areas may cut through strata filled with geodes lined with glittering calcite or quartz. Often these can be found where they have been washed into the stream itself.

Southwestern Maine, around the town of Paris, and the rugged area north and east of San Diego, California, have long astonished collectors with magnificent crystals of tourmaline, pink beryl, and other gem minerals. These occur in a coarse-grained granite known as pegmatite. Prospectors look for pieces of quartz and mica, then try to trace the long narrow pegmatite bodies, called dikes, looking for stains or changes in the pattern of the quartz and feldspar mass that would lead to a pocket of crystals. North Carolina and the Black Hills of South Dakota are also regions attractive for rose quartz and other minerals found in pegmatites.

Such prospecting is similar to the search for iron-stained quartz that may betray a gold deposit or the green stains of copper minerals that led to rich mines in Arizona and Montana.

(Left) Quarry in Val di Serra, Trentino, Italy. On the front of the rock surface, a dark patch is plainly visible against the lighter background. This is basalt imbedded in a mass of dolomite and indicates the presence of interesting minerals such as magnesium hydroxide (brucite), basic magnesium carbonate (hydromagnesite), and zeolites. These have been formed by contact between the incandescent basalt and dolomite.

(Below) Quarry in Val Bragaglia, Sondrio, Italy. The white veins in the rock are signs of minerals. Shown here are pegmatite and veins of quartz which often indicate the presence of beryl, tourmaline, rutile, titanite, apatite, and other minerals.

2

PLACES TO SEARCH

From time immemorial, man has put stone to use in every way he could think of. With increasing technical skill, mining and shaping of minerals became increasingly important. As time went on, man ventured underground to hunt for veins of minerals; these he transformed into metals for making tools and, unhappily, weapons of war. He also practically tore the heart out of mountains to get stones for his temples, pyramids, and obelisks. As in the past, but now with radically different techniques and procedures, mining is carried on in the open and underground in quarries and mines.

ACTIVE MINES AND QUARRIES

Since working mines and quarries are traditionally the places to find minerals, you can be confident of a rich harvest if you work in their vicinity. Ore extraction goes on so rapidly that there's always a fresh pile of rocks to go through. The quantity and quality of what you find will vary with each mine. Extraction techniques differ as they are adapted to the natural form of the mineral being mined. The unwanted material extracted along with the mineral being sought is often thrown to one side. Many modern underground mines do not bring waste rock to the surface, and what they do bring up is finely ground to extract the metal or other valuable constituent. But most old mines have left behind extensive dumps. Notable are those in the upper peninsula of Michigan, where much of the world's copper was produced in the last century. Here are hundreds of prospect piles or massive waste rock piles containing pieces of copper, sometimes bits of native silver, zeolite, calcite, and quartz crystals, and masses of green-stained rock that is the raw material for unique bookends. Many collectors have searched such dumps with metal-detecting equipment and have now and then been richly rewarded. Most of the mine entrances themselves have been closed by waste rock bulldozed into the shafts so that the mines would no longer be deathtraps for humans or animals.

The itineraries that you will surely study before setting out on a trip will help you to formulate a precise program and will suggest suitable equipment and techniques. Following are some general suggestions for finding specimens once you have reached the mine or quarry:

In quarries, examine the roadways, mine approaches, and the areas from which material has recently been taken as well as the dump itself. By doing this, you can pick up small bits of whatever material is being quarried. Then look at the rock walls to see if there are any signs of interesting minerals.

If the mine owners permit, examine the area in front of the mine shaft and the ore in the trucks. In

QUARRIES AND MINES

When you see the words *quarry* and *mine,* you expect the former to refer to digging in the open and the latter to digging underground. In fact, there is also a difference between the two based on the nature of the mineral being mined. Metal-bearing ores, materials for refractories, and coal are *mined.* Marble and ornamental stones used in building are *quarried;* sand and gravel are dug from pits. There are both subterranean mines with shafts and tunnels and surface mines.

The largest mines in the United States are open pits, such as the enormous copper mine at Bingham Canyon, Utah, although here some tunnels, known to miners as drifts, have been dug to facilitate the operation. Both underground and open pit methods have been used in the copper mines at Globe and Bisbee, Arizona, but the older mines in that state were underground. At the other great copper center, Butte, Montana, former underground mines have been opened to the sky and worked as open pits.

Coal mines at one time were almost entirely underground, with the shafts reaching down to drifts along which the coal was broken out and brought to the shaft to be hoisted to the surface. With the development of gigantic earth-moving machines, more and more coal now comes from strip mines, where the topsoil is stripped off to bare the coal seams.

Marble, granite, and slate are usually produced from open quarries, even though much overburden or inferior-quality rock must be removed to expose the commercial product. In the waste dumps, minerals may often be won by patient search.

an open pit, you may be working near unstable rock walls, where a hard hat must be worn and extreme care should be taken not to cause a rock fall. Rarely are collectors allowed to get near the mining machinery or the miners at work. Keep away from any ponds in the area where mud has been discharged as a result of ore processing. There might be pockets of quicksand in this mud. In combing through dumps, be sure to work from the top toward the bottom so that you can be seen by the mine workers. If you're out of sight, you are in considerable danger of being buried by a fresh discharge of waste rock.

Don't try to get permission to go down into a mine shaft. It will always be refused, and with good reason. These working shafts are only a few feet square, badly lit, and often slimy. There isn't much to be found, so there's no point in running a useless risk, especially with plenty of material out in the open, already broken into conveniently small pieces.

Miners and foremen are friendly people, usually generous with help and advice. Don't get in their way, or annoy them by wandering around aimlessly. Do what they ask and don't attempt anything more than they have given you permission to do. When you leave, thank them, and, if it seems appropriate, give them a present, such as a piece of handmade jewelry.

Make sure to keep your mineral piles and baggage a good distance from where the men are working. Otherwise, everything might accidentally be swept away by a truck or bulldozer.

You will note that the areas around the mine or quarry are neat and orderly, although at first they may not seem so. So don't scratch around piles like a chicken, scattering material in all directions. Spend a little time cleaning up before you leave. This will assure a favorable reception on some future occasion and give you a reputation for courtesy.

ABANDONED QUARRIES AND MINES

Not infrequently, you may read about or hear about the marvelous things to be found in such-

WORKING MINES

Surface mines:

1 View of a mine at Bingham Canyon, Utah.

2 Strip coal mine near Gillette, Wyoming.

Underground mines:

3 Mine portal at Fenice Capanne, Grosseto, south of Florence, Italy.

3

1

2

4 Red granite quarry at Oltrefiume, Baveno, Italy.

5 Crushed stone quarry near Trento, near the Swiss border.

6 Basalt quarry near Altavilla, Vicenza, northwest of Padua, Italy.

5

4

6

ABANDONED QUARRIES AND MINES

1 Dumps of abandoned Brosso mine (Turin, Italy).
2 One end of canyon, with the crumbled front part of a tunnel, in an antimony mine near Siena, Italy.
3 Crushed stone quarry near Cerezzola, Reggio nell'Emilia, west of Bologna, Italy.

4 Dumps and ruined bits of old construction in a manganese mine near Praborna (Aosta), Italy.

5 High up there are old tunnels, one of which can be seen in the picture. Minerals can be found in the dumps or in the outcroppings near the tunnels.

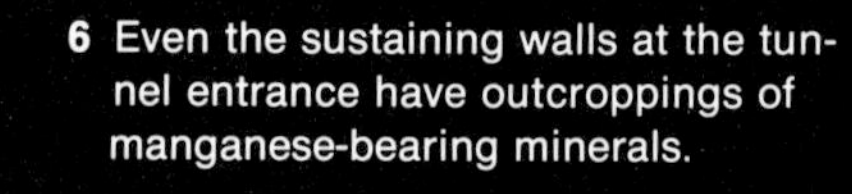

6 Even the sustaining walls at the tunnel entrance have outcroppings of manganese-bearing minerals.

and-such quarry or mine. On reaching the place, you find that it has been turned into a sordid, smelly town dump, the shafts closed or blocked by slides, and the rock wall so covered with thorny vegetation that there is nothing left.

Quarries and mines often have a short operating life; nevertheless, an old lead may turn out to be a good one. True, the showy specimens you had hoped to find may be gone, but your attention may be drawn to inconspicuous pieces that otherwise would never have been noticed. This may lead to interesting discoveries. The heavy gray lumps that the gold seekers at Leadville, Colorado, discarded were later recognized as the ore that made Leadville one of the world's silver bonanzas.

Minerals long exposed to weathering take on a patina or coloration which hides their true nature and can fool the collector. Mosses, roots, lichens, and soil fill small depressions in the rock and conceal crystals embedded there. Usually these changes are superficial. If they are broken out carefully, washed, and brushed, rocks from such places often yield good specimens. Handle them carefully, because such specimens may be something new, interesting, and quite rare. Excavation alters the natural conditions under which the minerals were formed and held in balance, allowing new minerals to form with the passage of time. These may be on the dumps or near old mine workings.

An advantage of prospecting in abandoned places is that usually there is no need for permits, no worrying about tidying up the site. But resist the temptation to go nosing into old tunnels, and never, for any reason, venture underground. Hidden pits, crumbling rocks, or other unforeseen dangers could injure or kill you. While in the open, watch out for possible landslides, precariously balanced rocks, and shafts and excavations hidden by underbrush.

IMMOVABLE ROCK MASSES

Minerals, of course, are found not only in quarries and mines but also in cliffs, peaks, and other rock masses, as well as on the ground. Rock masses usually refer to formations not yet mined. But minerals which might otherwise be hard to get are often made fairly accessible by weathering, espe-

ROCKS AND MINERALS

A close look at a solid fragment taken from the earth's crust will often reveal that it's made up of varicolored particles. This isn't a single mineral, but a heterogeneous entity composed of minerals held together in a compact mass. This conglomeration of minerals is technically known as *rock,* which differs from a true *mineral* in that the latter is homogeneous, having essentially identical characteristics at every point.

Scientific terminology aims at precision and avoids general terms like *pebble* or *stone*.

There are, however, rocks made up of only one mineral, as for instance, marble and limestone, both of which are essentially formed of calcium carbonate. So actually rocks can be one mineral or a combination of minerals. They are not only those hard, solid substances usually denoted by the word *rock,* but sometimes rather loose combinations of materials, like sand from riverbeds or beaches. Take a close look at a fragment of Rutland, Vermont, marble. Notice the clear pure color, the granulation, and the way it sparkles in the light. We could call this fragment calcium carbonate or marble. Both terms are correct.

The term *calcium carbonate* might also be used for a fragment of opaque grayish limestone, likewise formed of this mineral. In describing the one fragment as marble you are referring to a rock which not only is calcium carbonate, but which was formed in a special way. So marble is distinguished from other calcium structures not only by appearance, but by its unique origin. To sum up: rock is characterized not only by its mineral composition but also by the natural phenomena that created it.

cially thawing and freezing, and other natural action. The building of roads, tunnels, and other constructions may also leave material easily available to the collector.

Prospecting in heaps left over from construction work isn't much different from working in quarries. Prospecting a living rock mass can be tiring and not very fruitful, but it can yield other satisfactions. You are bound to discover marvelous walks in beautiful mountain country, filled with delightful views, and there is always the chance of discovering some unreported and desirable mineral.

Rock masses are not usually in easily accessible places. They vary widely in appearance and are often hidden by vegetation, debris, or surface discoloration. To locate and identify them requires either a detailed itinerary or perhaps the help of an experienced guide. When you reach your destination, you may find nothing because a landmark is hidden by overgrowth, or, as might happen on the edge of glaciers or gravel pits, no landmarks remain. Moss growth, loam deposits, or oxidation may have changed the rock color into something different from what had been expected. Carefully examine dry walls enclosing farms, all rock outcroppings, gravel, landslides, fallen boulders, and any small bits of rock freshly fallen from the main rock mass. Inspect beds of streams, brush aside scrub and underbrush, and see what may lie hidden underneath.

WHEN AND HOW TO GO

In many climates the best season to prospect on a mountain side is in the spring, when snow and ice have disappeared. Freezing and thawing will have caused rock falls, so that a search at the foot of the mountain may disclose plenty of untouched material and save a difficult, possibly dangerous, climb. The Toal Canyons, cut into the Monzoni Mountains in the Trentino in Italy, illustrate this. Climbing there is difficult and dangerous, except in the spring. At that season a great variety of splendid minerals can be obtained.

Nowadays, roads, aerial railways, and chair lifts have made access much easier to many spots high in the mountains. Of course, the climb always seems endless with a pack on your back, and so does the return trip to the car. It's wise, therefore, to lighten the load by carrying only what is indispensable and bringing home only the most interesting specimens.

Since mountain climbing is always tiring, it is well to alternate short periods of climbing with spells of rest. When tired, stop and rest. Suck on sweets for a quick pick-me-up and drink as little liquid as possible. Remember that the descent can be more tiring than the climb, so don't overload your knapsack, and do put everything back in its proper place to equalize the load on the way down.

When it's possible to reach a rock cliff or a peak by car, the collector will be tempted to overload his pack. Resist the temptation; remember that too heavy a load can exhaust you. It's impossible to estimate in advance the weight of the rocks that may be found on the trip, so travel light. Overestimating one's strength can lead to the most unpleasant consequences. If, by good fortune, the rock mass at the collecting site has had a road cut through it, be careful not to litter the sides of the road with material you have loosened. Before leaving, clear the gutter and the roadbed of stray fragments. And don't fail to examine the material removed by the road workers; this may be scattered at the entrance to the cut or near it. It could contain excellent specimens.

AREAS OF LOOSE ROCK

Sand, gravel, and moraine materials are loose, noncoherent rocks created by the destruction of solid rocks that have been crushed, pounded, and transported by water, wind, or volcanic action. The sand in streams may come from rocks that were originally formed many miles away.

The Saint Peter's sandstone that underlies much of the midwestern United States is believed to have been transported as beach sands by ancient seas from mountains that once stood off the eastern coast. Most of this fertile land around the Great Lakes is buried deep with soil, pebbles, and boulders that were brought by glaciers a thousand or more miles from what is now Canada. In southern Oregon, hundreds of square miles are littered with fragments of lava and ash ejected by the gigantic explosion that blew off the top of an ancient volcano and created beautiful Crater Lake.

Such states as Nebraska and Kansas—the High Plains—owe their fertile soil to erosion of the pred-

(Above) Toal Canyons in the Monzoni mountains in the Trentino Alps. Excellent minerals can be found here.

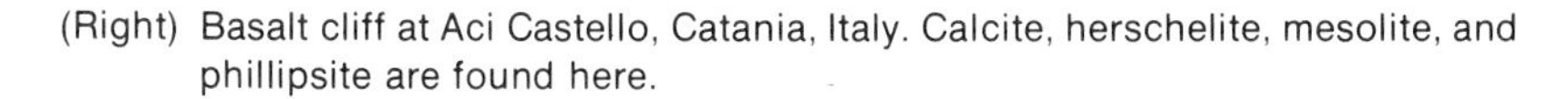

(Right) Basalt cliff at Aci Castello, Catania, Italy. Calcite, herschelite, mesolite, and phillipsite are found here.

ecessors of the present Rocky Mountains, which in turn have been carved by glaciers that spread broad fans of sediments across the level plains. Agates and petrified wood fragments as well as specimens of hundreds of types of rocks can be found wherever ice, wind, water, and mother nature's other abrasive tools have strewn the land with their products.

Prospecting in such areas is not without problems. There are usually no fixed guide points, and farmers may resent intrusion into their fields unless permission is first obtained.

Most sedimentary soil areas are level, but clay masses hollowed into deep gorges by water erosion can pile up steeply and could occasion a bad tumble. When working in such an area—the side of a steep slope, for example—level out a place to stand and another place for gear and minerals. Exploration of stream beds and the rocks the stream has eroded and carried down can be profitable. Sometimes the boulders must be broken up with hammer and chisel. The main hazard here is the possibility of slipping on wet rocks. In such places, don't carry sharp tools in your pockets or attached to your belt. And keep your hands free; you will need them to help over difficult spots. One more warning: mountain streams may rise suddenly from a distant rainstorm or release of water from dams or power stations higher up. Such a sudden flood could have serious consequences.

Moraines are hills of rock and earth that glaciers have carried along and left behind when the

1

2

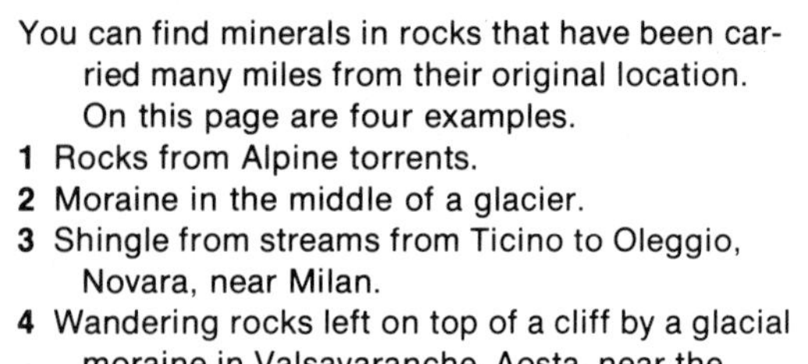

You can find minerals in rocks that have been carried many miles from their original location. On this page are four examples.

1 Rocks from Alpine torrents.

2 Moraine in the middle of a glacier.

3 Shingle from streams from Ticino to Oleggio, Novara, near Milan.

4 Wandering rocks left on top of a cliff by a glacial moraine in Valsavaranche, Aosta, near the Swiss border.

3

4

glaciers receded. These moraines sometimes contain rock specimens, quite large, known as wanderers or erratics, striated and polished by glacial action.

Farmers clearing a field often pile such boulders around a tree growing in the field or use them for rough walls. Occasionally some rock of interest can be obtained from such an accumulation. In cities, small boulders once were used for building material, and some large ones have been allowed to remain on lawns as a center of interest or to display tablets commemorating notable events. Landscape architects employ them for creating rock gardens, but such uses, of course, put the rocks out of reach of the casual collector, even though he can enjoy the sight of a sampling of the rocks of half the continent brought together by the glaciers. Most such rocks have little mineral interest left after the abrasive and chemical ordeal of their glacial journey.

The surface ridges of glaciers and the ground in front of them yield rocks in better condition, and often good specimens can be collected there. Again, the search won't be easy. But if you love mountains—and mineralogy—and are responsive to the sublime beauty of the sights, you'll enjoy a rich harvest of minerals as well as a thrilling experience.

3

WHAT MINERALS LOOK LIKE

Before going into the field, some acquaintance with the appearance of minerals is important, both for recognition and later for proper preparation of the rough stones into collectors' specimens.

Minerals appear in many forms. Some crystals are freestanding, others are embedded in rock. Sometimes they combine into aggregates and odd formations that are beautiful. At other times, they form compact, shapeless masses.

FREESTANDING CRYSTALS

In such environments as water or fused rock masses, mineral particles are free to migrate easily and to cluster around a core of attraction. This results in the formation of a crystal which, free to grow in all directions, takes on a well-defined form, almost as if shaped by man. If the environment in which the crystal has grown changes, through evaporation, decay, or dissolution of the matrix, the crystal is left to stand by itself, free to display its elegant structure. Freestanding pieces of beautiful quartz can be found in the mountains near Hot Springs, Arkansas, where cavities in quartz veins gave them room to develop.

Frequently, crystals originating and growing in close proximity combine in various ways. When two or more crystals join so that they share a common face, the resulting crystal is called a twin. If they join haphazardly, they form a structure called an aggregate.

Freestanding crystals often absorb foreign matter that touched them as they grew. Several areas in the eastern United States yield crystals that contain cavities filled with water, often with a movable bubble, or with sand, or clay.

On occasion, crystals cluster in rounded kidney shapes, called reniform structure from the Latin word for "kidney." While growing, these crystals have arranged themselves so that they radiate from a central point. When the cluster is split, the surfaces look rather like a Japanese fan.

Not all freestanding minerals are sufficiently attractive or interesting to warrant a place in a collection. Some crystals are mere granules or flakes in sandy riverbeds, barely visible to the naked eye. There are two reasons for this: either they were misshapen from the beginning when they were crowded up against other crystals; or moving water or ice stripped them from their rocky bed and, in the course of a long, punishing voyage, reduced them to their present condition.

There are no general rules for finding good specimens. After selecting a promising area, try to break off pieces corresponding more or less in size to the crystals that you hope to find. If some pieces appear to contain crystalline veins, take them home and enjoy the pleasure of freeing the crystals at leisure and with the proper tools.

CRYSTALS: GEOMETRICAL FORMS CREATED BY NATURE

Some minerals fascinate us by their beauty or strangeness. Looking at them can be an aesthetic experience and make us eager to learn more about them. For example, look at the octahedral crystal illustrated. It occurs exactly this way in nature; man has had no part in shaping it. The appearance is that of a geometrical polyhedron. Of course, it is not quite perfect; it has a few scratches, fractures, bits of foreign matter, and it is not highly polished. Nevertheless, its symmetry is apparent.

The orderly external arrangement of its plane surfaces and the angles at which they meet arise from the atomic pattern of the elements of which it is composed. Thus its symmetry is a property of the whole crystal. Every other crystal of the same mineral, while its appearance may show some distortions arising from the accidents of its growth, will nevertheless have its plane faces arranged at the same relative angles characteristic of the mineral species.

In the vocabulary of the collector, there are three major words for the objects that interest him. A *mineral,* such as the one discussed, is a natural, inorganic substance with a definite chemical composition, which composition expresses itself by orderly internal structure and definite external shape. Some minerals that have enjoyed favorable opportunities to grow, as in a geode or cavity, are found as crystals. A *crystal* is a solid bounded by planes that meet at definite angles characteristic of the mineral substance of which it is composed and which express the orderly arrangement of the atoms within.

Crystals may be tiny, such as unworn sand grains, or huge, as the crystals of spodumene weighing many tons found in the Black Hills. Some crystals are so small that they can be seen only through a microscope lens, and some have had to grow together so closely that they never had room to assume their characteristic shape. These are called cryptocrystalline, from the word meaning "hidden," and many of the quartz species used for jewelry, such as chrysoprase, can be defined by this word.

The third word that interests the collector, as has already been mentioned, is *rock,* which is an aggregate of one or more minerals, usually so crowded together that much of their crystal shape is lost. Granite with its quartz, feldspar, hornblende, and mica is an easily identified rock. A fourth group that the collector will deal with comprises the materials that lack crystal structure, such as obsidian, found with other volcanic ejecta, and opal.

Minerals are classified according to their structure into six crystal systems. These are discussed further on pages 88–91.

Photomicrograph of a perfect octahedron of anatase, a dioxide of titanium, $1/25$ inch high.

Veins of calcite require particular attention, for beautiful and rare specimens are sometimes found in them. To free these specimens, the calcite matrix has to be removed, but never attempt to do this in the field. The beauty of the specimen will be ample reward for the extra work of lugging the rock home. Fortunately, the envelope of rock and massive calcite provides protection for transporting the delicate crystals.

During a field trip, you may be tempted to work spots where the calcite has been eroded, leaving interesting material visible. This would be a mistake. Such an exposure is no longer in its original condition; the colors of the calcite may have

Reniform marcasite 5 inches in diameter, with crystals radiating from a central core. When the specimen has been split, the radiating structure of the inner surface is apparent. The specimen is from France.

changed, and the crystals may be worn or etched. It's better to look for a healthy vein and carry away good-sized chunks from it.

CRYSTALS IN ROCK FORMATIONS

Separate crystals grow under conditions that change with the passage of time and in settings that may be destroyed as they grow. If no destruction has occurred, crystals may be found embedded in the rock when it is broken open. Many rocks contain crystals interesting because of their beauty or rarity; many don't. Sometimes it's easy to find them; there could be thousands in a single area. Elsewhere, they may be so scarce that the collector is lucky to find one.

If a seam or cleavage in the rock runs along the faces of the crystals, the crystals won't be smashed along with the rock but will appear on the surface of the break. Another time, it may take a lot of careful hammering to release even a single undamaged crystal.

DRUSES AND CRYSTAL CAVITIES

While crystals are forming, they become embedded in a matrix, which may be of the same mineral as the crystal or a different mineral or a rock formation, such as granite or lava. Any crack or bulge in the rock could be lined with crystals. *Could be,* but isn't necessarily. Convinced that a treasure is within their grasp, collectors sometimes tear down half a cliff, only to find at last that the rock wall is barren.

The matrix may be in one of several forms. A druse is a rock surface, usually fairly level, that is covered with crystals. A geode is a shell of mineral, such as the cryptocrystalline quartz known as chalcedony, filled with crystals of the same mineral and, perhaps, other minerals. It will usually form within a natural rock cavity. A geode that is thin-walled and hollow is likely to contain the biggest crystals. Some types of crystal cavities are called vugs or pockets, depending on their size. A related form is the nodule, which is a mass of mineral that develops to fill a cavity without forming its own walls. The so-called thunder eggs dug from the lava beds in Oregon are nodules of agate, often associated with opal.

TWIN CRYSTALS

Crystals commonly develop in clumps or groups, one next to another. But occasionally something exceptional happens. The result could be mistaken for a single crystal but is actually a combination of two or more crystals. This is known as a twin. A twin may be defined as a symmetrical combining of two or more crystals of the same kind. If the twinning is composed of more than two singles, it is known as a multitwin. When one crystal crosses into the other, they are known as penetration twins. When they join along a plane surface, they are called contact twins.

Twins occur typically in certain minerals and have a characteristic appearance. Mineralogical collections may include such beautiful twins as geniculated rutile (titanium dioxide), "tin-beak" cassiterite (tin oxide), and pyrite (iron sulfide) with characteristic "iron cross" formation.

The gem mineral chrysoberyl, which is beryllium aluminate, is perhaps the best known example of an even more complex form of twinning. Six crystals create a hexagonal grouping that resembles a snowflake in contour. Represented in most collections is a related form, the less common calcium carbonate called aragonite, and its famous pseudohexagonal twins from the province in Spain that gave the mineral its name. These resemble a column with flat terminations. Witherite, which is barium carbonate, crystallizes as repeated twins that look like shallow pyramids, and so does its close chemical relative, strontianite, which is strontium carbonate, the stuff that gives the red glow to fireworks. Cerussite, the carbonate of lead, forms several kinds of twins, including six-rayed starlike groups.

Staurolite's penetration twins are popularly known as fairy crosses when the crystals meet at ninety-degree angles. These are prized as ornaments. Virginia and Georgia are major sources of such crystals.

The group of aluminum silicates known as feldspars is noted for several common types of twinning. Two forms assumed by orthoclase, a potassium member of the group, are the Carlsbad and the Baveno twin habits. A Carlsbad twin appears to have been formed by pushing one crystal lengthwise into the middle of another so that the tips of each project. A Baveno twin forms a nearly square prism, although more complex habits exist. One form gets its name from the city in Germany; the other from an Italian source. Beyond this brief discussion, the complexities of feldspar twinning belong to specialists.

Quartz crystals are commonly twinned, so much so that synthetic single crystals are now manufactured for the production of the thin wafers of quartz used to set the wavelength for electronic communications. The twinning is so complete that it is possible to detect it only by the position of small faces near the crystal apex, by striations on the crystal, and by optical tests. The form known as the Japanese twin, however, is spectacular, as it consists of two flattened crystals joined at nearly a right angle at their bases. They are ornaments of any collection. Selenite is another commonly twinned mineral. (See illustration below.) In this, two single crystals unite by joining surfaces. This is contact twinning.

Lancehead or swallowtail twin crystal of selenite, calcium sulfate, from Agrigento, Italy.

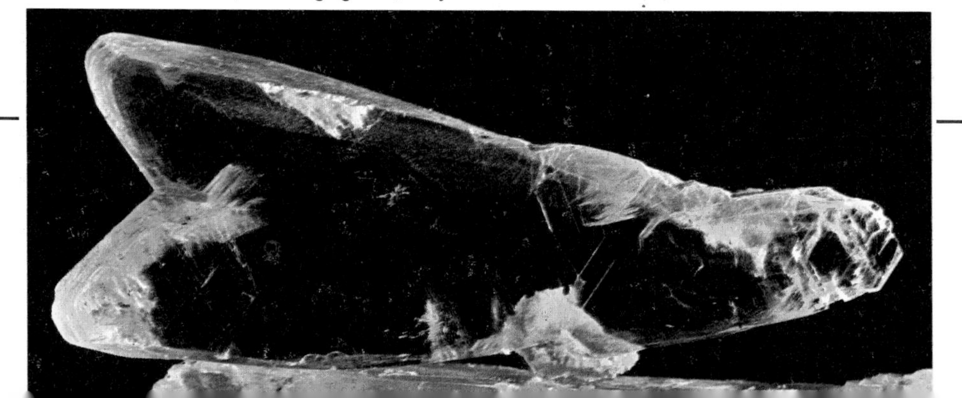

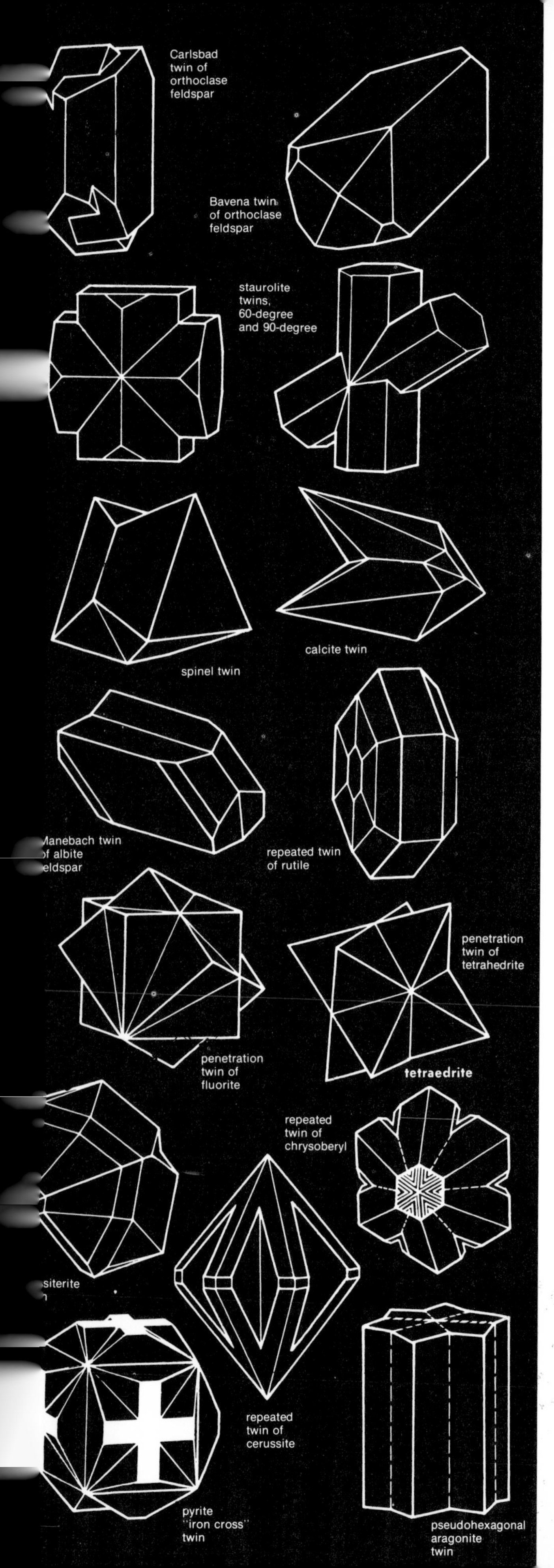

1

2

3

Photographs of Twin Crystals.

1 Calcite.

2 Aragonite, a pseudohexagonal twin, Spain.

3 Sanidine feldspar.

4 Cassiterite (tin dioxide) with tin beak.

5 Fluorite penetration twin, Cumberland, England.

4

5

The famous pegmatite rock mass of Piona, Italy, has stimulated many people to become rock collectors. Pegmatite is a rock mass composed of coarse crystals of quartz, feldspar and other silicates, sheets of mica, and numerous other minerals such as beryl and tourmaline. Some crystals were able to develop because they had formed before the quartz and the feldspar enveloped them rigidly. Such pegmatite veins are found in many other places in the world and are almost always good places for fieldwork. The pegmatite here has been quarried for use by the ceramic industry, but even though the veins have been worked almost to extinction, a sharp-eyed collector can still find a fine specimen in the debris. The biggest vein here is called the Malpensata and is on the road leading to Piona abbey, very close to the abbey itself.

(Far left) Pegmatite vein at Malpensata, located on the road to the Piona abbey, north of Como in Lombardy, Italy.
(Left) Pegmatite from Piona, composed of a variety of minerals.

Sometimes drusy crystals form on a dense hard rock from which it is difficult to remove a group without damage. Elsewhere, however, the rock matrix may be loose or of a consistency that is easily broken free. Geodes and pockets are difficult to remove intact from hard rock and it is best to look for them where the rock is disintegrating or naturally friable.

Collectors can work in pairs, one to tap a sharp chisel along the hoped-for line of cleavage, the other to hold and maneuver the chunk of rock so that it is not damaged.

Often specimens can be picked up in quarries and mines where, while the ore was being removed, other minerals have been broken out that will enhance the collection.

Crystals in all forms are so eagerly sought by rock hunters nowadays that it's no longer easy to find a specimen of exceptional beauty. Fortunately, while searching for spectacular pieces, prospectors often overlook less noticeable ones. These may turn out to be real prizes for the sharp eyes that discover them.

In collecting from rock walls, look for fractures or seams along which cavities lined with crystals may be expected. Break out the material, examine the surfaces, and wash the pieces to get off the dirt. It will then be possible to assess the potentialities of the site.

Both luck and good judgment play their parts in successful collecting. Dale Sweet, a neophyte, knew that gem tourmaline had been found in past years in the old, almost abandoned Dunton mine near Rumford, Maine. Following the maxim that the most promising place to look is where others have found crystals, he hacked away at an inconspicuous seam in the rocky pegmatite wall of the open pit until he broke into a small pocket that contained gem material. With the help of a companion, he opened up the pocket and to their as-

Geode of amethystine quartz from Mexico. **1** When this rock sphere was broken in half, it disclosed a cavity lined with crystals. **2** To illustrate this more clearly, see diagram below left **3.**

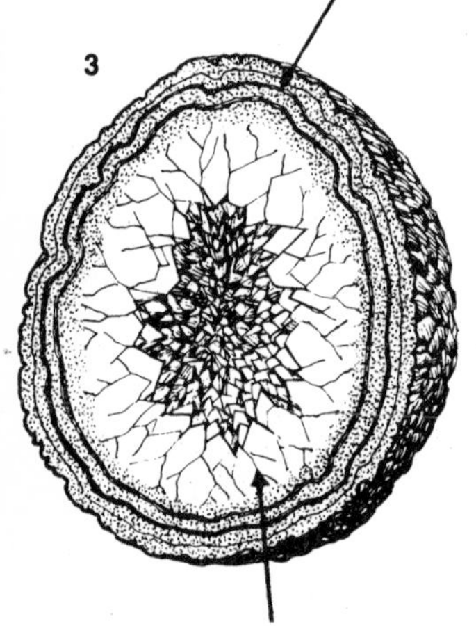

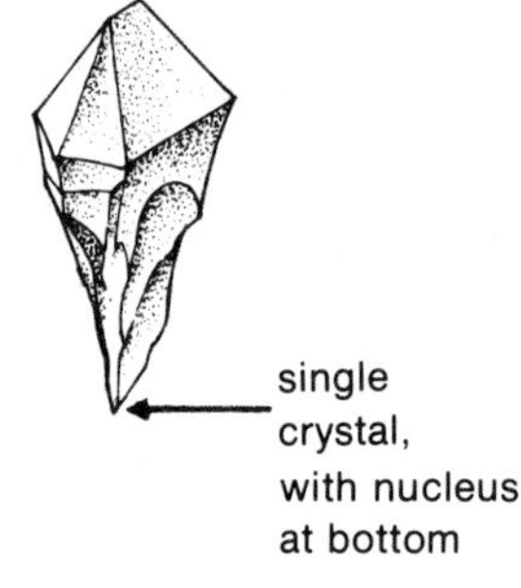

tonishment they found that it led to a series of almost room-size pockets lined with colorful tourmaline. It was reported that the gem crystals were taken away in bushel baskets.

Equally successful have been the geode hunters in the area where Missouri, Iowa, and Illinois come together near the Mississippi river. In the banks of the streams, geodes filled with calcite crystals, some stained black by bitumen, can be pried carefully from the soft rock, and in the waste rock of quarries similar prizes occur, especially near Hamilton, Illinois.

COMPACT AND SPECIAL FORMS

Almost all minerals are crystalline, but many appear in compact granular or fibrous forms which do not yield distinct crystals. Even though they are not as spectacular as big crystals, it's a good idea to collect these minerals, too, because they are typical of a certain area, represent the ore of a specific mine, may have some scientific interest, or simply because they're curiosities.

Collecting such specimens is easy. Often they are scattered in the open, at the entrance to a quarry, although occasionally a little hammering may be necessary to obtain a piece of suitable size. But don't confine yourself to specimens of only one mineral. Select pieces that represent as many minerals as possible.

The dumps of the copper mines of the upper peninsula of Michigan are particularly rich in tiny crystal-lined pockets in the black or reddish basaltic rocks. These rocks may even show flecks of bright copper where they are broken. Many of the old mine dumps in Arizona and New Mexico, such as those at Jerome, Arizona, betray their mineralization by green or blue stains on the rock. Likewise, all around the old bonanza town of Virginia City, Nevada, stand huge dumps where traces of silver minerals are by no means uncommon. Where there's a mine dump, there's opportunity.

AMORPHOUS FORMS

There is no need to say much about opals and a few other substances that lack crystal structure. The extraordinary speed with which a natural glass such as obsidian formed allowed no time for it to develop an orderly crystalline internal struc-

Translucent quartz druse from Madagascar.

Examples of minerals that show minor evidence of crystallization. (Far left) Granular pyrite, below; compact, above. (Near left) Satin spar, a fibrous gypsum.

ture. These amorphous materials could be compared to a pile of bricks scattered at random as they were dumped from a truck, or to the glass of a windowpane whose atoms have no ordered structure either. The United States has a number of notable localities for obsidian, such as the great cliff outside Yellowstone Park, the Glass Buttes near Hampton, Oregon, and the small nodules found near Superior, Arizona, commonly called Apache tears. A rare, beautiful form is snowflake obsidian, a dense black flecked with white lacy spots found in Utah.

Amorphous fire opal from Mexico.

MINERALS THAT AREN'T MINERALS

Every collector, no matter how expert, has been misled at least once into exchanging a mineral for a chunk or shard of glass. Indeed, such material is often so beautifully formed that it fools the most knowledgeable. Carborundum, copper sulfate crystals, and slag from glass or steel plant furnaces can certainly be puzzling, especially if offered by someone bent on fooling you. These specimens may well deserve a place in a collection as curiosities, but don't give up good minerals for them.

Slag is often beautiful for its color and swirls of pattern, and it is easily obtainable near any glass factory. Plastics also can be deceiving to the eye, and one unique fake material is the lacquer broken in chunks from walls and pipes in booths where automobile bodies are sprayed. This builds up in thin layers of a great variety of colors, like Joseph's coat. Repaired broken crystals are another trap for the unwary collector. The glue, however, will show up under ultraviolet light.

Slag from a steel plant; this can easily be mistaken for a mineral.

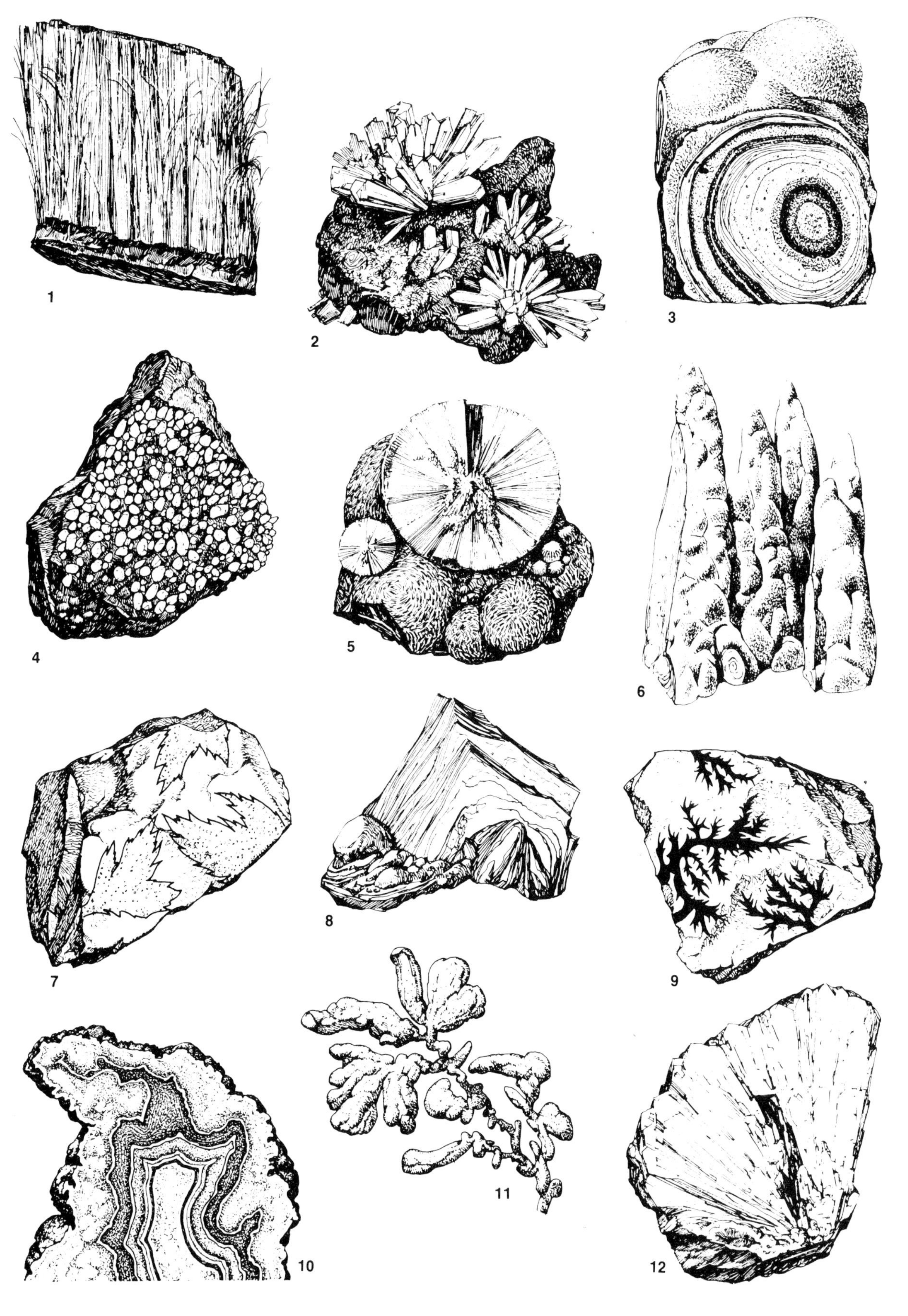

Crystals that combine into an aggregate may assume a variety of shapes. Each of these is identified by a special name. Here are a few examples of aggregates.

1 Compact fibrous aggregate: asbestos.
2 Diverging, lamellar aggregate: hemimorphite.
3 Mammillary aggregate: malachite.
4 Granular aggregate: olivine.
5 Radiating aggregate: wavellite.
6 Stalactitic aggregate: goethite.
7 Foliated aggregate: muscovite mica.
8 Micaceous aggregate: mica.
9 Dendritic aggregate: psilomelane on rock.
10 Banded aggregate: agate.
11 Arborescent aggregate: copper.
12 Lamellar radiating aggregate: stilbite.

4

PHASES OF ROCK COLLECTING

Suppose you are climbing a hill at the top of which is a mineral deposit. If you're lucky, it will yield a generous harvest of specimens. *If you're lucky.* It is worth repeating this as you climb, because occasionally the search will be fruitless. On reaching the top, you may find that the deposit has been disturbed, or that other collectors have been greedy and have practically cleaned it out. At other times, you may not strike the right vein; perhaps the light isn't good, or you may just miss spotting the vein. But even if you have bad luck, there is no reason to feel downcast. At least you've been outdoors and gotten a lot of good exercise. The excursion has been worthwhile for itself alone.

In the big quarries or in operating mines, the first thing to do is to ask permission from the superintendent or whoever is in charge to enter and search for minerals. If permission is granted, you can then explore rock walls and rock piles and wander at will in unworked areas within any limits set by the management. Always get permission from the proprietor before working in a meadow, orchard, or woods—even if the land is unfenced. If it is a farm, assure the owner that you won't harm anything growing. And when you're done, clean up after yourself. Fill in holes and don't leave piles of rock fragments or gravel on the roads or in the ditches beside them. Above all, do not tinker with the farmer's machinery, alarm his livestock, or use any explosives or firearms. Leave gates as you found them, open or closed. In collecting, always be courteous and considerate of the rights of others, if only to avoid making life difficult for collectors who come after you. At best, you are a guest; at worst, a trespasser.

INSPECTION AND GATHERING

Having established a base camp for tools and baggage, the next step should be to divide the surrounding area into search zones among members of the group. It may be necessary for a group to stick together if most members are not familiar with the deposit and need to remain with a leader who does know the site. But usually it is more efficient to fan out singly, according to planned itineraries. This prevents several persons from going over an area where material already has been collected when they might be working in fresh territory. Of course, the searchers should remain in hailing distance of one another, ready to help if anyone runs into trouble or if one person finds something warranting everyone's inspection.

The initial reconnaissance should be a quick one. Just mark the promising spots with scratches, paper, or plastic tags; use bright-colored markers—red or yellow—so that they can be picked out at a glance later on. It will take some will power, of course, but *don't* pause during the initial tour to do any hammering. The first rock you come across might offer specimens of minor inter-

Metamorphic Rocks. To break up this type of rock, such as serpentines, **1** Chisel along the schist line. **2** Then use the chisel as a lever. **3** Never attack the rock in a direction perpendicular to its strata. It's almost impossible to break it that way.

1

2

3

Stratified Sedimentary Rocks.

1 Thrust a long-handled chisel between the strata, and use it as a lever to loosen the piece. **2** To break up the dislodged piece, and to see if it contains a mineral or fossil specimen, hit it lightly with a prospector's pick in the direction of the strata.

1

2

Veined Rocks.

1 Never tackle this type of rock head on if you want to break off pieces. **2** Always work from the side. Then apply leverage against the rock itself.

1

2

est. Stopping to hammer it will use up valuable time which could otherwise be utilized later to search for specimens of much greater interest.

The initial inspection allows for planning the work to make it as productive as possible, to determine what tools are needed, and, finally, to assess any hazards in the area. There is another reason for proceeding deliberately and not skipping the reconnaissance: frequently, careful inspection leads to finding quantities of splendid specimens that have crumbled from the rocks or become detached by blasting in a mine. And these can be had without lifting a hammer!

After the reconnaissance and before starting to collect, consult with the group and decide whether to continue alone or in pairs. At this stage, it is sometimes better to be in pairs to avoid losing anything chipped off in chiseling and also as a safety measure. Start, of course, with one of the more promising of the marked spots. Unless you are experienced, it might be well not to begin with the most promising objective of all. Instead, when working on a rock cliff, for example, try sections of lesser interest to accustom your hand to the task before going after the biggest prize.

While working in hard rocks, don't use your chisel wherever it merely shatters the rock into small pieces. It's more effective to knock off good-sized chunks with a sharp blow of the hammer. These larger pieces will be easier to handle in preparation of the specimens. The chisel will come in handy mainly on stratified rocks and as a wedge.

As you collect, put your specimens into little piles identified by colored markers. Don't stop to ponder whether a specific find is worth keeping. Just include everything that looks interesting enough to warrant further examination.

For easy identification, anchor a cloth on each pile of specimens. Use white or red—any color that stands out clearly.

PICKING

When the day's search is done, the time comes to decide what your best finds are and what to take home. Leave the ones that aren't quite as good as your best for someone who will come there after you have gone or for you to return for if later you find yourself short of material. Rejoin the group and sort your specimens roughly, discarding those that appear undesirable. This is a ticklish job; sometimes it is advisable to lug all the material back to base camp and consult the other members of the group before making final selections. If you come across a promising but unwieldy rock mass and don't have the proper tools to break it up, carry it home as it is to work on later. Don't risk losing a fine specimen by hacking at it with the wrong tools.

If you're searching alone, whatever you find is yours. But when you're part of a group, it is a friendly custom to share your haul with those who have been less fortunate. One way to do this is to pool the various collections, divide the pool into the same number of piles as there are collectors, making them as equal in size and quality as possible, and then draw lots for them.

PACKING

Packing winds up the day's activities. Wrap each specimen in several sheets of newspaper; place it carefully in your pack, first being sure to line the section of the knapsack that hits your back with either a soft sweater or corrugated cardboard. Don't overload the pack. If you have boxes or fruit crates in the car, place the specimens in them at once, even if this requires several trips to the car. Don't leave rocks lying loose in the car trunk. Bumps or jolts could damage them and in an accident they might become flying missiles.

If you have fragile material, such as calcite crystals, zeolites or artinite, use a small individual box for each piece, and wad tissue paper around it to prevent movement. If no little boxes are available, wrap each piece separately, cover the small packages with a loose blanket of folded newspapers, and fold the entire bundle in more newspapers so that nothing can harm the delicate crystals.

Small, freestanding crystals that are not likely to break can be packed in plastic bags. Selenite crystals should be packed individually because they suffer damage—ugly white marks—when they rub against one another.

Some minerals require special packing. One is laumontite, which must be wrapped in wet cloth or paper because its color changes and it crumbles as soon as air strikes it. Another is rock salt, which should be packed in several thicknesses of plastic. It is extremely sensitive to moisture.

LEAVING

After a visit to an operating mine or quarry, remember to thank the superintendent. If the workers have supplied useful information, reward them suitably. Before leaving, check your baggage to be sure that nothing has been forgotten. It is easy to forget equipment when everyone is tired at the end of the day and eager to get home. And you are pretty sure to be tired, for if the area has been rewarding, you will have kept hammering away as long as you could. Oddly enough, many of the day's best finds often are made just as the collector has to leave for home.

5

THE HOME LABORATORY

One of the problems that collectors face is finding a place to put the specimens they bring home. The house isn't big enough; the rocks get it dirty; the cellar already is overflowing. There's barely room enough in the garage for the car, and not one more thing can be jammed into the attic.

But the problem is not insoluble. You can always find a spare corner if you're determined to do so. Start by discarding things no longer needed; put away some of the once-cherished knickknacks now rarely looked at; clear a little space somewhere in the house.

To make the most of small space, pick and choose selectively while you're still in the field. Discard inferior specimens and pieces that are not typical or are too bulky. When you get home, don't put off work on specimens. The accumulations of several trips can pile up and create a real storage problem. Discard the bits and pieces chipped off the stones as you go along. Be as orderly and organized as possible and keep only a few duplicate pieces, including some for trading with other collectors.

HOW TO ORGANIZE STORAGE SPACE

Obviously, the easiest way to store a good many specimens in limited space is by using shelves, provided the floor is strong enough to hold them safely. Ready-made shelves are available, but with a little initiative, creativity, and skill at carpentry, you can build ones specially adapted to your requirements by using salvaged material. Ask at stores for empty wooden boxes or crates. Nail them to wooden risers so that they are attached one above the other, with nine to ten inches between them. This will provide enough storage space to hold recently acquired specimens as well as those you've previously worked on and are keeping for trading purposes.

No matter how many shelves are put up, there is never enough space. The shelves will get so crowded that finding the exact piece you want when a friend comes in to trade becomes a problem. So try to discipline yourself: save only the most beautiful and interesting pieces and throw away those for which there is really no room.

THE WORKSHOP

With a little ingenuity, the space cleared to store incoming specimens can almost always be used as a minilaboratory, too. Fix up a small workbench; on it put a vise, grinding wheels, a wood block, a tool rack, and a bright lamp. Workshops vary according to the space available. There's only one general rule: keep it as neat and clean as possible. You'll need only a few tools, and these will be discussed later.

A well-equipped home workshop.
1 The vise, the wood block, and the grinding wheel are visible, while a taller wood block stands at one side. Specimens to be worked on are arranged in shelves made of shallow wooden boxes. This can be seen more clearly in **2.**

2

1

(Below) To break down pieces that can stand hammerblows, use a hardwood block as an anvil. When the piece is fragile, squeeze it between the jaws of a vise, like the one shown on the left.

GETTING SET TO WORK

Much rock material, laboriously acquired and carried home, is damaged or destroyed because of overeagerness to get at the specimens without first considering how to go about preparing them.

Preparation is usually delicate: undertake it slowly and patiently. Collecting is a hobby, and the subsequent preparation of specimens should yield as much enjoyment, albeit of a quieter kind, as the outdoor activity that precedes it. Some aspects of it can be made to occupy an idle hour; others will require several hours at a time—a rainy afternoon or a weekend morning. Allow plenty of time for studying each specimen and deciding how to remedy its imperfections and bring out the loveliness that nature has endowed it with. The reward of skillful and patient application is to see a beautiful specimen emerge from the work of your hands, a specimen that you will be proud to exhibit.

Don't start work unless you have a reasonable stretch of time free, and be sure to allot a few minutes at the end for cleaning up. Put away the finished pieces, clean your tools, and clear away the mess. A self-respecting mineral collector finds a broom, shovel, and plastic litter bag just as necessary as a hammer.

TOOLS FOR WORKING AT HOME

The tools for arranging, shaping, and polishing specimens are not those used in the field . . . but they are no less important. Specialized equipment, such as little hammers, diamond saws, and special cleaning devices, is not needed by the beginner. Such tools are expensive, but they permit the advanced collector to do delicate work more quickly and easily than with common tools. A few tools, and skill acquired in their use, will make possible results about as satisfactory as most specimens require.

THE EQUIPMENT

Listed below are the tools that are essential:

A workbench. If you build one, make it sturdy, approximately 32 inches high with a surface 28 inches by 40 inches. Put in a lower shelf, 8 inches off the ground. This will brace the legs and provide a convenient storage space for whatever you're working on. An excellent framework for this type of table can be purchased or made. Use pierced angle iron to hold the shelf, adjustable to any height. Everything you need for this is obtainable at a hardware store.

A wall rack for hanging tools, made of a frame with wooden strips running across it. Drive nails into the strips to position the tools where you want them.

Two hammers, weighing from 10 to 18 ounces. These are in addition to those used in the field.

A hardwood block to serve as an anvil when splitting specimens. The bigger it is, the better it will muffle the noise of your hammerblows, but a small block, about 8 inches in diameter and of the same height, is adequate. A lumberyard or sawmill will be the likely place to obtain one. Let the block dry thoroughly and then bind it with metal bands, top and bottom. Nail the bands securely so they won't work loose later. Keep the wood block protected from bad weather and ground dampness. A big boulder of granite or diorite in a garden where you can work on specimens would make an excellent anvil.

Chisels for home use, with edges ¼- to ½-inch wide, in addition to those you have for the field. When buying them, be sure to state that they're for use on hard stone.

Needles for delicate work, such as freeing crystals from surrounding mineral. Darning needles with small round eyes serve very well for this purpose and are available at any notion store. Mount them in wood handles, like those used for small files. These have a small opening. Insert the eye of the needle in the opening, first coating it with vinyl glue. Then, holding the needle with pincers, tap the pincers a few times, driving the needle into the wood about a half inch.

Fine chisels for the delicate work of removing matrix from crystals. To make a fine chisel, insert a darning needle into a handle, this time point down, with the eye outside. With a grinding wheel, remove the eye of the needle, leaving a flat, sharp chisel edge.

Grinding equipment of some sort is necessary in a well-equipped shop. Its nature depends on the use that will be made of it. If it is to serve only to sharpen chisels or grind off small spurs on a specimen, a hand-operated one will be sufficient. It should be of silicon carbide and of the proper composition for grinding steel. But if the collector expects to grind and polish mineral surfaces, or

1

2

3

1 The beam press is a useful but somewhat expensive device for breaking rocks. Put the piece to be broken under the chisel. Then rotating the beam of the press will force the chisel down **2** and it will split the rock **3.** This equipment makes it possible to free the crystals you're after without shattering them as the vibration of a hammerblow might. The chisel penetrates the rock with an even pressure; therefore, no damaging shock waves are set in motion.

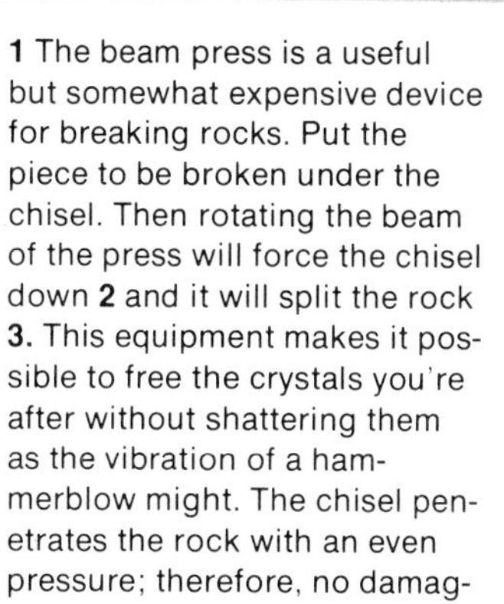

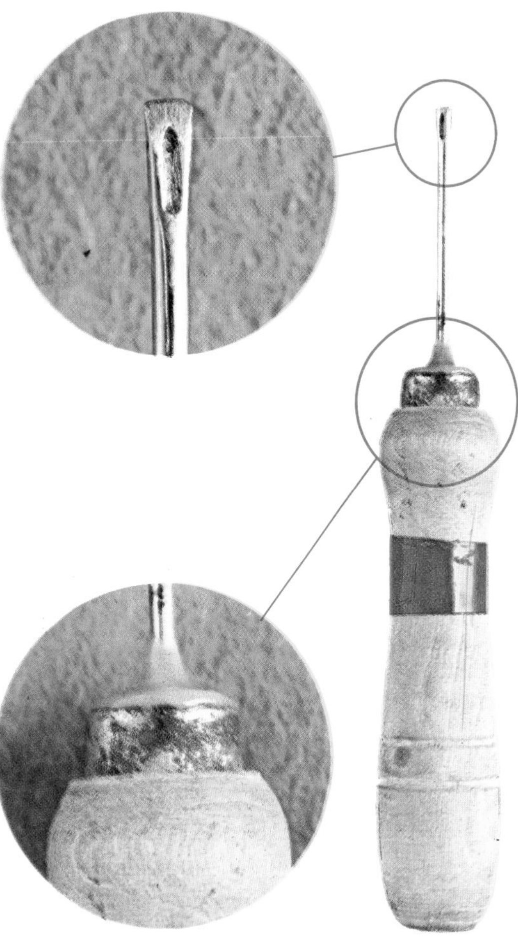

This slender chisel is useful for delicate work. It is made of a darning needle with a small eye inserted point down into a handle.

cut gemstones, he will need power-operated grinding wheels with provision for a spray of water on the periphery of the wheel or wheels. Usually two wheels, of 80 grit and 200 grit, are used on one shaft. As wheels for metal and for rock differ in the bond that holds the grit together, tools should not be ground on rock wheels.

Wet grinding has many advantages over dry grindings. It is dustless; the operator is not breathing rock dust; and it cools the wheel and the ground surface so that metal is not "burned" and a mineral surface does not fly apart from expansion caused by overheating. It is well to wear goggles or safety glasses when running any wheel at high speed, to stand aside when it is starting and stopping, and to be sure that the water spray is turned off so that the wheel is not waterlogged and thus out of balance when it stops.

A *vise* is expensive but provides a sure grip while you are breaking up big pieces and holds chunks securely for working on them. The bigger and stronger the vise the better, but a modest 3-inch vise is sufficient, provided that you are careful not to push it beyond its capabilities.

To assure a firm grip on the piece you're working on, insert strips of rubber, wood, or cardboard between the specimen and the jaws of the vise. If the shape of the specimen isn't such that the vise grips it firmly when pressure is applied, try some other means of holding it. Otherwise, it may slip from the vise and be damaged, or excessive pressure may break the vise.

One way to break specimens is to insert a wedge or steel blade between one jaw of the vise and the specimen. Its sharp edge will press against the specimen as the vise closes. The blade is likely to slip during the work unless care is used in tightening the vise, and the method is for that reason adaptable only for specimens of favorable shape.

ACCESSORIES

Some of the tools you'll need are the ones used in the field; goggles, magnet, and pocketknife. Others, such as pliers and pincers, are usually available in the house. To these add a flashlight or high-intensity lamp for extra illumination where you need it, and an apron or coveralls such as gardeners wear to protect your clothing. For washing specimens and treating them with acid, you'll need a scrub brush, one paintbrush for varnishing and one for water colors, a bucket, and some small plastic bags. Keep a few old towels for drying your hands. And be sure you have a box of pressure-sensitive labels, small tags (about 2 inches by 1 inch), as well as pencils and pens.

REAGENTS AND COSMETIC TECHNIQUES

Several reagents are used for improving the appearance of specimens and bringing out their details. The principal ones are hydrochloric acid, oxalic acid, and sodium thiosulfate, which is the photographer's "hypo." The correct way to use these is described in the next chapter. Hydrochloric acid, also known as muriatic acid (available in drugstores), dissolves the carbonates that surround crystals. Sodium thiosulfate (at chemical supply houses) and oxalic acid remove rust and other stains.

Here is a list of beauty aids for your specimens:

Waxes. Contrary to the opinion of some purists, skilled preparation makes a specimen much more attractive without destroying any of its essential character. When crystals are covered by foreign matter or blackened by minute corrosions, their beauty is dimmed. You'll notice that immediately after washing a specimen, its color and brilliance are much more evident than later when it has been dried and is lying in the display case. But use a little wax on it and it will retain that sparkling look. Colorless floor wax or even clear shoeshine wax will do. The wax will not harm the specimen and can always be removed.

Glues. From time to time, when you're working on a specimen it may break or a crystal may fall off. You can salvage the piece by putting it together carefully with a quick-drying adhesive such as Elmer's Glue-All, or a plastic cement such as Duco. If you're skillful, your piece will look as good as new. A repaired specimen, however, should be so identified if you sell or trade it.

Sprays. Some minerals are unstable, such as halite (salt), mercury globules on rock, and laumontite. A thin coat of clear plastic, commercially available in aerosol cans, will prolong the life of your specimen notably. Laumontite is best preserved by a dip yearly in a laundry starch solution. A bath of mineral oil will often suffice to keep halite from disintegrating.

Rock salt, or halite. This type of mineral is sensitive to moisture, and requires a protective coating.

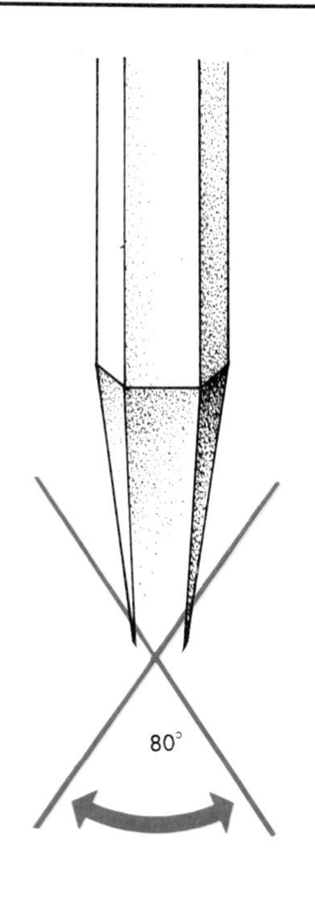

CARE OF EQUIPMENT

Simple equipment is not expensive, yet it represents an investment in a hobby that can best be justified by taking good care of tools and making frequent use of them.

Keep your tools sharp and clean, with the handles in good condition, so that they'll function at peak efficiency. Store them in a place that is neither damp nor too dry.

When you know you won't be using your tools for a while, coat them lightly with grease before storing them. Never leave any clothing, shoes, or knapsack in a damp place. Each time you return from a trip, check their condition. A loose button or a broken shoelace can cause inconvenience in the field at a most inopportune time.

CARE OF CHISELS

Keep the cutting edges of your chisels sharp. This can be done by the regular use of a grinding wheel. For working on rocks, the angle of the chisel's cutting surfaces should be about 80 degrees. Occasionally, a chisel will need tempering; this is a job for a cutlery shop. A rock chisel should not be so hard that it is brittle, but it must be tough to keep an edge. Be sure to grind off the burrs caused by hammerblows on the base of chisels. They may break loose when the chisel is struck and inflict a nasty cut.

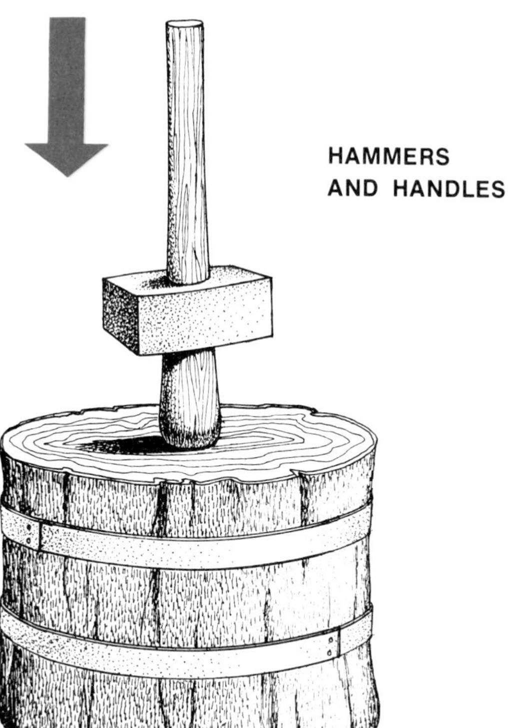

HAMMERS AND HANDLES

Since hammer handles are usually the first equipment to wear out, they deserve special emphasis. When they're not in perfect condition, they can cause unpleasant accidents. If they show any signs of weakening or cracking, change them at once. They're inexpensive, and any size can be obtained at most hardware stores.

Wood contracts in drying, so to assure a firm fit to a handle, first dry it thoroughly in the sun or on a radiator. Then put the narrow end of the handle into the opening of the hammerhead and pound it on a block of wood so that the handle is forced into place. If the handle doesn't quite fit, shape it with a wood file and remove any remaining roughness with sandpaper. Next, examine the head and file down any ragged edges of metal. Finally, plunge the finished hammer into water. The wood will swell and press against the metal, making a tight grip.

Don't polish or varnish the handle; it would slip in your hand. Bind the end of the handle with bright strips of red or yellow adhesive tape for easy identification on field trips. Finally, cut a seal, your initials, or some other distinctive mark on the handle. This will save arguments about whose hammer it is when a group is working together.

6

PREPARATION OF SPECIMENS

Practically everything collected in the field has to be worked over to make it suitable for display. Some specimens need to be ground down and polished so as to bring out their scientific interest without, however, neglecting aesthetic considerations.

Your collection should be a harmonious unit, not a random assembly of stones. In designing a display, follow the principles that guide architects, sculptors, and painters. Use the play of light, shadow, and color to highlight the parts of your collection you wish to emphasize. For each specimen, spotlight an outstanding crystal, some interesting formation, or some other praiseworthy characteristic.

Everyone has some feeling for beauty. You can sharpen yours by analyzing why any stone seems either beautiful or ugly to you, and by studying composition. *Composition* is the key word in successful display—the word used by artists to describe the organization of shapes and colors in their work that appeals to the eye.

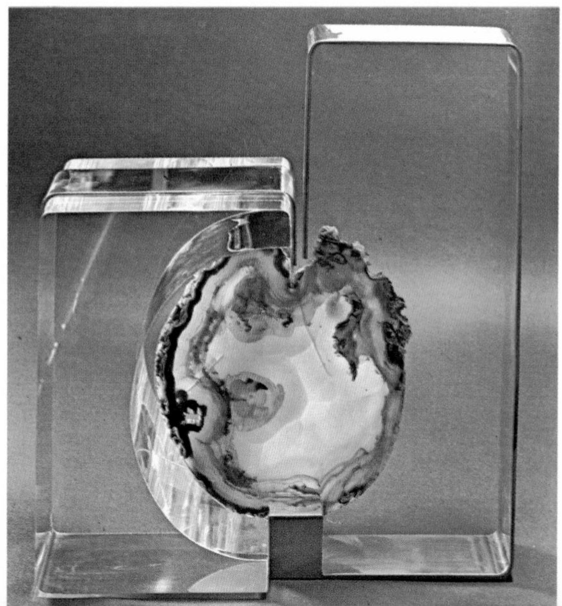

Minerals are sometimes incorporated into works of art, as in these sculptures. (Above) Milk white quartz is used with free-form molded copper. (Right) A slice of Brazilian agate framed with plastic and stainless steel.

DISPLAY FORMATS

In arranging specimens, be guided by your own taste and the space available. Make provision for adding new specimens occasionally. Obviously, stones as big as watermelons are too big for display, even if you live in a castle, and a collection made up of particles no bigger than gooseberry seeds will be only a collection of little boxes. Specimens best adapted for home display range in size from a strawberry (½ inch by 1 inch) to a tangerine (1½ inches by 2 inches) up to a grapefruit (3 inches by 4 inches).

The usual sizes for minerals in collections:
3 inches by 4 inches; 2 inches by 3 inches; 1½ inches by 2 inches; ½ inch by 1 inch.

The format for displaying your collection as a whole will vary with circumstances. In general, however, the larger, more beautiful pieces should be shown on shelves in glass cases and the smaller pieces should be put into boxes. Large display cases are suitable for specimens that can't be trimmed, such as big crystals. Smaller cases are satisfactory for showing separate crystals, and for specialized collections, which will be discussed later.

POSITIONING YOUR SPECIMENS

Suppose you are trying to arrange a number of parallelepiped-shaped specimens mounted on rectangular bases. Each could be placed in any of three positions. Choose the position that turns the most interesting face of the specimen toward the front of the case. Arrange the specimens on a shelf in two rows, those in front in a horizontal position, and those in back standing vertically.

Two examples of how to place minerals so as to show their beauty to the best advantage: (Left) Crystals of quartz and wolframite from Panasqueira, Portugal, covered with zinnwaldite. (Right) Banded jasper from Morocco.

Don't overcrowd the shelf; every piece should be clearly visible. Be sure each specimen is securely mounted; it mustn't teeter or fall over. If there's any danger of this, it may be necessary to enlarge its base to keep it steady. If you can't do this without damaging the specimen, supply an auxiliary support. (See page 58).

It is important to limit the size of your specimens. Too many heavy pieces could break the shelves holding them, and a case filled with only large pieces is not as attractive to the viewer as one in which there is variety of size as well as of mineral species.

In the lower part of the case put the larger pieces, including the heaviest crystals and those darkest in color. These will form the base of the design. On higher shelves put the smaller individual crystals and those lighter in color. When you've finished arranging the case, look at it in a strong light to see whether the design automatically draws the eye to the most interesting pieces.

TECHNIQUES OF PREPARATION

Choice of the proper way to deal with each specimen depends on its physical and aesthetic characteristics. All the techniques are simple and should present few problems. What may be difficult to supply are the time and perseverance needed for this work. Before you start on a fine specimen, try a practice run on a piece that has little or no value. Experience gained on it will help you to prepare a specimen for your collection of which you can be proud.

Separate crystals. First wash them thoroughly, scrub them with a small brush if they are not fragile, and go over each one with a needle to rid it of any trace of foreign matter. Then spread the crystals on a cloth stretched over a metal frame, and put them aside to dry.

Druses and crystal pockets. These splendid crystals are among the highlights of any collection. They are too delicate to be subjected to vigorous hammering or rough brushing, so you must wash them, rid them of excess matrix, give them a stable base, and shape them harmoniously without using the hammer. Instead of a hammer, use a grinding wheel, pliers, pincers, and a vise for this work. Often a specimen is better left as it was when found rather than run the risk of damaging it by overzealous preparation. This is a question of judgment the collector must make.

Do only necessary cleaning of these specimens because there is always the danger of knocking off a bit of precious mineral or of changing the specimen's characteristic appearance. Don't remove crust—even if it seems to obscure some of the crystals—because it is really an integral part of the specimen. Stains, however, are not.

For the finishing touches, use a soft brush and do only what is absolutely necessary. Be careful not to knock off the tips of crystals that are part of the specimen. Such damage could spoil the piece.

Crystals in matrixes. Many specimens you start to work on will have crystals peeping out on one face. These should be brought to light insofar as is possible. Occasionally, however, you'll bring home big pieces that present many difficulties in exposing the hidden crystals.

Try breaking the pieces of crystalline rock by squeezing them carefully in the jaws of a vise. While doing this, you'll hear a distinct crackling noise. This is caused by little internal cracks occurring along the planes of cleavage as the pressure separates the crystals inside. Don't increase the pressure of the vise on the specimen until the crackling stops; then continue until the piece falls apart. This technique will often bring the hidden crystals to light. They'll show to best advantage if you work delicately and crumble off as little as possible of the surrounding matrix. Use a fine-needle chisel and follow the planes of cleavage if possible. Don't wash these specimens: water might dull the freshness of the crystal faces just exposed by the break.

If the rock you're going to prepare is granulated or brittle, the vise will break it, and bringing the crystals into the open will offer no special problem. Keep wetting the rock while you're working to prevent ugly whitish streaks from appearing on the crystals. These streaks result from scratching by pulverized matrix. Be careful not to leave ugly ridges around the crystals when you're using the fine chisel. If these appear, plane down the surrounding rock.

If you are eager to get really spectacular specimens from soft rocks, and have plenty of time and patience, gently chisel the matrix slowly away from the crystals. When you've brought a bit of the crystal into plain view, continue working with a needle.

A talclike (greasy) rock will compress but won't

Use a fine chisel to expose crystals embedded in soft rock. Hold the specimen firmly in a vise by interposing a piece of corrugated cardboard between the jaws of the vise and the specimen.

break either by hammering or by the pressure of a vise. Find the schist planes, where there is least resistance, chisel along these lines, and the rock will split easily. Lift off several layers, and along one of them you may expose the crystals you're looking for.

Sometimes, when working on soft rocks too enthusiastically with your needle, you may scratch the crystals. Try to avoid this, because little can be done to repair the appearance of the crystals afterward. When preparing a specimen where the crystal mass forms the greater part of the surface, you can often remove the soft matrix concealing the crystals with either a fine chisel or a wire brush used very carefully.

When the crystal is embedded in limestone or calcite, acid is the best agent to bring it to light. For more information on this, see page 44.

Massive and compact specimens. There's not much to say about the preparation of such specimens. Usually, there are a great many of them in the field, and you can select the shapes and colors you like best. When you get them home, look them over again to see whether any conceal crystal formations. Retain only those specimens that have fresh surfaces and a pleasing shape.

When working on special forms, such as dendrites or stalactites, take a little time to find out how best to handle them, so that you won't spoil either their unique character or distinctive shape.

Two special mineral forms. (Left) Dendrites of manganese oxide in Jurassic limestone from Solenhofen, Germany. (Right) Stalactite of chalcedony from South Africa.

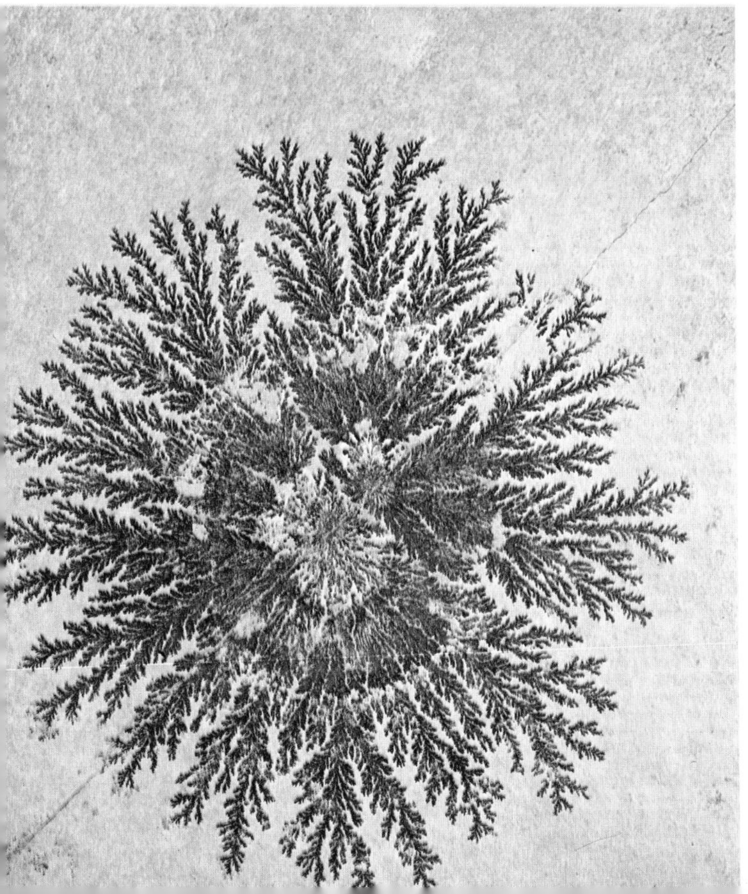

1

2

3

4

5

6

Cleaning a mineral.
1 Using a stiff brush, clean the rock from which the crystal is to be freed. **2** Remove the matrix from around the crystal with a chisel and hammer. **3** Dust the specimen to remove any chips and dust left on it after using the chisel and hammer. **4** Sponge the specimen with water to soften the rest of the rock to be removed. **5** Examine the specimen carefully with a lens from time to time to see how you're progressing. **6** Use the chisel to remove any matter still clinging to the crystal. **7** Finish by using the drill to remove any bits of rock that haven't come off with the chisel. An electric drill is a useful tool for preparing specimens. A large variety of such drills and accessories can be purchased in hardware stores.

7

7

WASHING AND PROCESSING

Before washing it, give the specimen a preliminary cleaning by going over it with a needle. Then soak it for twenty-four hours and, to get out deep-seated dirt, use a scrub brush, a penknife, and the needle again, if necessary. Put the specimen in running water or in a bucket of water, changing the water several times. Don't wash it too vigorously. This could spoil the specimen or detract from the freshness of its appearance.

Obviously, this treatment won't work for minerals that dissolve in water or that crumble easily. When you have to wash a mineral covered with small sharp points or one that scales easily, don't use the brush. Instead, run water over the specimen carefully and examine its condition frequently while you're washing it. Once in a while you'll be processing a specimen of which only a small part will need finishing. Turn it upside down, so that the area to be cleaned faces downward, and wash it with a wet brush. In this way, water will be kept from spreading over the entire surface of the specimen.

DRYING

Dry the pieces thoroughly after washing them to prevent mold from forming, as this can cause surface changes. Residual humidity can damage specimens even after they're stored in closed cabinets or drawers. Work in an open, well-ventilated area and take enough time to be sure the stones

Equipment used in the chemical treatment of specimens. Top, left: A cabinet for reagents. On the worktable: two trays; the one on the left contains acid, the other water. Beside the trays: A metal mesh frame on which specimens are dried.

are completely dry. If they're being dried outdoors, take them in at night and put them back out in the morning. Stones absorb moisture from damp night air.

A simple drying frame is readily made of a wood frame covered with galvanized or aluminum wire mesh. This will allow the moisture to drain off, and the specimen will be ventilated on all sides.

In some regions the wash water is so full of salts that it will leave whitish streaks or a scum on pieces washed in it. Even if these blemishes aren't plainly visible, they will detract from that specimen's brilliance. There is a simple test to discover whether the water is too hard—that is, whether it contains an undesirable quantity of salts. Spill a few drops on a piece of glass, and let them dry. If white spots appear, you'll have to give the specimens a final rinsing with boiled water or, better yet, distilled water, like that used in auto batteries. You can buy this at gas stations and many grocery stores.

ACID TREATMENT

As has been mentioned, crystals of beautiful minerals are often found embedded in calcite or limestone. The fastest way to free them is to dissolve the calcite in acid. This gets rid of the calcite and leaves most other minerals unharmed. Some, however, such as other carbonates, are damaged by this procedure. So before going ahead, test both the crystal and the matrix for resistance to acid.

To treat your specimen with acid, put it in a nonmetallic tray with the surface to be worked on face down. Pour enough acid solution into the tray to cover the face-down surface, but not enough to cover the whole piece. After treatment, wash the specimen thoroughly until all traces of the acid solution are removed and put it on the metal screen to dry.

Hydrochloric (muriatic) acid is cheap, easily obtained, and convenient to use. It is available at drugstores. Use a solution of three parts of water to one of acid. Pour the acid into the water slowly to avoid splashing. *Never pour water into acid.* Place the specimen in a plastic or glass vessel, so that the surface to be etched is face down. Pour in enough acid solution to cover the part to be treated, but don't submerge the specimen completely. The acid will foam up immediately. To prevent it from flowing over the sides of the container, pour the acid in a little at a time. The action of the acid on the calcareous matrix produces carbon dioxide gas, which causes foaming of the solution. This treatment should be checked periodically to keep it from going too far. A nylon cord tied around the specimen before immersing it will enable you to pull it out of the solution occasionally and dip it in clear water. If the acid treatment has gone far enough, remove the specimen from the acid and place it in a pan of water.

To push the acid treatment to the limit, leave the specimen in the solution until all bubbling stops. Then fix a fresh solution and immerse the specimen, leaving it there for at least twelve hours before taking it out and putting it into clear water. It isn't always advisable, however, to push this treatment to the limit. Sometimes the crystals are embedded so deeply in the rock that the specimen would be destroyed by acid bite. Some crystals are so delicate that they need some matrix left around them for support. Usually you'll prefer to leave some matrix because the specimen will then also show the nature of the rock in which the crystals grew.

Once in a while, you'll have to deal with a matrix that does not yield so readily to acid as calcite. Some carbonates, such as magnesite, don't react to cold acid and must be dissolved in a hot solution. Do this work outdoors, if possible, or with windows wide open. Put the specimen in a heatproof glass vessel such as a laboratory beaker, and, in double boiler fashion, place the glass vessel in a pot, but not one made of aluminum. Fill the vessel containing the specimen three-quarters full of acid solution. The level of this solution should be about the same as the level of the water in the pot. Raise the glass vessel about a half-inch above the bottom of the pot by some device such as a piece of shaped wire mesh. This will provide a platform for the glass vessel and will permit the

PRECAUTIONS WITH ACID

Hydrochloric acid must be used with great care. It's vital to follow the basic rule: *always* pour the acid into the water. Remember AAA: *A*lways *A*dd the *A*cid. Put the container for the acid on a sheet of plastic so that any spilled drops won't mar your work surface. If you can, work outdoors or with the windows wide open, because acid fumes in an enclosed room may damage your tools. Keep a bucket of water at hand to wash off any acid that accidentally falls on your skin. And wear a coverall or big apron to protect your clothing.

1

2

3

4

A direct way to remove calcareous material from a specimen is to apply hydrochloric acid with a small brush. **1** To make the solution, pour the acid into a glass vessel containing water, in the proportion of three parts of water to one of acid. (Never pour water into acid.) **2** Moisten the brush. **3** Brush the solution on the mineral to be cleaned. **4** An immediate effervescence will result from the action of the acid on the calcite. To avoid acid burns, it's prudent to wear gloves.

Amethyst quartz as it looked before cleaning (left) and after cleaning (right).

water to circulate freely between the pot and the bottom of the glass.

Keep the flame low; don't cover the pot, and wait patiently. Let the apparatus cool before taking out the specimen with an attached nylon cord or plastic to see whether the treatment has worked. If it has not been entirely successful, try it again. Add cold water to the pot during the boiling to slow down any sudden rise in temperature which could crack the glass vessel.

Some crystals react markedly to acid, and they must be treated in a special way. If they are embedded in dolomite, you'll have to remove the matrix by hand, because dolomite reacts reluctantly to acid. But if you're working on a calcareous matrix around such a crystal, first remove as much of the matrix as you can with a needle and a small chisel. Then get rid of the rest with a little brush dipped in acid concentrate. After each stroke of the brush, when the foam subsides, plunge the specimen into cold water. To eliminate any delayed effect from acid residue, soak the specimen in a weak solution of bicarbonate of soda (one teaspoonful to a quart of water) before washing and drying it.

NEUTRALIZING, WASHING, AND DRYING OF ACID-TREATED PIECES

The preservation of any specimen treated with acid solution depends on the care with which you wash and dry it. Even a trace of acid can harm the specimen and contaminate other pieces in a display case. Be sure to allow sufficient time for the wash water to absorb all acid from the specimen. This can be done by immersing the specimen in a bucket of water and changing the water once a day for five successive days. Then put the specimen on the screen to dry. You have at your command one of the best tests to ascertain whether all the acid has been removed; apply the tip of your tongue to the specimen. If it tastes tart, which is unlikely, you'll have to do further washing.

Any acid is dangerous. Use it with care; protect your hands with rubber gloves and avoid splashing it in your eyes or on work surfaces; use it in glass, porcelain, or stainless steel vessels, and keep an acid solution out of the reach of children or anyone who may not be aware of the solution's nature.

But even after application of the preparation methods described above, some specimens may not yet be ready to appear in your collection. You'll have to look them over and decide what more is needed to shape them to your liking.

TREATMENT WITH THIOSULFATE

Superficial black scales and stains can be removed or minimized by treating specimens with

GETTING RID OF ACID SOLUTION	You can use the acid solution again and again until it no longer reacts to carbonate rocks. When that happens, dilute the acid, one glassful to a full bucket of water, and pour it down the drain slowly, while water runs from the faucets. This will prevent the acid from damaging the pipes or polluting the water. An even better way is to neutralize the acid solution with bicarbonate of soda or a lump of limestone until all traces of bubbling stop. Let the solution stay in the glass container for a day, then pour it down the drain and wash the container.

sodium thiosulfate, which has a bleaching effect. To do this, make a cold solution of thiosulfate, using two teaspoonfuls to a quart of water. Immerse the piece in it for forty-eight hours, then wash the specimen. If it is not brittle, give it a vigorous brushing to remove the blackish residue. If it is acid-proof, give it the acid treatment to remove what stains may have been loosened by the thiosulfate. If one treatment doesn't yield satisfactory results, repeat it.

Oxalic acid, a granular substance obtainable at drugstores or hardware stores, is especially effective in removing the iron stains that often disfigure quartz crystals. A saturated solution is made by pouring the granules into water until no more will dissolve, and the specimen is soaked in the colorless acid until the stains that will come off have been removed. Oxalic acid is a mild poison and should be handled with care. Wear gloves when working with it and do not leave the solution where children might get it. The solution can be used repeatedly. Its most common function in the mineral field is to polish marble.

A highly effecive method of cleaning crystals has become popular now that the electrical machine for that purpose has become less expensive. This is the ultrasonic cleaner—a tank containing water through which ultrasonic vibrations are transmitted to the mineral. Dirt is literally shaken loose by the treatment, along with a great deal of other foreign matter. Use of the device, of course, is limited to fairly robust minerals. Small machines are on the market at a price that any serious collector can afford, but the ones that will accept large specimens are still in the luxury class.

PROTECTIVE AND REMEDIAL MEASURES

Some minerals have a tendency to absorb water, others to lose it. Still others change color and luster from exposure to air. Your first impulse may be to protect these chameleon minerals by putting them in sealed containers. But if you don't want your collection to consist of an array of boxes, you can protect these specimens with a spray of clear lacquer, available in aerosol cans. To do this, tie a string around the piece, whirl it rapidly, and, with the other hand, spray it from a distance of a foot. Do this out of doors, away from any open flame, and repeat the process when the lacquer is dry.

Some crystals fade, crumble, and disintegrate after a while. If this starts to happen, stop the process by coating the piece with petroleum jelly, repeating the treatment every six months or so.

Some crystals with wonderfully vivid colors have pockmarked surfaces or are covered by a dull film. To bring up the full beauty of these crystals without altering their scientific worth, wax them. After preparing the piece and exposing the crystals, remove surface blemishes by rubbing crystal faces with waterproof silicon carbide cloth of 240 or 400 grit. By folding the cloth and using the edge, you'll be able to work on small surfaces. Keep the specimen moist, and rub lightly so as not to damage it. Brush the treated surfaces frequently with a small brush dipped in water. When the blemishes are no longer evident, wash the piece thoroughly and let it dry before waxing.

Clear liquid waxes, such as those used on floors, are best for this work because they don't have to be polished vigorously to bring up the luster. Apply the wax to the surfaces of the crystal with a watercolor brush. To fill in small pockmarks, use a suitable shade of shoe polish diluted with turpentine, and apply it with a small brush. After waxing them, clean the crystals with a cotton cloth and polish them with a bit of wool or a small stick of balsa wood. Use care in applying this beauty treatment that you do not let the wax spread and stain and disfigure the matrix.

STRENGTHENING TREATMENT

Some matrixes are fragile or crumble easily. You can strengthen such pieces and make them easier to handle by treating their surfaces. Put the piece into a solution composed of two parts of a vinyl acetate glue, such as Elmer's Glue-All, to ten parts of water. Take it out after ten minutes and wipe off the excess liquid with paper or a rag. After it has dried, the film of adhesive will bind the crumbling matrix together without materially affecting the color or luster of the crystal.

Collectors generally look askance on specimens that have been waxed, stained, or repaired, unless these measures have been kept within severe limits and have been done without intent to deceive a possible customer. Such treatment should be reserved for exceptional situations and should be described on the specimen's catalog card. One unquestioned way, however, to improve the luster of a crystal is to rub it with the kind of silicone-coated papers supplied to clean and polish spectacle lenses.

CUTTING AND POLISHING

When there is an excessive amount of matrix to deal with, you may have some doubts about how well the removal techniques discussed here will work. In that event, take the specimen to a rock shop or some person who has a diamond saw and grinding wheels to shape the specimen to manageable dimensions.

Polishing of certain specimens, however, is not necessarily difficult, especially when you're working on soft minerals such as marble. It can, in fact, be an agreeable pastime.

If polished stones such as agates, ground to show the pattern, form only a small part of your collection, it would be sensible to seek professional help. But if polished stones bulk large in the collection, why not consider acquiring the necessary equipment for use at home? First give some thought to how much extra space you'll require, and it is advisable to consult several experts about the merits of various equipment manufacturers before buying.

One piece of equipment that will turn stones into desirable specimens is the tumbler. Its use requires little skill; it need not be expensive; and its product is in demand. There are many types of these machines, but all operate on the principle of forcing a number of stones to rub against one another until they round and polish themselves.

GLUING

A broken specimen, especially a beautiful and typical one, can be made presentable, if it is not too badly shattered, by gluing the parts together. The glued piece will no longer have as great value as an unbroken piece, but it can be a joy to the owner, just as is a fine Etruscan vase when properly restored.

For repair work, use an all-purpose glue, available in tubes. First test the joining; find the exact position where the two pieces fit together perfectly, and decide how to hold them together while the glue sets. Carefully clean the surfaces to be glued. Then cover each with a thin coat of glue and press the two pieces together firmly with your fingers for a few minutes. Then tie or clamp them tightly together, or bind with a rubber band.

If the specimen is broken in more than one place, glue one break at a time and allow a full day for the glue to dry before going on to the next break. Repair work of this nature should be done indoors in a dry and dust-free area that is neither too warm nor too chilly.

(Left) Tumbler-polished stones. First row above, left to right: jasper from Nepal; rose quartz and amethyst quartz from Brazil; carnelian from India. Bottom row: agate and aventurine from Brazil and sodalite from the Union of South Africa.

(Top) To polish stones, mix them with abrasive powder and rotate them in tumblers, as is being done in this commercial establishment.

Abrasive grits and polishing materials are added at various stages of the operation. The photos above show a mass of tumbled stones, mostly of the quartz and chalcedony family—agates and jaspers—and large tumbling barrels in a commercial establishment. Slabs as well as rounded stones can be tumbled, and many offered for sale have been made attractive in this way.

CHOOSING SPECIMENS

You probably made a rough, provisional selection among your finds while still in the field. But when you line up on the workbench those that you have kept and take a second look, you must decide, once and for all, which specimens to add to your collection and which to use for trading and as gifts to friends. This is a pleasant task, but not an easy one. Which piece is best? Among three equally beautiful specimens, which shall I keep? Shall I keep only one specimen of each mineral for my collection? If the piece contains several minerals, how should it be cataloged? Which pieces should I use for trading, which for gifts?

Your collection should include the specimen of each mineral that has the most perfect structure—healthy, regular crystals with fresh-looking surfaces—and that also represents the typical appearance of that mineral. If space is limited, keep only one of a kind. A duplicate takes up space that could be allotted to a different mineral; furthermore, the duplicate could be traded for that different new piece. If you are reluctant to part with your duplicates, keep them and rotate them in your display. This will satisfy you and please your friends.

You should have a separate specimen to illustrate each mineral represented in your collection. Select these so that each one emphasizes the mineral you wish to feature. As an example, a pegmatite may yield specimens that contain beryl, tourmaline, feldspar, mica, and quartz. Several of these may occur as distinct crystals, but in one specimen the beryl may overshadow the other minerals; in another smoky quartz crystals may predominate. Consequently, several specimens from that same pegmatite may well appear in the collection.

After you've made your first choices, lay aside some pieces for trading and presents. Pick them carefully, too, because they will be representative of your taste and collecting skill.

SAVING DUPLICATES

Duplicates are useful both for trading and for gifts. Often, they may reveal some novel feature which went unnoticed on first inspection. So take the same good care of them that you give to the other pieces in your collection. Choose a storage place that is easy to get at and that will protect the choice specimens from dust, dampness, and excessive dryness. Don't pile one piece on top of another. Wrap beautiful specimens suitable for gifts or for trading in paper and put a written description of the contents on the outside. Your less desirable duplicates can be stored anywhere—in the cellar, on the sun porch, or in the garage.

Many specimens contain crystals so small that they may be overlooked. Put a colored arrow on the specimen pointing to the inconspicuous crystal.

LABELING SPECIMENS

Labeling is the last step in the preparation of specimens for display. Put a number on each piece. Use arrow pointers where needed to call attention to special features.

Numbered labels and arrows. The primary purpose of numbering a specimen is to provide reference to the descriptive record of it in the catalog of your collection. Numbers can be written by hand in India ink or typed on paper, then glued to the bottom or some other inconspicuous place on the specimen. The professional way is to paint a small rectangle of white lacquer on the specimen and, when it is dry, write the number on the spot with India ink and seal it with a dab of clear lacquer. The small bottles of fingernail polish are convenient for the purpose because they contain a small brush for application of the lacquer.

If you are going to use glued-on numbers for cross-referencing specimens to your catalog, type out about a hundred numbers in sequence and cut them apart when you're ready to use them. If you're going to number an extensive series of specimens, group them according to the localities from which they came. Cut up five labels at a time and put them face up on a piece of dark paper. Being so small, they're easy to lose. Then put a drop of glue on the bottom of each specimen to be labeled and apply the label with a small brush. When you've finished numbering, go on to the next step, which is recording.

Some collectors also prepare another label. On it they write a brief description of the mineral and note details about radioactivity, fluorescence, etc. This label is pasted on the bottom of the specimen next to the number label.

Pressure-sensitive labels are good only for temporary identification. They drop off after a while, and they have little resistance to washing.

Some specimens are too small to hold a label. Put information about these on the boxes that contain them.

Indicator arrows. Many specimens contain important crystals so small that they could easily be overlooked. Call attention to these crystals with small red or yellow arrows, cut from adhesive tape. Put a bit of glue on each arrow and attach it firmly to your specimen, placing it so that it points to the crystal pocket.

8

CATALOGING

The memory is a remarkable machine, but it isn't an infallible computer. Consequently, it is necessary to keep a permanent record of the minerals in a collection. Catalog specimens without delay, registering all the essential facts at once. Supplementary details can be added later if you wish.

The first step in cataloging is to assign a serial number to each specimen. As soon as you've put the serial number on the piece, enter this same number in your index card file or book.

FACTS TO RECORD

The complete record of each specimen should include:

(a) identifying number
(b) name of mineral
(c) variety
(d) structure (crystal, compact, etc.)
(e) other important minerals accompanying it
(f) nature of deposit (on rock, embedded)
(g) where found (quarry, mine, canyon)
(h) district where found (township, county, state)
(i) how obtained (found, given, etc., with details) and date

Here is an example:

(a) #250
(b) beryl
(c) variety—aquamarine
(d) crystal
(e) with tourmaline
(f) in pegmatite
(g) Mount Antero, 12,000 feet
(h) Chaffee County, Colorado
(i) from the Smith collection 1/10/74

Lack of information may make it impossible to complete the record. Some of the chief difficulties are:

The kinds of minerals. Identification of a specific mineral is often quite haphazard. Sometimes it is by hearsay, or because a specimen looks like a piece seen in a museum, or because it is known to occur in a specific locality. After you've learned to identify specimens according to methods used in physics and chemistry, you will be better able to verify descriptions. But even then you'll often be faced with rare or atypical minerals that present special problems. These raise a lot of questions, but sooner or later the answers may be found. In the meantime, if you're in doubt about the name of a specimen, write a provisional name on its card in pencil, with a question mark, and try to get accurate information later.

To save space and time in keeping records, use symbols. There are some that have come into general use over the years. Others are not universally used but have been devised, one by one, as the need arose. Following is a system of symbols that has been in satisfactory use for a long time:

X	Single crystal
XX	Several crystals
XS	Separate—freestanding crystal
MC	Compact mineral
in	Embedded in matrix
on	On matrix
R	Radioactive
F	Fluorescent
V	Variety
⚒	mine in operation
⚒	abandoned mine
∩	quarry in operation
∪	abandoned quarry
≡	rock deposit
C	Collected—specimen found by you
G	Gift—specimen given to you
T	Trade—specimen traded with_____ on _____
B	Bought—specimen bought from_____ on _____

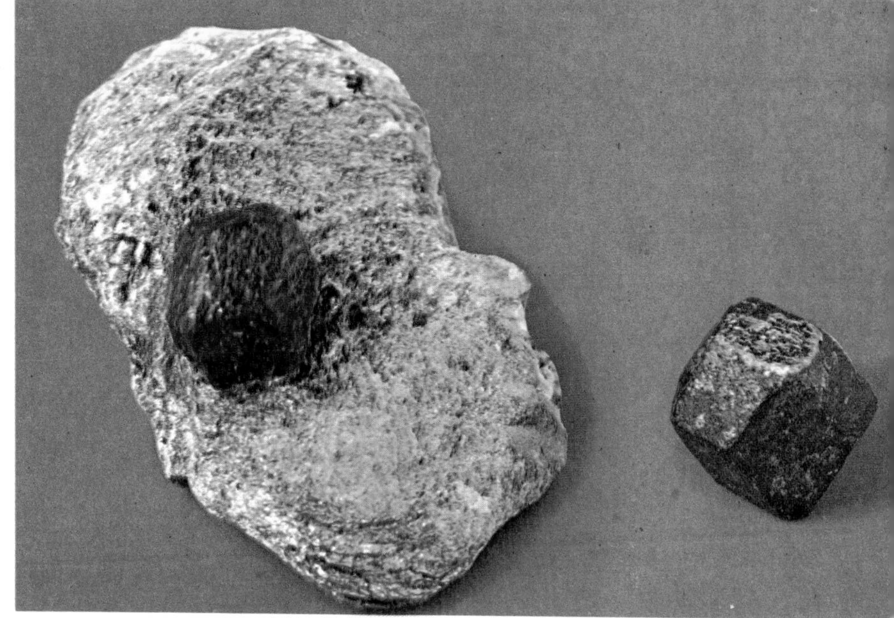

(Top) Garnet crystal on matrix (X on _____) and separate crystal (XS).
(Bottom) Beryl crystal embedded on quartz (X in quartz).

Mineral names. Use the generally accepted name of the mineral, not some archaic name, even though it may appear with a specimen that comes from an old collection. For example, write *diopside,* not *alatite.* Similarly, write *vesuvianite,* not *idocrase.* For the correct choice, consult such a book as Dana's *A Textbook of Mineralogy* (John Wiley and Sons), or *The Glossary of Mineral Species,* by Michael Fleischer.

Varieties. Some minerals are varieties that differ from the basic mineral either in their crystal habit or because they show some accessory characteristic. Here again the best solution is to follow the classification system used in a good textbook, recording the name of the basic material and then giving the name of the variety. For example, record *cuprite var. chalcotrichite* since the latter is a hairlike variety of cuprite.

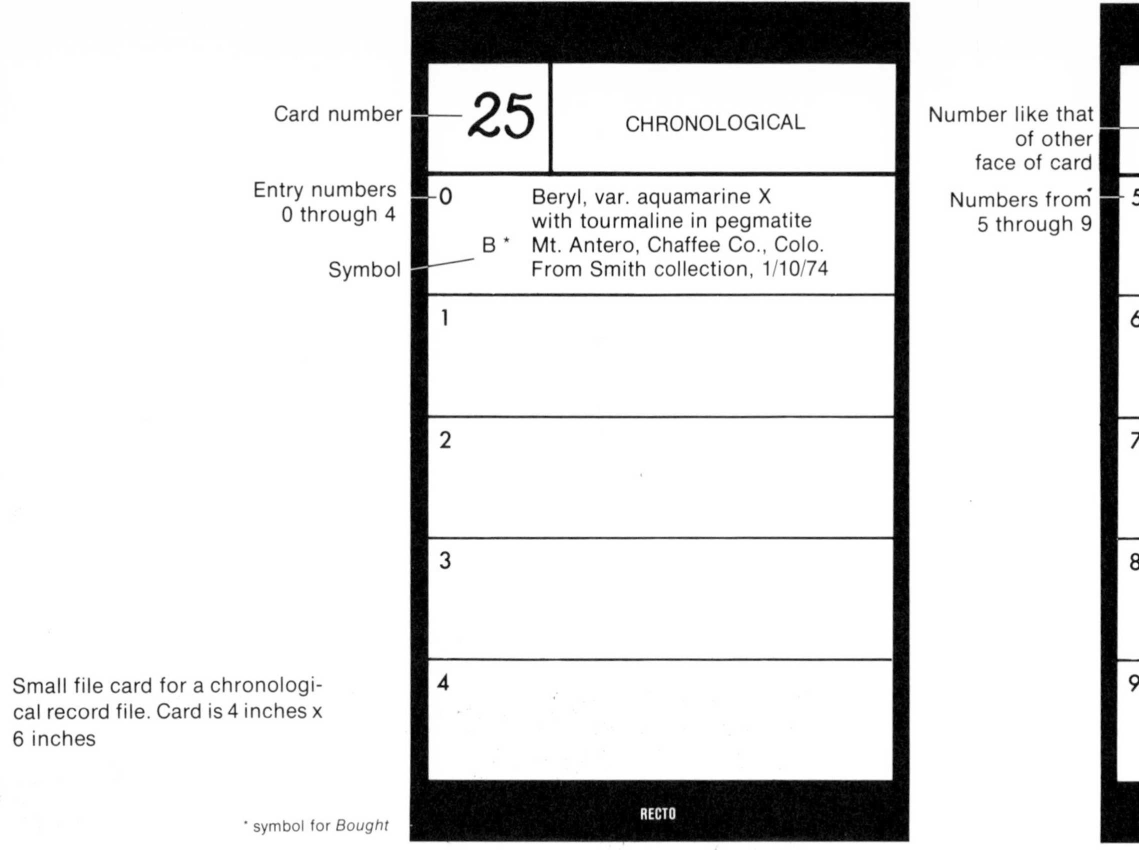

Small file card for a chronological record file. Card is 4 inches x 6 inches

* symbol for *Bought*

Composites and names with multiple meanings. Some minerals are a composite of two or more identifiable minerals. One such is wolframite, an iron-manganese tungstate, which is the general name for a series of mixtures of ferberite, the iron tungstate, and huebnerite, the manganese tungstate. Another source of confusion is use of different names for a mineral, such as the hydrous zinc silicate which is known in the United States as hemimorphite but in some countries is called calamine.

As you accumulate scientific knowledge, uncertainties such as these tend to disappear. For now, record the available names.

Matrixes. It is often far from easy to identify the rocks on which minerals are found, or in which they are embedded, partly because the terminology is not as well established as is that of minerals. That is one reason for making a record of the exact place where a specimen was found, because local rocks are named on geological maps.

The difficulty of identifying the various types of rocks will diminish with practice, and in the process you will learn a surprising amount about lithology and the origin of minerals. You will also begin to understand that there is a connection between the nature of a rock and its mineral content.

Catalog each specimen under the name of the mineral you wish to emphasize, not necessarily the one most prominent in the specimen. By doing this, you'll have a record of what is in the deposit from which the specimen came.

Often you will acquire a specimen, perhaps by purchase of a collection or of an attractive mineral in an antique store or some other unlikely place, which, unhappily, has no name or pedigree. Some collectors give it a catalog number and hope that by study or chance it will become identified. Others will refuse to accept it into their collections. This is a matter of personal preference.

The places. Often you won't know the name of the town in an area where you went hunting. If it's a small place, hidden away in the mountains, itineraries won't always show it. But rock collectors usually identify areas by local features, such as the name of a canyon, a quarry, or a mountain, so note precise topographical features of the area. These can be identified for you by people in the area. When you're not entirely sure of the town, put it down with a question mark. But do record the precise location.

As for the specimens that you didn't collect yourself, record whatever information you can get, subject to later revision.

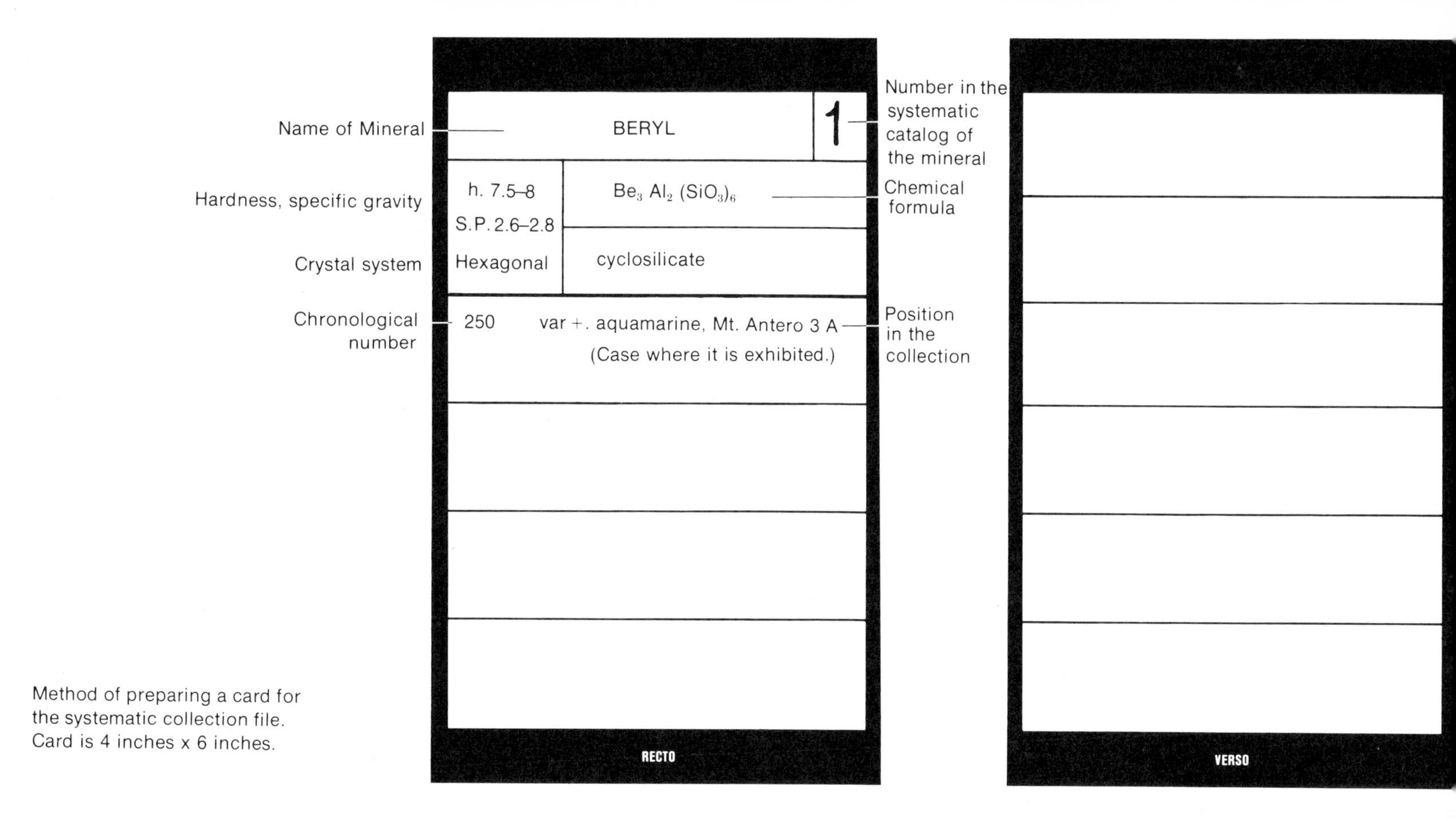

Method of preparing a card for the systematic collection file. Card is 4 inches x 6 inches.

WHERE TO RECORD

A complete record of a collection should include two catalogs. One is what a librarian would call an accession catalog, which records each specimen in the order in which you acquire it. The second will group together like minerals in what is known as a systematic catalog.

The chronological or accession catalog should be kept in a small copybook or on file cards. Records kept on loose sheets are easily lost and with them go vital data. Keep this record near the collection for easy reference. Small copybooks are inexpensive and take up little space. After a while, however, they may begin to look shabby and may be difficult to find when you wish to refer to them.

A box of file cards is not as easy to carry around and costs somewhat more. But the cards are easier to use, less likely to get torn, and when a record proves incorrect it's easy to substitute a new card. It is wise to set up such a file as soon as you start collecting. Don't wait until you've acquired a lot of specimens, because then you'll have to copy casual records into the file. This can be time-consuming. Record every fact clearly, using pen and ink, but pencil in data requiring verification.

For file cards, use white or colored ones about 4 inches by 6 inches. Each will provide enough room for data on ten specimens, using both sides of the card.

The first thing to put down on each card when you start to fill it in is the number. This represents a sequence of ten, and should be written in the upper left-hand corner of the card, as shown in the illustration. For example, the number of the first specimen entered on card number 25 would be 25 plus the line number (the first would be 0), or 250. The next one entered on that card would be numbered 251, and so on.

These cards can be made from those sold in stationery stores and can be housed in a small wooden or metal file box. Or you can have them printed to order. The unit cost for printing file cards goes down as the quantity increases. So why not get together with several friends who also need cards, and make up a good-sized order? Don't stint on the quantity; it's economic to have an ample supply of cards in reserve.

SYSTEMATIC CATALOGING

The second catalog will be a systematic listing organized on file cards.

Start a separate card for each mineral in the collection. On this card, note systematically all pertinent data about the mineral itself (name, formula, group to which it belongs, hardness, specific gravity, crystal system). In addition, write its chronological number, where it was found, and, in pencil, the place assigned to it in your collection, such as a glass case or cabinet drawer. Arrange these cards in alphabetical order in a file box. A collection will rarely contain more than 600 kinds of minerals, without counting each mineral's varieties. These varieties should be entered by name on the card for the primary mineral. You'll need about 800 cards, allowing for future expansion. They should be the same size as the chronological cards, but of a different color.

This systematic catalog provides an immediate, overall view of your collection. It compels you to write down the important data about each specimen and to learn the characteristics of any given mineral. It shows where the specimen was found and where it is placed in your collection. If you consult it every time you're about to add a specimen to your collection, it will prevent you from piling up duplicates.

EXPLANATORY LEGENDS

There are two other procedures which you may find useful. The first is to mark with a symbol on a map the name of the mineral that is in your collection from that area. This will be helpful when you look for specimens to complete your representation from that area.

The second suggestion is that you place small cards with selected specimens in your display case, briefly describing the specimens for the visitor as he views your collection. Don't overdo the use of these cards; they are needed only for minerals that have some exceptional quality that might not be obvious. Don't include in your cabinet, even as background, route maps or written cards and other material that will spoil the look of the display.

USING FILE CARDS

Unless you remember the details clearly, refer to your systematic file before you put a specimen into your collection. You may already have an example of that particular mineral from that area. If so, compare your new acquisition with the old example and decide which one to keep. It may be a difficult choice, especially if the specimens are of equal interest, but try to resist the temptation to keep both. If the piece is new or is to replace an inferior specimen, number it and record it both on the chronological and the systematic file cards. You can cross out the data relating to the discarded piece. Keep the number for the discarded piece open, and don't use it again. The numbers in sequence should show the order in which specimens are acquired, not the actual number of pieces that you own.

NUMBERING DUPLICATES

Store your duplicates carefully, preferably in boxes, although there is really no methodical way of keeping track of them. Put with each one a small card that notes the specimen number and where it came from and when. Location is the vital element in the record of a mineral specimen. Its nature can be redetermined if lost, but a location record gone is often gone forever. Such an orphan specimen has lost half its value and most of its scientific significance.

NEWSPAPERS AND MAGAZINES

Some rock hunters have formed the habit of keeping a logbook, a record in which is noted, as they appear, news items about their hobby. This is a valuable memory refresher which preserves important pieces of information for future reference.

As time goes on, the information in the logbook will be useful in many ways. For instance, it could be a source in preparing papers to contribute to magazines and even scientific journals or for talks before mineralogical societies. But don't cram too much into the logbook; be selective and write concisely.

9

THE HOME COLLECTION

Detail of a cabinet built to hold a mineral collection.

Collecting isn't the be-all and end-all of interest in mineralogy. Love of the outdoors and observation of nature are part of the hobby, too. But the collection does bespeak the effort, luck, and study that have gone into the collector's activity.

There is no simple formula for assembling a collection. Often it is necessary to make compromises, balancing the choice of one specimen against another. So adapt your collection to your taste and space limitations and don't try to give it the character of a museum. Museums, especially in the past, have transformed earth science into a grim, bespectacled muse by trying to show too much and explaining too little of the significance and allure of the mineral kingdom.

BASES AND CONTAINERS

A statue looks unfinished without a pedestal, and a mineral loses some of its display value without a suitable base. A wide variety of bases is available, but in making a choice remember that simplicity is preferable to originality. Usually it is advisable to choose a plain base 1 inch high with standard dimensions of either 2 inches x 3 inches or 3 inches x 4 inches, with one side beveled to take a label. Such bases used to be made of wood, painted black, and were rather expensive. Styrofoam, a polystyrene, generally is used today and has several advantages. It's economical, light, and strong enough to hold a heavy specimen. It adds only ounces of weight to the shelf, often a matter of real concern. It's easy to cut—you can make a hundred bases in a couple of hours. And it's easy to press the specimen into it to hold the latter in perfect position.

Styrofoam can be purchased in sheets at technical supply stores and building material dealers. Cut the sheets with a thin, sharp handsaw, holding the material firmly pressed to the tabletop. This is essential because it has a tendency to crumble. The loose bits take a charge of static electricity and fly into the most unlikely places; you must clean up thoroughly when you've finished. If you want the color of the base to match the specimen, buy a can of white water paint, used for walls, and four little bottles of red, yellow, blue, and black tinting colors. With these you can mix any desired shade.

Bases are less conspicuous if they are cut fairly thin, but the thickness will depend on the shape and weight of the specimen. A flat-bottomed, well-balanced specimen can be attached to a thin base with just a spot of glue, while one with a jagged base must be pressed down into a thicker base until it is securely held and then fastened in place with glue. Braces of the base material can also be glued to the back or side of the base to place an awkwardly shaped specimen so that it shows its best side. If for any reason it is desired to separate base and specimen, this can be done easily by pulling the specimen loose and soaking off any adhering glue and scraps of the base.

Some minerals have to be stored in special containers, either because of their size or their unusual physical and chemical characteristics.

Following is a list of easily obtained containers:

Specimen boxes. Some specimens must be kept in boxes. If you have only a limited number of such pieces, it is wise to buy specially designed plastic mineral boxes, which come in a number of sizes. These contain a Styrofoam base to which the specimen can be glued, and a label can be affixed to the back of the inside of the transparent lid.

Boxes for small specimens. Plastic trays are useful for holding small specimens and fragments that should be saved. Since they are modular, you can assemble them into any desired width or height. They are on sale at department stores and technical supply houses in various colors. Specimens stored in these little containers should have cotton batting or sponge rubber stuffed around them to prevent them from jiggling when the boxes are handled.

Compartmented boxes. If you have a choice collection of separate crystals and gemstones, you will naturally want to show them off. Small, compartmented plastic boxes are recommended for displaying these little pieces. You can get them in department stores in a variety of colors. Another

SUPPORTS

Some specimens are so oddly shaped that they are difficult to display on a base. For such specimens, a bit of putty or similar substance often will do the trick; or the specimen can be made to stand up with a small, well-hidden wedge of wood or plastic, or a stand can be contrived of wire. Several types of ready-made stands are on the market. Putty has an odor and also has the disadvantage of staining many minerals. The easiest way to support a difficult specimen is to press it into a suitably shaped base of Styrofoam, which will yield to its shape readily with a little pressure. Put a touch of glue in the hollow and hold the specimen on the mount until the glue is dry. The specimen can always be removed by pulling it free and soaking the glue off in water.

The habit of wedging bits of other minerals under specimens to support them is unwise. Such props are an unreliable form of support and they add weight on the shelves.

A specimen is shown to advantage on a suitable base. This standard model is wood, beveled for easy labeling **1.** When a specimen has an odd shape, so that it doesn't balance properly, make a support out of putty, as shown. This will keep it in proper balance **2.**

1

2

attractive showpiece is a collection of miniature specimens, each no bigger than a thumbnail—one for each kind of mineral—to use for reference. Such a collection can be displayed in compartmented boxes or in the individual boxes mentioned above.

Hermetically sealed containers. A few minerals change in appearance when exposed to air. For these buy little plastic containers that snap shut and are practically airtight, especially if you have only forty or fifty such specimens to show. You can improve the seal on these with strips of cellulose tape.

When preparing display minerals that absorb moisture, put a little packet of dehumidifying salt into the container with the specimen. You can buy this at chemical supply houses.

For minerals that lose moisture and discolor in a dry atmosphere, put a small dampened sponge into the container. For minerals that react to oxygen, use dry ice (carbon dioxide) to expel all air from the container. Put the dry ice into the container. It will vaporize when it comes into contact with the air there. The gas given off is heavier than air, so it will push the air out of the container. After a little while, put your mineral into the container, closing it tightly.

Minerals that discolor from exposure to light, such as proustite, should be preserved in opaque containers, and those that are so delicate that they shouldn't be cleaned, such as artinite or jamesonite, will need hermetically sealed boxes. An array of these boxes won't enhance the appearance of your cabinet, so store them in a drawer or a closed case. Of course, they should be recorded in your systematic catalog.

THE ROCK ROOM

Every collector dreams of having a rock room for his minerals, with space for well-lighted display cases, instruments and books. Few, however, can afford such a luxury. If you have a country place, it could house your collection but then you could give it your full attention only during vacations when there's already too much to do. If you happen to live in a studio apartment, you might design

1

2

3

Minerals can be displayed in special plastic containers **1, 2,** or wooden boxes **3.** Note the interesting collection in the third tray. Every specimen is quartz, illustrating different varieties of this mineral.

ingenious furniture pieces for your collection, fitting them, for example, neatly between bed and bookcase. But if you're young, you are likely to move to a new place in a few years and might have to leave the cabinets behind. So even if it clips your wings a bit, make do with a modest display for the time being. Later on, when you're settled in a place where you expect to stay, you can indulge in more elaborate installations. Whatever you do, try to keep your display in harmony with your home and its furnishings, and generally pleasing. A well-displayed mineral collection adds to the attractiveness of a living room, hallway, or den, and its scientific value is in no way impaired by being attractive, too.

Basements, sun porches, or garages are often used to house collections, but none offers facilities as satisfactory as a room inside the house. Basements are often damp, which is harmful to minerals affected by moisture. Sun porches are subject to sharp changes in temperature and humidity, which can also damage specimens. In a garage the collection may have to share space with household discards. Another disadvantage to the garage: your pride is hurt when you invite your friends over to admire your treasures and you have to take them into a service area. So, in selecting a place for your collection be guided by judgment and taste and try to make room for at least a part of it inside the house.

ROTATION: HOW TO KEEP A COLLECTION LIVELY

Limited space is a problem for almost everyone, even the world's most famous museums. It's impossible for them to show the hundreds of thousands of examples they own. Even if they could, such a flood of specimens would bewilder visitors. To make it possible for visitors to see and study entire collections, museums now rotate specimens, replacing those on display with others held in reserve, and they do this at regular intervals. This rotation is finding favor with amateurs as well, because of the many advantages it offers.

Rotation of specimens in a display case enables you to use a smaller case yet show all your collection. By using this method, you will be able to key the cabinet to the size and shape of the room instead of to the number of specimens you've collected. It also forces you to review and reorganize your collection periodically. While doing so, you may uncover a good specimen that you had forgotten about and that you can now show occasionally when you change pieces. Rotation also provides an opportunity to arrange special displays, such as theme exhibits built around color, crystalline structure, or chemical formulas. Many ideas will occur to you once you start thinking about your collection in this way, and you will undoubtedly be stimulated to more vigorous collecting activity.

1

Still another benefit is that your visitors won't have to spend hours looking at all your minerals and won't feel surfeited by being offered too much at a time.

All in all, the advantages of rotation of specimens outweigh the natural pride that all collectors have in showing what a large and varied display they have assembled. Active work through rearranging the collection and the added appeal to visitors of a choice, smaller display are more important than satisfaction of vanity.

Examples of cabinets for minerals that are also decorative pieces.

1 Cabinet constructed with glass display cases above and drawers below. Each drawer is divided into compartments.

2 Minerals are placed on a layer of cotton batting in the compartments.

3 An arrangement of shelves with room for about 2,000 specimens. The deep shelves are staggered and adjustable.

4 Metal shelving set up in a hallway, with adjustable shelves and sliding glass panels. Its capacity is about 700 specimens.

2

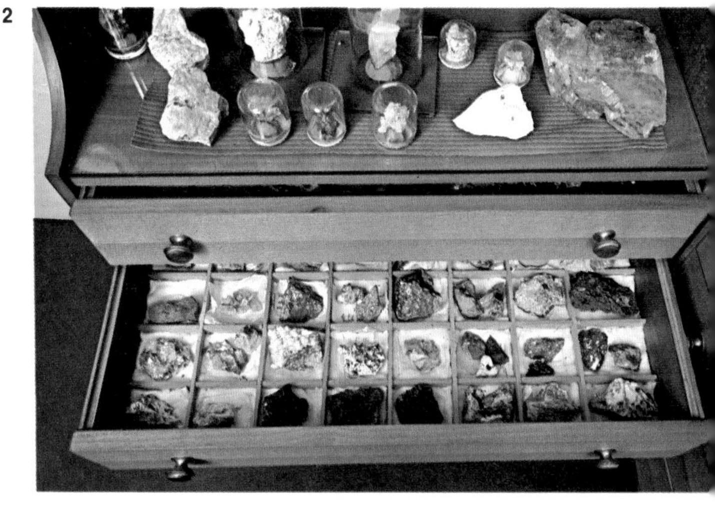

3

4

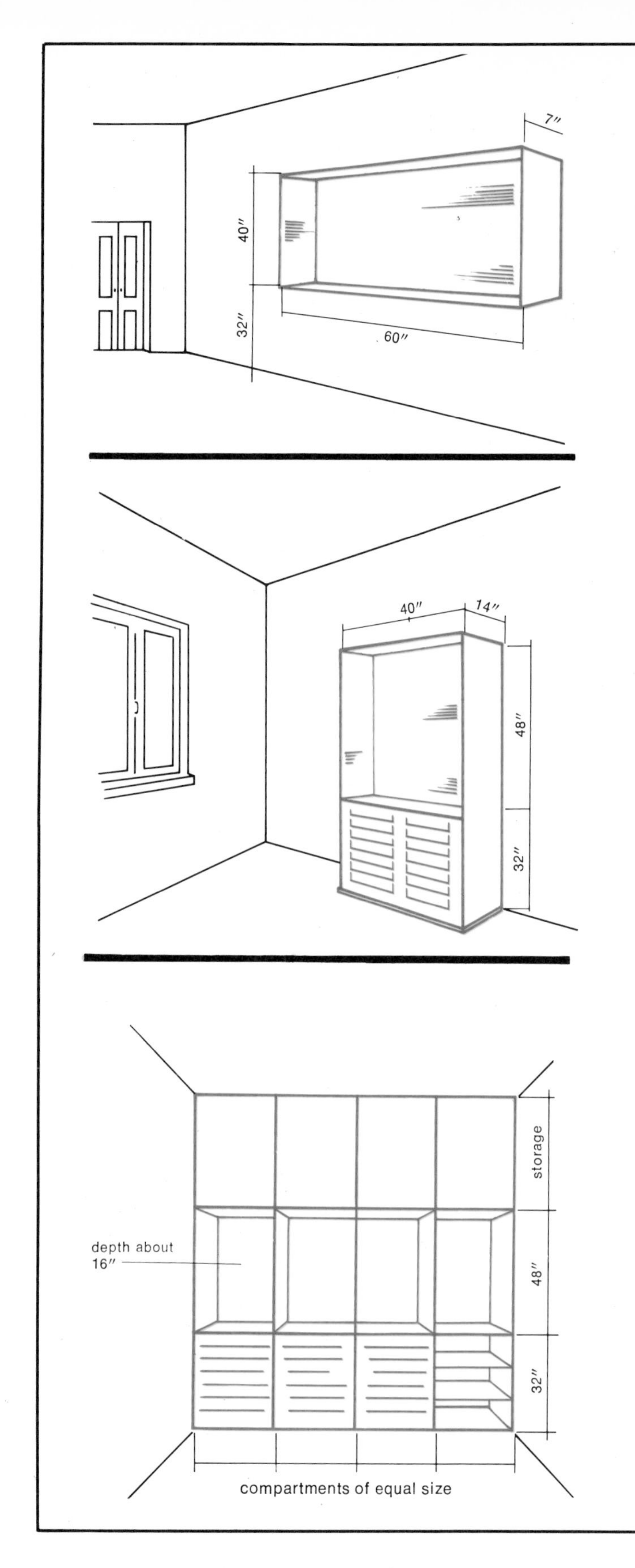

GLASS WALL CASES

These are suitable for use in hallways or on small premises. They should measure no more than 60 inches by 40 inches by 7 inches and should be hung on the wall with the bottom shelf about 32 inches above the floor. With this type of case you can take advantage of wall space in passageways, which is often wasted.

CABINETS OF MEDIUM HEIGHT

The outside dimensions of these pieces are about 40 inches by 80 inches by 14 inches and they can be put alongside one another. The bottom section is made up of storage drawers. The upper part, above the 32-inch line, is for glass shelves. Internal illumination for these shelves is usually necessary.

CABINETS OF CEILING HEIGHT

These are the most expensive, but they accommodate an incredible amount of material. They can be 16 inches or more in depth and are divided vertically into compartments, each not more than 32 inches. Horizontally, they divide into three sections. The bottom one, for storage, is composed of two sets of shallow shelves and one of deeper shelves. The latter can hold instruments and the books you're using for reference. The middle section, some 32 inches to 80 inches above the floor, is a glass case for displaying specimens, with its shelves stepped back. This should be illuminated from inside. The top section which goes to the ceiling has simple, adjustable shelves to take bigger specimens, books, and used instruments. Both upper and lower sections should have sliding doors, and the central section should have sliding panels of heavy glass.

If your cabinets take up an entire wall, you won't need a back panel, side panels, or a top piece. The plaster walls will serve instead if they are coated with a light, dust-resistant, opaque paint.

GENERAL RULES

When designing and building a display cabinet, try in every way to keep it in harmony with its surroundings. Some suggestions:

Show only your most beautiful pieces behind glass and never crowd them. Other specimens should be stored in drawers to protect them from dust, which could affect their color and freshness.

Choose the position of your cabinet so that the specimens will not be exposed to direct sunlight; it can fade colors and cause other damage. The space between shelves should be governed by the size of your specimens.

The zone of maximum visibility for a cabinet is from 32 to 80 inches above the floor. Below that, you'll have to stoop to see, and above it stretch your neck like a giraffe. The best place to stand to view the complete installation is about 20 to 25 inches away, so try to position the cabinet so that it has at least that much space in front of it.

Sliding doors are recommended, and be sure they slide back and forth easily. Don't consider any type of fixed closure. Cases or cabinets that have to be opened with keys or screwdrivers are annoying when you will be handling your minerals constantly and wish to have them easily available.

See to it that the cabinet framework is sturdy because minerals are heavy. The floor where you place your cabinet should be strong enough, of course, to carry the weight of the collection plus that of any visitors who may crowd around to look at it.

Glass shelves are elegant but they're expensive and breakable. Wooden shelves with supports are safer even though not as attractive. Be sure that the shelves are rigid enough to take the weight of the specimens without sagging. One great advantage of wooden shelves is the dust is less visible on them than on glass.

WHAT TO DO ABOUT NEW ACQUISITIONS

As soon as an orderly and pleasing arrangement has been achieved, you will acquire a new specimen that you will wish to squeeze into the collection. If you have had the foresight not to crowd your cabinet, you will be able by a little judicious rearranging to find a suitable place for the new arrival. It's a good idea to keep new acquisitions together until you rotate the specimens in your display cabinet. Then these new pieces can be shown. Not only does such an arrangement allow you some time to decide where to put the new pieces, but it also gives you time to study them and enjoy them while you're doing it.

One final word: Don't use your collection cabinet as a catchall. Keep it neat, orderly, and ready to be shown at all times.

LIGHTING

A good strong light is needed to illuminate specimens; it's difficult to appreciate their quality or to judge structure and color values without it. The light should not be too bright or too close to the specimens, because excessive light causes glare from some white minerals and the lustrous surface of others.

You can actually "model" your minerals with light and shade if you position them skillfully in relation to the lighting. Use daylight fluorescent tubes to keep the colors as natural as possible.

For shallow cases that can't be lighted from within, you'll have to devise a way of putting the lighting fixture outside. Keep the fixture in harmony with the cabinet and place it so that the light

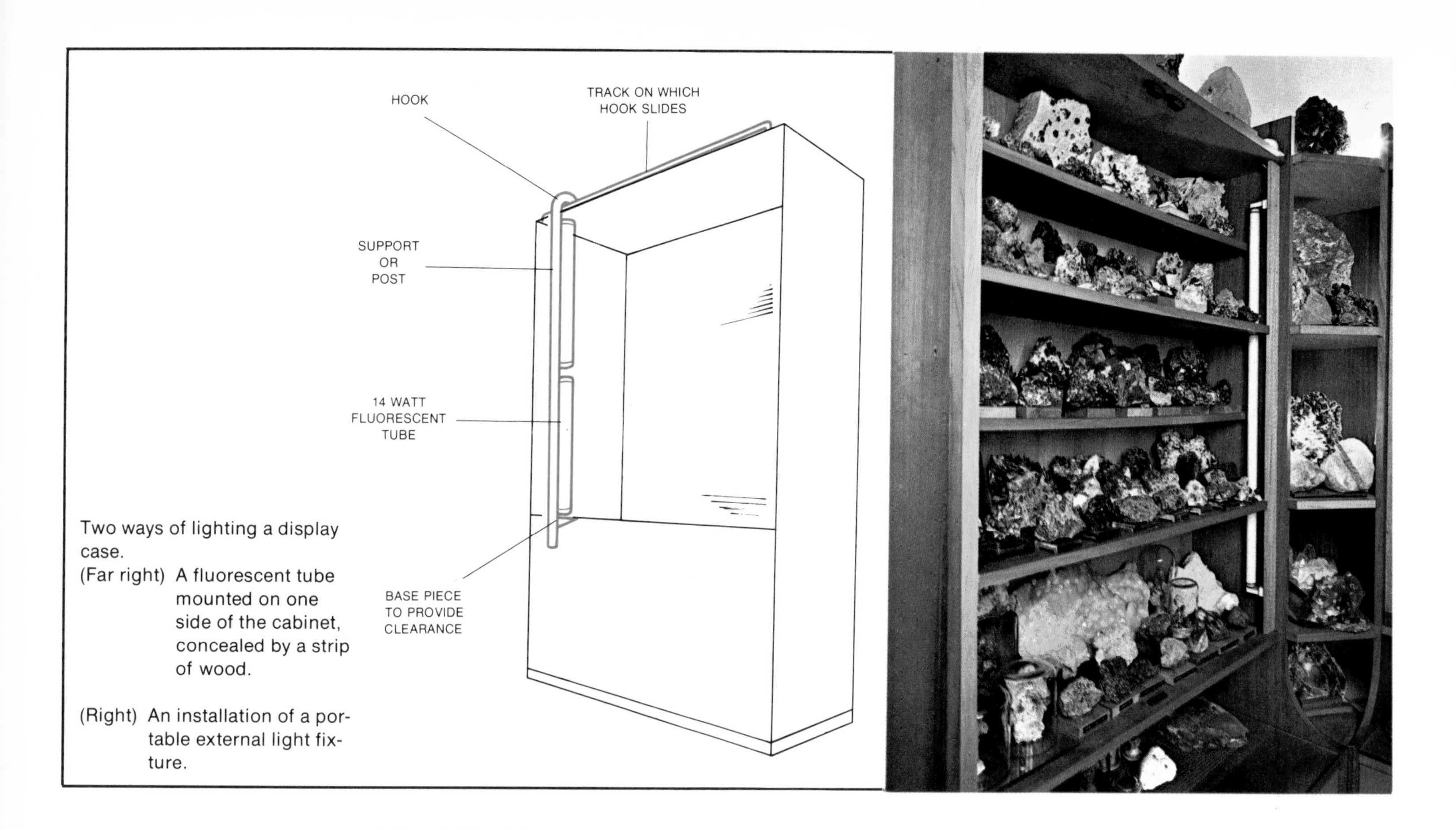

Two ways of lighting a display case.
(Far right) A fluorescent tube mounted on one side of the cabinet, concealed by a strip of wood.

(Right) An installation of a portable external light fixture.

CLEANING

Even in tightly closed cases and cabinets, some minerals are subject to gradual deterioration, which regular maintenance can slow down. All the specimens will in time become dusty.

You already know how to handle those unstable minerals that change in texture and appearance and that often damage specimens near them or the cabinet itself. Lacquer some of these specimens, put others into closed containers, and discard the most troublesome ones. As has been mentioned, washing in the long run harms specimens, and it is not advisable to expose pieces excessively to sunlight and heat.

Most specimens, however, can be kept clean in spite of these difficulties. Use soft brushes or small watercolor brushes and go at the job patiently and carefully. Do the work on a window ledge with the window open, or on a balcony, so that the dust raised doesn't get back into the house or settle on the pieces just cleaned. It's a good plan to use two boxes when cleaning specimens. In one, put the pieces to be cleaned, in the order in which they came off the cabinet shelf. After cleaning, put each piece back in the other box, in the same order.

Some minerals that are too delicate or fragile for frequent brushing may develop tiny cracks in which dust collects. You can clean these with the vacuum cleaner, reversing the action so that it blows air from the tube instead of drawing it in.

Cleaning does take time and patience, but it will keep your collection fresh and sparkling if you do it regularly. Most collectors clean their specimens when rotating them, because it gives them time to examine long-neglected pieces with a fresh eye.

won't cause glare from the glass front or shelves.

In deeper cabinets and those with stepped-back shelves, the fluorescent tubes can be put under the shelves. If the shelves aren't deep enough, the tubes can be mounted upright on the sides of the cabinet and concealed by strips of wood or some other material.

For cabinets with stepped-back shelves containing fluorescent minerals, you can put a 20-watt ultraviolet tube under a shelf. It's useful to place a white light next to the ultraviolet light and control both with a switch (for *off-ultraviolet-white*) so that you can compare the way a specimen looks in daylight and under ultraviolet light. Keep the ballasts out of sight on top of the case. Use the smallest possible switches and mount them on the doorpost of the cabinet. Arrange the entire lighting installation with as much artistry as you can, concealing all wires.

One way to manage this is to use a long support or post hooked onto a slide rod on top of the cabinet, and on which a fluorescent or incandescent light tube is mounted. This is, in effect, a portable lamp, as it can be moved to illuminate any part of the display cabinet.

Fluorescent tubes give more light and are cooler than incandescent lamps, but they do not bring out all colors as faithfully as the latter. For most displays this is not a major objection, however.

10

TYPES OF COLLECTIONS

Mineralogy is a hobby with so many possibilities that a devotee can form a collection reflecting his own special interests and background. If he has a scientific bent, his collection will reflect it by the precise way the specimens are described according to crystal class, chemical formula, and the like. Another, who likes to travel, will group his specimens by the localities from which they came. A third, who has a well-developed artistic sense, will primarily arrange his display according to aesthetic principles. And one who can afford it will go in for collecting gems. If a collector has all of these characteristics and plenty of time and storage space, he can put together several different collections.

No matter what kind of collector you are, you can't get far without a highly developed sense of order. Mineral collecting requires orderliness, willingness to study, and perseverance. Unless it reflects these qualities in the collector, his collection will be just a random display of rocks without any significance.

If you are going to make mineralogy your hobby, be prepared to study. This may be tedious at first, but don't be discouraged by abstruse concepts and difficult terminology. If you get yourself a good textbook, ask advice occasionally from friends, and persevere, material that seems incomprehensible at first will gradually become clear. From then on, the way will be less difficult. The types of collections most commonly seen are:

THE SYSTEMATIC COLLECTION

This collection groups minerals in classes, families, and series in accordance with their chemical and crystallographic similarities, ranging from the simplest, an element such as copper, to the highly complex tectosilicates, such as feldspar. The general classification is an accepted one, but there are small differences over details. In organizing your collection along these lines, use one of the better textbooks as a guide, such as Dana, Hey, or Strunz.

Forming a systematic collection offers several fringe benefits. First, it will increase your knowledge of chemistry and crystallography. Second, it offers the opportunity of showing one type of mineral from many different deposits in one cabinet. And along with this master display can be shown other minerals related to it in chemical composition and crystal structure.

THE TOPOGRAPHIC COLLECTION

The topographic collection is not arranged according to as scientific a method as the systematic one. It groups specimens found in a specific area, regardless of how they look. The area could include a mine, a valley, and a quarry, and the other places usually included in an itinerary. This type of collecting has many practical advantages. One of

CLASSIFICATION OF MINERALS, ACCORDING TO DANA, WITH EXAMPLES.

CLASS 1
Native elements—antimony, silver, arsenic, carbon, mercury, copper, sulfur
CLASS 2
Sulfides—bornite, chalcopyrite, cinnabar, galena, pyrite, pyrrhotite, realgar, sphalerite, wurtzite
Selenides—berzelianite, tiemannite
Tellurides—calaverite, sylvanite
Arsenides—niccolite, skutterudite, domeykite
Antimonides—dyscrasite
CLASS 3
Sulfo-salts—livingstonite, miargyrite, tetrahedrite
CLASS 4
Chlorides—halite, sylvite
Bromides—bromargyrite
Iodides—iodyrite
Fluorides—fluorite, cryolite
CLASS 5
Oxides—cassiterite, chrysoberyl, chromite, cuprite, magnetite, rutile, hematite
Hydroxides—becquerelite, brucite, diaspore, goethite, manganite
CLASS 6
Carbonates—aragonite, azurite, calcite, dolomite, magnesite, siderite
CLASS 7
Silicates *
Nesosilicates—phenacite, garnet, olivine, willemite, zircon
Subnesosilicates—kyanite, titanite, topaz
Sorosilicates—hemimorphite, epidote, ilvaite, vesuvianite, zoisite
Cyclosilicates—beryl, dioptase, tourmaline
Inosilicates—augite, diopside, rhodonite, wollastonite
Phyllosilicates—apophyllite, biotite, muscovite, talc
Tectosilicates—albite, anorthite, leucite, natrolite, orthoclase, sodalite
CLASS 8
Titanosilicates—titanite
Titanites—perovskite
CLASS 9
Niobates—pyrochlore
Tantalates—tantalite
CLASS 10
Phosphates—apatite, monazite, pyromorphite, variscite, xenotime
Arsenates—adamite, erythrite, mimetite
Vanadates—carnotite, vanadinite
Antimonates—bindheimite
CLASS 11
Nitrates—soda niter
CLASS 12
Borates—boracite, colemanite
CLASS 13
Uranates—uraninite
CLASS 14
Sulfates—barite, anglesite, celestite, selenite
Chromates—crocoite
CLASS 15
Tungstates—wolframite, scheelite
Molybdates—wulfenite
CLASS 16
Oxalates—whewellite
Mellate—mellite
CLASS 17
Hydrocarbon compounds—curtisite, amber, petroleum

* A modern expansion of the Dana classification.

Superb examples of minerals worthy of inclusion in a collection stressing aesthetic values. These include (back row, left to right) selenite roses, white aragonite from Sardinia, a beautiful slab of rhodochrosite from Argentina, and (front row, left to right) Brazilian tourmaline, azurite and malachite, and cuprite.

them is that in discussions with friends you may mention that certain minerals are available in a certain place. Then you can point out specimens conveniently grouped according to the topographic method. Another advantage is that any gap in this type of collection becomes obvious, and this could lead you to redouble efforts to complete the exhibit.

A topographic collection takes up about as much space as a systematic one, but because beauty isn't the prime objective you can store the pieces in cabinets together with typical rocks from that same area if you do not have examples of these rocks as matrix of mineral specimens.

A regional collection is a topographic collection embracing one region or zone (for example: southwest Maine; Arizona and New Mexico; or Oregon). Usually, a collection of this type is assembled by a collector who knows his own area inside out. Such knowledge, perseverance, and enthusiasm often bring remarkable results.

THE AESTHETICALLY ORIENTED COLLECTION

Collecting for aesthetic satisfaction can be the most costly kind. It is difficult to find undamaged specimens of exceptional beauty, and if you buy examples, as you almost certainly will, the expense mounts up. Such specimens, however, have high resale value if you ever wish to dispose of them.

If you do have a collection of beautiful pieces, be guided in arranging them solely by how the piece looks next to others in the grouping. Don't try for any scientific order, and don't crowd the pieces in the case. Put them in an attractive cabinet and place it in the room so it will be an important part of the decor.

COLLECTIONS OF MINIATURE SPECIMENS

For some time, there has been a vogue for collecting specimens that do not exceed one inch in any dimension. These are called thumbnails. Such a collection has unquestioned advantages: somewhat lower costs than large specimens, the possibility of obtaining small examples of many rare minerals, and the limited space required for housing them.

Another somewhat larger class—the miniatures—which do not exceed two inches in any one dimension, are also popular. They enjoy many of

A collection of specimens in a plastic case. In these small specimens are beautiful crystals which, seen in all their perfection through a microscope, appear like those greatly magnified below. These crystals are about 1/25 inch in size.

1 Rutile (titanium oxide) from Switzerland.

2 Azurite (basic copper carbonate) from Tsumeb, Southwest Africa.

3 Wulfenite (lead molybdate) from Mexico.

the advantages of thumbnails, but can be quite expensive.

Most convenient of all are micromounts, which are minerals that can be seen and enjoyed only through a microscope. These well-crystallized miniatures are mounted in tiny boxes which have inside dimensions of ¾ inch by ¾ inch. A small case will hold an entire collection. Such specimens make no claims to having aesthetic appeal to the naked eye. But when the specimens are seen under the microscope, it's another story. Then they're magnificent. Such specimens can give the owner immense satisfaction, and in addition there's always the possibility of discovering rarities of exceptional scientific value among the tiny crystals. These collections of miniatures are discussed at greater length on page 109.

COLLECTOR'S CHOICE

With so many ways of forming a collection, how will you decide on which to concentrate? Before coming to a decision, resist the temptation to try to get together several different kinds, all at the same time. This would require a great deal of space, take up much time, deplete reserve trading stock, and crowd the house with inferior duplicates. Once a choice is made, your taste, judgment, and bank account will all come into play in forming the collection. Later on, new interests and changed circumstances may set you off on a new

1

2

3

1	2	3	4	5
6	7	8	9	10
11	12	13	14	15
16	17	18	19	20
21	22	23	24	25

A collection of rocks keyed to the color chart.

IGNEOUS INTRUSIVE ROCKS:
1 white granite
2 rosy granite
3 syenite
(a quartzless granitic rock)
4 gabbro
5 labradorite
(a plagioclase feldspar)

IGNEOUS EXTRUSIVE ROCKS:
6 porphyry
7 granitoid porphyry
8 basalt
9 pumice
10 obsidian

SEDIMENTARY ROCKS:
11 flint
12 red Verona limestone
13 travertine
14 limestone
15 alabaster
16 tufa
17 sandstone

METAMORPHIC ROCKS:
18 gneiss
19 hedenbergite
(a calcium-iron pyroxene)
20 Candoglia marble
21 slate
22 mica schist
23 chlorite schist
24 Carrara marble
25 quartzite.

THE LITHOLOGIC COLLECTION

This is an assemblage of various types of rock. Lithology (from the Greek *lithos* for "stone") is a complex discipline, and one that is constantly evolving. When you start collecting, pick only specimens typical of a class; varieties and subvarieties offer a baffling problem which only the professional in his laboratory can solve. Rocks do not have a definite chemical composition, so classify them according to the natural phenomena that produced them. Rocks fall into three main categories:

Igneous rocks, created by the solidification of molten masses called magma. When such rocks solidify within the earth, they are known as intrusive, and when this occurs on the earth's crust, they are known as extrusive.

Sedimentary rocks. These are formed by deposition of pieces from older rocks. Flowing water, frost, the sun's heat, and wind erode rocks and cause periodic and radical changes in them. The fragments are carried by streams and deposited on lake and ocean bottoms. From such deposits and chemical precipitates sedimentary rocks are formed.

Metamorphic rocks. Because of geological changes within the earth's crust, igneous and sedimentary rocks may be exposed to widely varying conditions of temperature, pressure, and chemical environment. These variables cause the mineral elements to change and regroup into new combinations, which are called metamorphic rocks (from the Greek *metamorphos* meaning "change").

Within each of these three categories are subdivisions, classified according to the minerals of which the rocks are composed. The coarse-grained gray and red-and-white igneous rock familiar from its use in buildings and tombstones is granite. It is an intrusive rock composed of quartz, feldspars, and a few dark minerals, principally biotite mica. Rhyolite is formed of the same minerals, but because they cooled rapidly on the earth's surface it is fine-grained and light-colored, an extrusive rock.

The form of intrusive rock that lacks quartz is called diorite. Darker than granite, it is a drab rock composed of plagioclase feldspar, biotite mica, and hornblende, a black mineral. Like granite, the mineral crystals are clearly visible, but the comparable extrusive rock, andesite, is gray and fine-grained. Darkest of the igneous rocks are those made up of plagioclase feldspar, pyroxene, and olivine, of which gabbro is the intrusive, coarse-grained one and basalt is the extrusive form. The latter is the black rock of lavas; andesite is the gray lava.

Within these groups are some special forms, such as the very coarsely crystallized pegmatite, related to granite, and porphyry, which has a fine-grained ground mass that solidified rapidly near the surface but included already-formed large crystals carried up with it from the depths. The volcanic glass called obsidian is like granite in composition but it cooled so rapidly that crystals never had time to form.

The most common of the sedimentary rocks is limestone, which arises from several natural processes. Most of it was formed by precipitation of calcium carbonate from seawater, where it had been dissolved from calcium minerals crumbled by the weather and brought down to the sea by streams. Dolomite is like limestone in that it contains calcium but united with magnesium as a carbonate with a definite chemical composition. Thus dolomite and limestone are minerals as well as rocks. Both are usually light-colored.

Some limestone is composed of the remains of coral and algae colonies cemented together, and some is made up principally of shell fragments, such as the Florida coquina limestone.

Shale is clay and silt compressed into a layered rock. It is soft and usually dark, but some shales are light-colored. Shale formed where mud and clay were deposited by flowing water, such as on the bottom of a lake or ocean. Many shales will split easily into thin layers.

Sandstone might be regarded as a coarse shale because it is made up of sand grains cemented together. The grains of quartz, feldspar, and some dark minerals in it are easily seen by the naked eye, and for this reason sandstone is easy to identify. It formed where ancient beaches, dunes, and other sand formations once existed.

Conglomerate is the big brother of the sedimentary rocks, for it is made up of rounded pebbles cemented in a matrix of sandy material. It is a fossil gravel deposit where a rushing torrent slowed down and dropped the pebbles it was carrying toward the sea. If the stones in the conglomerate are angular rather than rounded, it is known as breccia, from the Italian for "broken."

The metamorphic rocks are derived from these igneous and sedimentary rocks through changes made by heat, pressure, and chemical fluids from deep within the earth. For example, gneiss (pronounced *nice*) is the product of metamorphic forces acting on such rocks as granite, diorite, and gabbro. It is coarse-grained and, unlike granite which it resembles in color and texture, is marked with bands of dark- and light-colored components.

Slate is derived from shale and owes its characteristics to the metamorphosis of clay particles into flakes of mica. These not only give a dull luster to its surface but provide the flat planes that make it easy to split into thin, even sheets. This is the quality that fits slate to be a suitable material for roofs.

Another metamorphic rock, phyllite, is like slate, but it has a more lustrous surface. It forms from further metamorphosis of slate.

The most easily identified of all metamorphic rocks is schist, in which flat flakes of mica, talc, or other minerals are easily visible. It cleaves easily with a wavy surface and the split surface glistens. Schists are often described by the prevalent mineral in them, such as mica schist, chlorite schist, and so on. They form from extensive metamorphosis of almost any igneous or sedimentary rock or an other metamorphic rock such as phyllite.

Jade, asbestos, and serpentine are products of metamorphism, and marble is composed of crystals of calcite metamorphosed from limestone or dolomite. Quartzite is a metamorphic sandstone in which the sand grains have been fused together.

tack. Perhaps along the way some exceptionally beautiful examples for your mantelpiece or library will be acquired. These need not form the nucleus of a new, aesthetically oriented collection; they have their own place as decorative objects.

You might get together a micromount collection because it presents minerals according to type and variety and will serve as a useful reference in identifying any mineral you're unsure about.

Everyone tends to work within limited geographical areas. Naturally, it's easier to assemble a regional collection than complete representation from a more extensive area, which is difficult to complete. There is no question, however, that the basic collection for any serious mineralogist is the systematic one, and it is recommended that you start with it.

COLLECTIONS ARRANGED ACCORDING TO CHEMICAL ELEMENTS

You might want to form a collection of minerals all of which contain the same chemical element, so you'd put together minerals with iron, with copper, with aluminum, and so on. As examples, some minerals containing iron and copper are listed.

Iron: chalcopyrite, goethite, hematite, ilmenite, lepidocrocite, limonite, magnetite, marcasite, melanterite, native iron, pyrite, pyrrhotite, siderite, vivianite.

Copper: atacamite, aurichalcite, azurite, bornite, bournonite, chalcanthite, chalcophyllite, chalcopyrite, covellite, cuprite, enargite, linarite, malachite, olivenite, native copper, stannite, tennantite, tenorite, tetrahedrite.

PRECIOUS STONES, GEMS, AND HARD STONES

A collection of precious stones, gemstones, and hard stones is a beautiful compromise between a mineral collection and a jewel collection. The objective is an assemblage of all stones that can be cut, polished, and carved to make jewelry or decorative ornaments. This is a highly specialized collection which could include all kinds of artistic objects as well as minerals—everything from crystal spheres to jade statuettes, from pebbles to diamonds, from cameos to paleolithic utensils, as well as from amber to coral, which are not compact minerals but organic materials.

Collection of gems, precious stones, and finished hard stones, arranged in descending order of hardness. Three diamonds (hardness 10) occupy the first little box at upper left. In the last box (bottom row right) is barite (hardness 3).

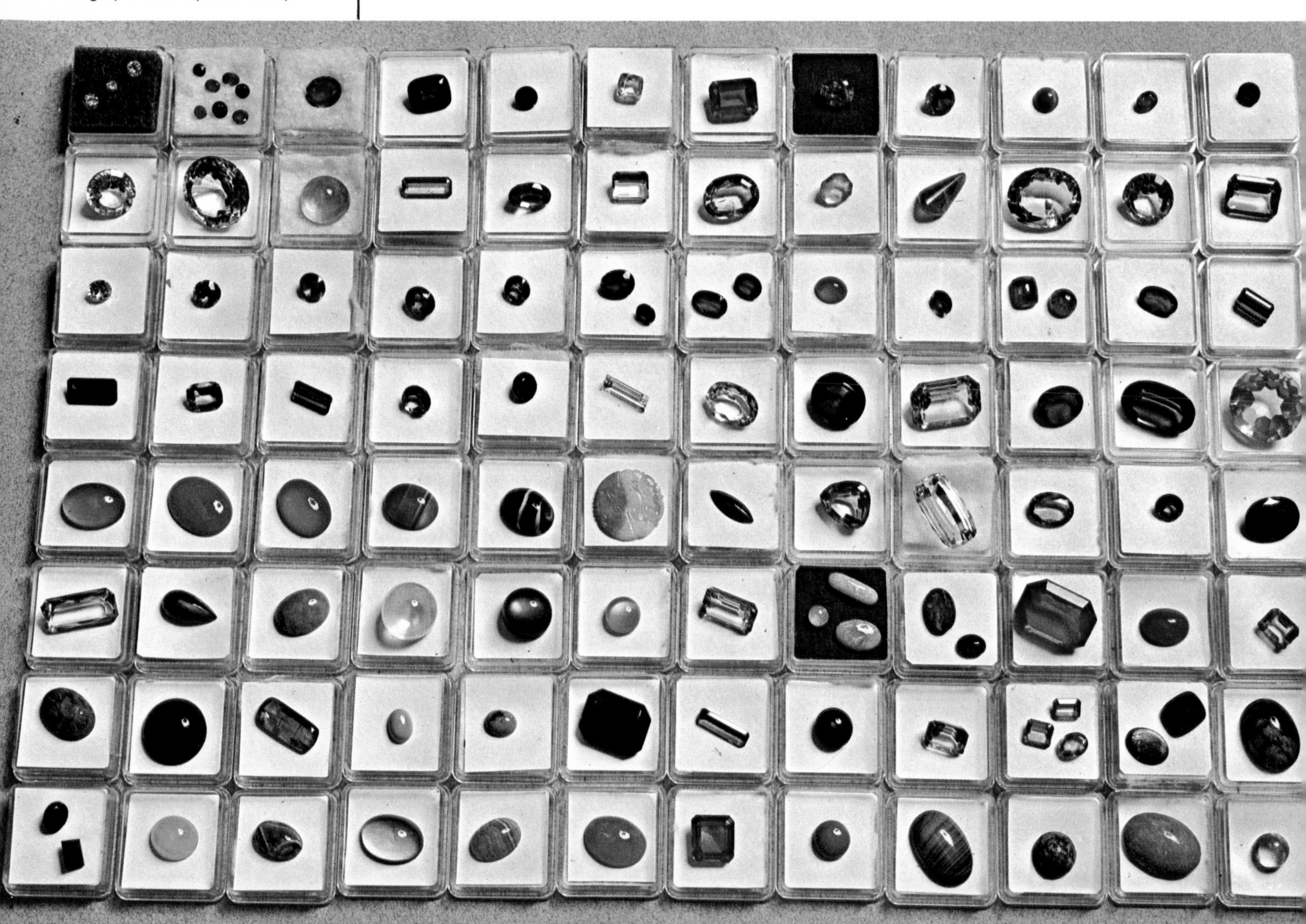

A collection of precious and semiprecious rough stones, keyed to the diagram below the photograph.

1 ruby
2 sapphire
3 amethyst
4 rutilated quartz
5 smoky quartz
6 group of smoky quartz crystals
7 chrysoprase
8 cherry opal in matrix
9 precious opal
10 cherry opal
11 biterminated topaz crystal
12 blue topaz
13 blue topaz
14 golden topaz
15 green tourmaline
16 blue tourmaline
17 red tourmaline
18 black tourmaline
19 almandine garnet
20 aquamarine
21 labradorite
22 Madagascar zircon
23 green spodumene
24 kunzite
25 blue zircon
26 jadeite
27 emerald
28 emerald
29 essonite garnet
30 demantoid garnet
31 brazilianite
32 amblydonite
33 Persian turquoise
34 apatite
35 fluorite
36 variscite
37 rhodochrosite
38 malachite
39 sphalerite.

11

HOW TO ENRICH YOUR COLLECTION

The best way to make your collection significant to yourself is by fieldwork. The primary aim of mineralogy is not to pile up rocks but rather to study nature, which is best done by trips into the field. A mineral you found yourself is bound to have more significance than one acquired in some other way.

Collecting has become much easier since certain tools and modes of transportation that were once restricted to the privileged few are now generally available. Take advantage of all these conveniences, but in doing so don't forgo the fascinating walks and rugged experiences that form such an important part of mineral collecting.

TRADING

No one can hope to visit all the gem or mineral deposits in the world. So to obtain specimens from places you can't get to, you will have to trade or buy.

Trading will be easier if you build up acquaintances with friendly collectors at home and abroad and if you attend conventions and rock swap meetings. Such affairs are sponsored by mineralogical societies and occur frequently.

When trading, most collectors tend to overvalue their own specimens. They remember the difficulties and fatigue experienced in obtaining the pieces and forget that the other fellow feels the same way about his minerals. When you trade, try to judge values as objectively as possible. Sometimes a trade will be proposed to you in a letter; sometimes you may suggest a trade this same way. When you do, send a detailed list of what you have available for trading and invite your correspondent to do the same. If a trade seems in the making, the one who wrote first should send specimens to the other for consideration. Then, depending on what is submitted in return, decide whether to make a deal or drop the matter. Normal procedure for this kind of correspondence is to confine your reply to technical comments on the minerals.

Sometimes you can make a trade with a dealer. Naturally, he will have to make a profit, but if you acquire a piece that's hard to find, the trade will be to your advantage, too.

TRADING DAYS

Swapping shows offer the best opportunities for enriching your collection—you can exchange specimens, make new acquaintances, and often pick up useful information.

Mineralogical societies organize these affairs, which draw a large attendance. You would do well to bring some of your best duplicates and arrange them tastefully.

A mineral swap held in a room of the Castello Sforzesco, under the auspices of the Lombard Mineralogical Society. This society has quarters near the City Museum of Natural History in Milan, Italy.

Pieces most in demand are those with good crystals, well formed, with good color, about 2 inches by 3 inches and 3 inches by 4 inches, except for fluorescent specimens. Wander among the exhibits, and when you see a piece that interests you, invite its owner to see whether you have anything that interests him. Actually, most trades are based as much on the desire to acquire a special piece as on the sale value of the specimens involved.

Mineral, gem, and fossil collecting and jewelry and lapidary work are all represented among the interests of a well-organized system of about a thousand clubs in the United States, organized into six regional federations and all generally included in a national federation. Most clubs sponsor annual shows at which members exhibit and dealers sell; the regional federations hold big shows annually, and each year one of them is host to the national convention and show, at which nearly all major dealers will be present with their merchandise and hundreds of hobbyists will show what they have done.

At many of the shows, rock swapping will be an organized activity. In addition, state groups of clubs hold annual rock swaps where specimens are exhibited on tables behind a trailer or camper

A collection of mineral specimens at the premises of a large dealer.

PACKING AND SHIPPING SPECIMENS

Too often, a fine piece is ruined because of inadequate packing and rough handling in transit. Proper packing is particularly important when sending minerals or gems by mail. Each piece should be packed separately. Wrap it in tissue paper, then put it in a box, packing tissue or cotton around it so it cannot move. Wrap the box loosely in a couple of layers of newspaper to keep the package soft. Then tie it up loosely. Wrap fragile pieces in two pieces of corrugated cardboard, placing them crosswise with the specimen centered on them. Fold the cardboard around the specimen and tie the package loosely. Put delicate minerals such as little tufts of artinite into small boxes. Wrap deliquescent minerals in plastic and then use ordinary double-wall corrugated paper containers. Pack the pieces as close together as possible in the container, stuffing wads of paper in all open spaces. Use heavy paper for wrapping the container. With paper tape or vinyl adhesive tape, seal the flaps of the carton and the outside wrapping, and tie the package with sturdy twine if the weight of the package seems to require it.

Put the name of the addressee and the sender on the package and mark it as fragile. Special handling or air express fees will generally insure more careful handling in the mails. Parcel post, of course, can be insured, but that will not replace damaged specimens. The maximum allowable weight for a package is 40 pounds and the maximum size is 84 inches for combined length and girth.

In the United States, Greyhound Lines and the United Parcel Service often assure more careful and faster service than the mails. Large sacks of heavy rocks can be sent cheaply as railroad freight.

MAJOR MINERAL COLLECTIONS

Representative museums and other public agencies that have mineral collections are listed below. There are many more local displays. Information about them may be obtained at those listed here. It may be necessary at some academic institutions to make prior arrangements to see the specimens.

Alabama: Museum of Natural History, University.
Arizona: Petrified Forest National Monument, Holbrook; University of Arizona, Tucson.
California: County Museum, University of California and University of Southern California, Los Angeles; Natural History Museum, San Diego.
Colorado: University of Colorado Museum, Boulder; Museum of Natural History, State Museum, and Bureau of Mines, Denver.
Connecticut: Peabody Museum, Yale University, New Haven.
Delaware: University of Delaware, Newark.
District of Columbia: National Museum of the Smithsonian Institution, Washington.
Florida: University of Florida, Gainesville.
Georgia: University of Georgia, Athens; State Museum, Atlanta.
Hawaii: Bishop Museum, Honolulu.
Illinois: Field Museum of Natural History, Chicago; Lizzadro Museum of Lapidary Arts, Elmhurst; State Museum, Springfield.
Indiana: Indiana University, Bloomington.
Iowa: Geological Survey Building, Iowa City.
Kansas: Natural History Museum of University of Kansas, Lawrence.
Kentucky: University of Kentucky, Lexington.
Louisiana: State Museum, and Tulane University, New Orleans.
Maine: Hamlin Memorial Hall, Paris; State Museum, Augusta.
Maryland: Johns Hopkins University and Academy of Sciences, Baltimore.

Massachusetts: Harvard University Mineralogical Museum, Cambridge; Smith College, Northampton; Mt. Holyoke College, South Hadley.

Michigan: University of Michigan Mineralogical Museum, Ann Arbor; Cranbrook Institute of Science, Bloomfield Hills.

Minnesota: Natural History Museum of the University of Minnesota, Minneapolis.

Missouri: University of Missouri, Columbia; City Museum, Kansas City; School of Mines, Rolla.

Montana: School of Mines, Butte.

Nebraska: University of Nebraska and State Museum, Lincoln.

Nevada: State Museum, Carson City; School of Mines Museum, Reno.

New Hampshire: University of New Hampshire, Durham.

New Jersey: Mineralogical Society Museum, Newark; Princeton University, Princeton; Franklin Museum, Franklin.

New Mexico: University of New Mexico, Albuquerque; New Mexico Mining Institute, Socorro.

New York: State Museum, Albany; American Museum of Natural History, Columbia University Geology Museum, Metropolitan Museum of Art, all in New York City; Vassar College, Poughkeepsie.

North Carolina: University of North Carolina, Chapel Hill; Colburn Museum, Asheville; National Park Service Museum, Spruce Pine.

Ohio: State Museum, Ohio State University, Columbus; Museum of Natural History, Cincinnati; Museum of Natural History, Cleveland.

Oklahoma: Gould Hall and Stovall Museum of University of Oklahoma, Norman.

Oregon: University of Oregon, Eugene; Museum of Science and Industry and State Department of Geology, Portland.

Pennsylvania: Bryn Mawr College, Bryn Mawr; Geologic Survey, Harrisburg; Academy of Natural Sciences, Wagner Free Institute, Philadelphia; Carnegie Museum, Pittsburgh.

Rhode Island: Roger Williams Park Museum, Providence.

South Carolina: University of South Carolina, Columbia.

South Dakota: School of Mines, Rapid City; State University of South Dakota, Vermillion.

Tennessee: Vanderbilt University, State Museum, Nashville.

Texas: Memorial Museum, Austin; Natural History Museum, Houston; Witte Museum, San Antonio.

Utah: University of Utah Geology Museum, Salt Lake City; John Hutchings Museum, Lehi.

Vermont: Fleming Museum of University of Vermont, Burlington.

Virginia: Virginia Polytechnic Institute, Blacksburg.

Washington: State Capitol Museum, Olympia; University of Washington, Seattle; Public Museum, Spokane; Ginkgo Petrified Forest Museum, Vantage.

Wisconsin: Lawrence College, Appleton; Beloit College, Beloit; University of Wisconsin, Madison, and Milwaukee.

Wyoming: State Museum, Cheyenne; University of Wyoming, Laramie.

CANADA

Alberta: University of Alberta, Edmonton.

British Columbia: University of British Columbia, and City Museum, Vancouver; Mineral Museum, Victoria.

Manitoba: Civic Auditorium Museum, Winnipeg.

New Brunswick: New Brunswick Museum, St. John; University of New Brunswick, Fredericton.

Newfoundland: Memorial Museum, St. John's.

Nova Scotia: Dalhousie University Museum, Halifax.

Ontario: National Museum, Ottawa; Queen's University, Kingston; Royal Ontario Museum, Toronto.

Quebec: McGill University, College de Montreal, Montreal.

MEXICO

Mexico City: National Museum.

rig as well as inside a tent or building. These are informal occasions which often open up the resources of a certain region as no other trading session can.

Larger cities in Canada have clubs and similar activities which are also organized into federations.

PURCHASES

If you lack an example that you haven't been able to find or acquire in trade, you'll have to buy it. Go to the best dealer you know, or see what you can buy at a mineral show or convention, where dealers will show their material. Getting a good specimen this way won't give the same thrill as if you had found it yourself, but often it is the only way to get a specimen from a recently discovered mine or from one so long exhausted that only when an old collection comes on the market is it available. This is true of Mexican and southwest African material and classics from German and Arizona sources, for example.

THE VALUATION OF SPECIMENS

The value of any piece depends on how eager a collector is to own it. This is also true for works of art and other collectible things. Dealers translate this eagerness into cash valuations, and that's how selling prices are established.

Although dealings in minerals are extensive, they haven't yet reached the level at which competition is the deciding factor. Prices from different dealers vary considerably; don't be in too great a hurry to buy. Take the time to compare offerings and prices from a number of sources. A good starting place for comparison shopping is a mineral society show where many dealers offer their wares. You can also learn a lot from mineral hobby magazines and dealers' specimen lists.

12

INTERESTING BYWAYS FOR COLLECTORS

Every true rock hound is by nature a student and keen observer, with a desire to accumulate information about his specimens. One way to broaden knowledge of mineralogy is by study of physics, chemistry, crystallography, and geology. Any good mineralogy textbook will give examples of the mechanical, optical, electrical, magnetic and crystallographic properties of minerals.

With these texts and using your own specimens, you can prepare exhibits in small boxes which will illustrate Mohs' scale (see page 99), color, specific gravity (page 96), examples of double refraction with Iceland spar, pleochroism with ruby, piezoelectricity with tourmaline (page 91), natural magnetism with magnetite (page 100), and others. You will have little difficulty in finding specimens to illustrate crystal systems (page 90). Making cardboard models of crystals helps to memorize the systems. When you've finished them, stow the exhibits away in a convenient corner. It will be an im-

Double refraction caused by a crystal of Iceland spar (calcite).
1 Pyritized fossil ammonite of the Jurassic period, from Brazil.
2 Kaolinized chalcedony with center of amethyst quartz.

1

2

1

2

Artificial crystals:
1 Crystals of potash and chrome alum deposited on quartz matrix.
2 Crystals of potassium bichromate deposited on quartz crystals by chilling a supersaturated solution.

portant information resource for you, and an attractive exhibit for your friends.

FORMATIONS

Along with these specimens, store such crystallographic oddities as rose-shaped crystal groups and twin crystals. You undoubtedly own examples of these, but they're probably scattered throughout your collection. Include other rock formations that you are unable to identify as specific minerals, such as zeolites, stalactites, dendrites, and pisolites. All of these are noteworthy specimens. Some fossils fit into this group, too, such as pyritized seashells and petrified wood.

ARTIFICIAL CRYSTALS

In addition to minerals found in nature, there are numerous artificial crystals that you could include in your special interest corner.

It will give you pleasure to make these yourself.

Heat a quart of water in an enameled pan. Add 9 ounces of potash alum (rock alum obtainable in drugstores) and stir. After the solution comes to a boil, remove the container to a place that is free from vibration, tie a fragment of noncalcareous rock, such as quartz, to a string, and suspend it in the liquid, keeping it at least an inch away from the sides and the bottom of the container. Insulate the container with cloth or Styrofoam and let it stand absolutely quiet for at least three days. When you take out the quartz you will be delighted to find it covered with clear crystals of alum. By dissolving varying amounts of chrome alum in the solution, you can get crystals of every shade of violet. If you use potassium bichromate you'll get yellow crystals.

In making artificial crystals, keep these general rules in mind:

There is a direct ratio between the amount of water and its temperature and the amount of material it will dissolve. Lowering the temperature or allowing the solvent to evaporate causes deposition of crystals on the fragment.

The larger the quantity of solution, the greater the freedom from vibration, the longer the cooling period—the more perfect the crystals will be.

ARTIFICIAL OR NATURAL MINERALS?

Since we are discussing artificial minerals, perhaps this is a good time to reevaluate your specimens and to question whether any that appear to be entirely natural could be regarded as the product of man's activity.

Man has altered many aspects of nature—he has dug tunnels, discharged great masses of material into the sea, and brought about conditions that have created such minerals as chalcanthite (copper sulfate). Other examples of these transformations connected with man's activities are minerals formed by the action of salt water flowing over dumps of ancient mines such as those at Laurium, Greece, and exposure to weathering at the United Verde mine dumps at Jerome, Arizona. Such minerals, created involuntarily by man, are recognized as natural, however, and should be represented in your collection.

13

WARNING AGAINST POSSIBLE DANGERS

Previous pages have emphasized that the rock hound is exposed to certain dangers. Some of these will be encountered on field trips and some in the preparation of specimens. There is no need for alarm, but do keep in mind that accidents—some of them potentially serious—can be avoided by taking sensible precautions. Most accidents are caused by negligence, ignorance, or heedlessness. Accidents can't be avoided entirely, but they can certainly be minimized.

IN THE FIELD

Never go on a trip alone; take a friend along. Use only good equipment, especially tools with good handles that are not slippery. Wear gloves, wear goggles, and keep your face as far away as you can from any piece you're hammering. Don't roll stones downhill when there are people further down; if you should do so accidentally, shout a warning. Be wary of large, precariously balanced rocks. When climbing over rock formations, make sure with each step that you have a secure footing. When examining active mine dumps, work from the top toward the bottom, first making sure that during your visit there will be no dumping from the mine. Keep away from danger spots such as wet slabs, wells, abandoned mine shafts, and overhanging walls. If a quitting time has been arranged in advance, stop collecting exactly on time. If time presses, abandon your specimens rather than lingering there. When it's necessary to seek cover from a storm, never stand under a tree. If you're walking up the bed of a mountain stream, first make sure that there are no dams or manufacturing plants upstream that could unexpectedly open their water gates and catch you in a flood, and that no mountain storm that could fill the canyon with water is expected.

Arrange your knapsack so that it rests firmly on your shoulders. It shouldn't sway from side to side—it might throw you off balance as you go downhill—nor should it thump against your kidneys. Carry your tools so that they can't jab into you if you fall; for example, picks should be carried with the points facing away from you.

Tetanus shots are advisable; the peace of mind they give is worth the small expense. Snakebite serum is indispensable; so is a little first aid kit. In desert or rocky country, always move stones with your pick and wear gloves, long trousers, heavy socks, and boots. A snake or scorpion might be under the stone. All wounds, no matter how slight, should be disinfected and taken care of.

WHEN PREPARING SPECIMENS

The dangers here are mainly pricks, scratches, blisters, and contusions from misdirected hammerblows; acid burns; and dust in your eyes. Most of these can be avoided by being careful and working slowly and calmly. Haste not only results in sloppy work; it also often causes accidents.

WITH THE SYSTEMATIC COLLECTION

Be sure your floor is strong enough to hold the weight of your minerals, plus that of visitors who come to see it. Remember that if you look directly at an ultraviolet lamp it can harm your eyes. So can prolonged use of the microscope.

Part II

HOW TO RECOGNIZE MINERALS

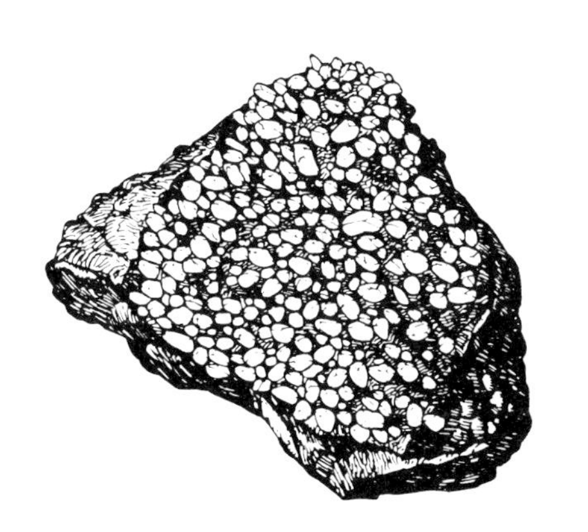

14

THE AMATEUR'S GUIDE TO IDENTIFYING SPECIMENS

When you see an unfamiliar mineral, you may ask, What is it? Especially if it has beautiful crystals. A dealer or an experienced collector will usually be able to give a prompt answer. In most instances the specimen will be accompanied by a little card, giving its name, place of origin, and perhaps its chemical formula and the date when it was found.

But if, during a trip, you should pick up a puzzling specimen, there will be no legend with it. It's easy to identify some minerals, such as the quartz crystals so common in rock cavities, especially after you've had a little experience, but others are more difficult. For example, if you see tiny shining crystals on the quartz crystals the chances are that you won't know what they are. As a rule, it's best to ask an experienced friend. Often, he can give you an answer at a glance, and will say, "It's titanite," or "It's albite" or "It's apatite," or whatever.

Occasionally, however, even an expert will be stumped. Because of this difficulty in identification, many interesting specimens (occasionally rare ones) are taken home only because they happen to have some fairly good quartz or beryl crystals. In Switzerland, collectors tell about some wonderful axinites (complex silicates) from Piz Va-

Clear quartz crystals in a pocket of pink rhodochrosite crystals.

Apatite on quartz from Panasqueira, Portugal. Quartz is easily recognized, but identifying the minerals accompanying it often requires special tests.

Vanadinite, a mineral that contains the uncommon element vanadium. The crystals are six-sided with flat terminations. Fine specimens come from Arizona and Morocco. This one is from Mibladen, Morocco.

lascha which lay neglected for a long time and were about to be thrown out by the owner because he was interested only in beautiful quartz crystals. Recently, in California, a rare beryllium borate—hambergite—was recognized among ordinary crystals discarded in the course of mining for garnets.

In Illinois, gravel pit operators ignored small geodes, but when the pit was abandoned, a curious collector accidentally discovered that these were filled with millerite, the rare nickel sulfide, and started a local stampede to the pit.

Likewise, in the Black Hills of South Dakota, the dark masses of triphylite were generally disregarded by seekers of rose quartz and big mica specimens, but modern X-ray diffraction analysis of these lumps has discovered a wide spectrum of rare phosphates. This also happened at similar deposits in Maine and New Hampshire, where glamour minerals alone caught the attention of collectors. No doubt there are countless other examples around the world.

Interesting discoveries can still be made, not only in the field but also by careful combing through dealers' stocks of minerals. The writer was once offered a specimen of legrandite (a rare zinc arsenate) from Mexico. But quite unbeknownst to the seller, this specimen also had beautiful crystals of paradamite, an even rarer mineral. Similarly, a rare specimen of copper arsenate (euchroite) was mistaken for an inferior example of dioptase (hydrous copper silicate), and sold in error as such.

Of course, the opposite can happen, too. Specimens of ordinary minerals may be offered as rarities. The best precaution is to buy only from a reputable dealer who does not misrepresent his specimens and who will make good on any mistakes.

In collecting, the amateur with the means and the ability to identify specimens is at a decided advantage. The problem is how and how far the enthusiastic amateur can go toward identifying the different minerals.

THE PROBLEM OF IDENTIFICATION

Usually, identification of a rare mineral calls for a great deal of work by an expert in a well-equipped laboratory. Chemical analyses are necessary—not just a qualitative analysis to identify components, but also a quantitative analysis to find the amount of each chemical element present in the specimen. These analyses must be done by trained tech-

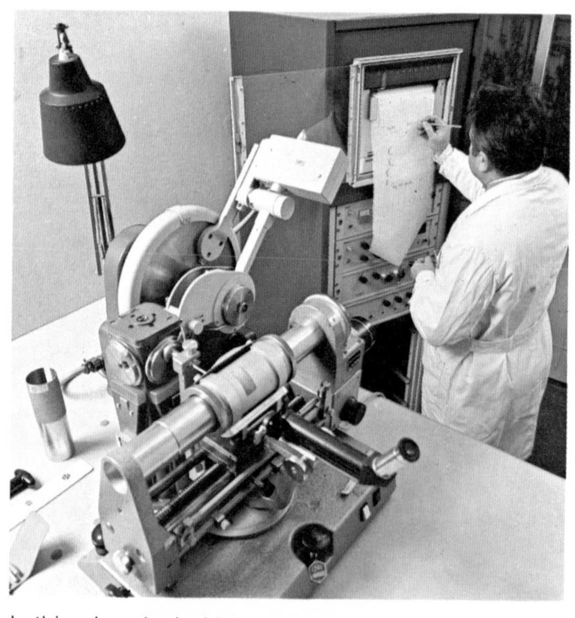

In this mineralogical laboratory, you can see the crystalline dust diffractometer, which uses X-rays to identify the type of crystal and, from that, the mineral from which the dust was taken.

1

2

3

nicians, and they take a lot of work, especially when dealing with small crystals that contain uncommon chemical elements such as the rare earths, niobium, zirconium, vanadium, and so on.

But chemical analyses alone are not enough. They must be supplemented by crystallographic examination because there are often two or more minerals of like composition, such as calcite and aragonite, sphalerite and wurtzite. Usually this crystallographic examination is done by taking an X-ray diffraction pattern photograph.

Constant reevaluation and reidentification goes on of specimens which have not been previously subjected to exhaustive testing, including many in famous collections and in scientific institutions.

Now, how should you go about identifying a specimen if identification entails so much work and specialized apparatus? Usually, when a mineral has not previously been found in an area, it should be studied in great detail. But if it has been found in the area before, often its appearance alone will tell what it is. Even in doubtful cases, there are usually only two or three possibilities, and a simple test often settles the matter.

A complete study can be done only in a laboratory with adequate equipment, but many interesting experiments can be done at home without difficulty. Practical experience, however, is by far the most important factor in the identification of minerals. Handling mineral specimens, collecting them in the field, examination of displays in museums and other collections, as well as study provide the basis for that extra sense that an experienced collector brings to identification of minerals.

The tests that will be outlined later in this book don't pretend to make exact identification always possible, but they will help the amateur to determine the nature of the piece he has found. Obviously, the better the equipment, the more likely an exact identification becomes. The available equipment for dealing with this problem will be discussed later.

Often the same mineral will appear in different habits, which sometimes makes identification by inspection difficult. An example is calcite, illustrated here in three forms.
1 Calcite scalenohedrons from Joplin, Missouri.
2 Foliated calcite in a chalcedony geode, from Mexico.
3 Calcite with sphalerite.

15

THE SYMMETRY OF CRYSTALS

Often in looking at labels on collections of minerals, or simply reviewing lists of names and the principal characteristics of the different types, you see things like this:

MANGANITE	MnO (OH)	Monoclinic
CHALCOPYRITE	$CuFeS_2$	Tetragonal

In this example, the first column gives the name of the mineral, the second its chemical formula, and the third the crystal system to which it belongs. Formulas and crystal systems need explanation.

NATURE OF A CRYSTAL

Most of the crust of our earth is composed of rocks and rocky material. Rocks, as has been explained, are usually made up of discrete grains or crystals of minerals. A few rocks, such as limestone, are formed of one mineral.

An ideal crystal has a regular external form, bounded by smooth planes, a form that reflects the orderly arrangement of the atoms that compose it. Common salt, for example, crystallizes as cubes, echoing the cubic packing into cells of the sodium and chlorine atoms that compose it. Thus a salt crystal reproduces in its gross shape the rows and rows of tiny cubic molecules of its structure.

Geologists have terms to define the relative perfection of a crystal's growth. If it has developed substantially all its proper crystal faces, it is said to be euhedral, from the Greek words for "well-

SKETCHES OF IDEAL CRYSTALS OF TYPICAL MINERALS ARRANGED ACCORDING TO THE SYSTEM TO WHICH THEY BELONG.

TRICLINIC SYSTEM
1 rhodonite
2 chalcanthite
3 albite feldspar

MONOCLINIC SYSTEM
1 pyroxene
2 orthoclase feldspar
3 gypsum

ORTHORHOMBIC SYSTEM
1 shortite
2 struvite
3 hemimorphite
4 sulfur
5 olivine
6, 7 barite

TETRAGONAL SYSTEM
1 rutile
2, 3 zircon
4 anatase

HEXAGONAL SYSTEM
1 beryl
2, 3, 4 apatite
5 dioptase
6 ilmenite
7, 8 calcite
9 hematite

ISOMETRIC SYSTEM
1 Diamond
2 Hauerite
3 Galena

based" or "well-formed." Such a crystal might have grown in a cavity where it was free of interference. If its faces are only partly developed because of the circumstances of its growth, it is described as subhedral, and if faces are lacking, like crystals commonly found in granite, it is anhedral from the Greek for "without form." These terms appear so often in mineralogical literature that they belong in the collector's vocabulary.

Definite internal order, consequently, is a crystal's essential characteristic. It would be easier to identify crystals of minerals if external form were as regular as internal. But even a fragment without crystal faces is nevertheless no less a crystal. In some minerals this is easily demonstrated by their readiness to cleave, such as galena. A piece of that lead sulfide will cleave into smaller and smaller cubes, which echo both the shape of a perfect crystal and the atomic cell structure within. Calcite, likewise, cleaves into rhombs reflecting its internal regularity.

A mineral without recognizable crystal form is called massive, but it is still classified as crystalline. It may be an aggregate of one kind of crystal, such as the sparkling surface of the calcite that composes marble, or it may be cryptocrystalline, like agate, in which the crystals of quartz are unrecognizable as individuals.

Crystallography, as these few paragraphs show, has its special vocabulary. It is a difficult science which relatively few amateurs have the opportunity to master, a science requiring familiarity with the higher mathematics and a capacity for visualizing abstract three-dimensional forms.

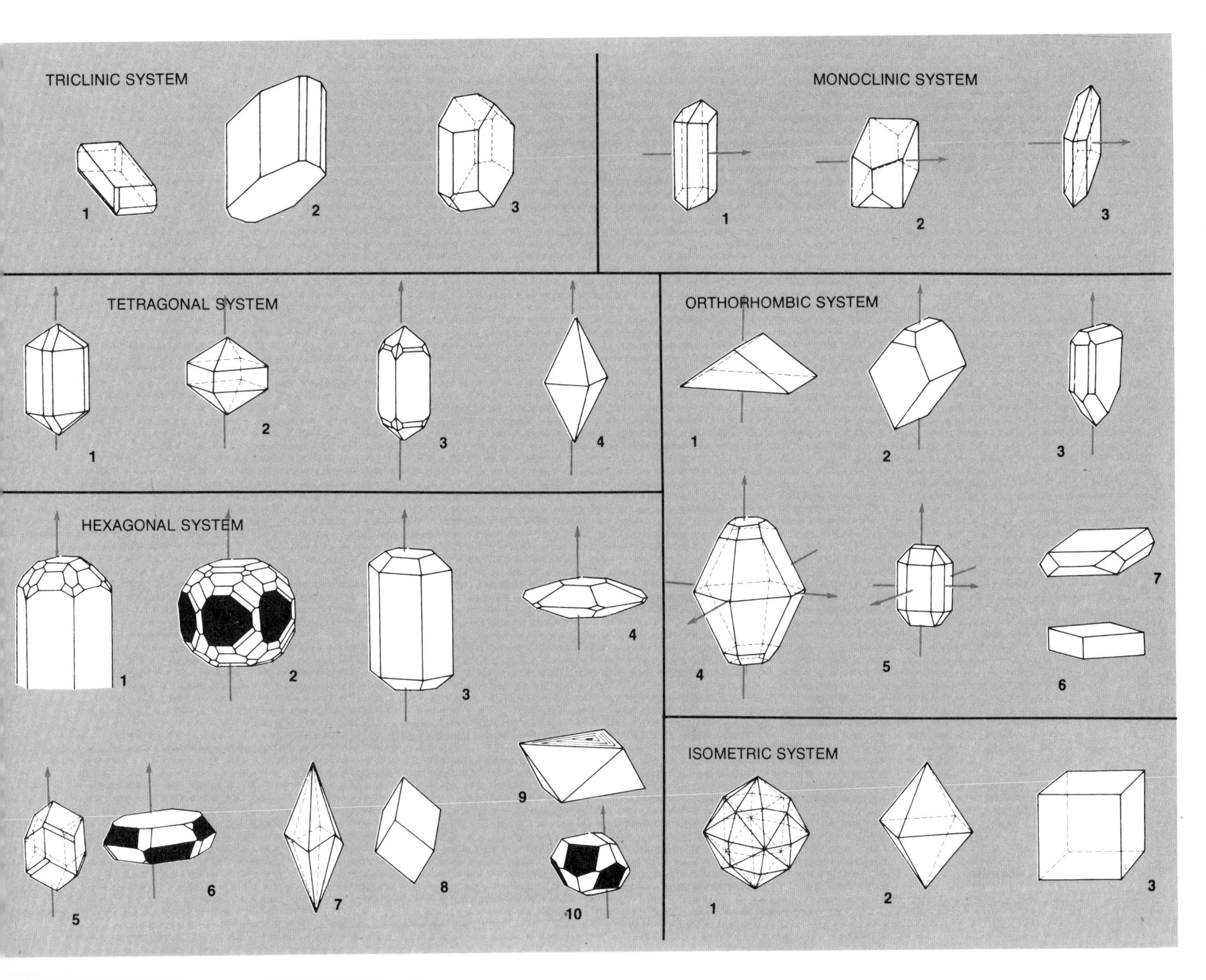

THE SIX CRYSTAL SYSTEMS

All crystals have been assigned to six systems, within which they are subdivided into thirty-two classes according to the relative degree of symmetry that they exhibit. Symmetry is expressed in terms of planes, axes, and a center that can be constructed in an ideal model of the crystal form. A cube of salt, for example, can be shown to have nine planes of symmetry, thirteen axes, and a center—the most regular class of the isometric system. Calcium thiosulfate of the triclinic system is at the bottom of the order with no symmetrical aspects.

A plane can be likened to a sheet of cardboard placed so that it divides a crystal into two parts that are identical mirror images of each other in faces, angles, and edges. To take an analogy outside the subject, a human face divided down the middle will show bilateral symmetry because the left side is a mirror image of the right. An axis can be likened to a needle penetrating a crystal where, as the crystal is revolved on the needle as an axis a certain number of degrees, the crystal will repeat

MINERAL SYMBOLS

Chemical formulas for minerals indicate by symbols the nature and quantity of the elements that compose them and something of the associations of the elements in groups in the formula. The subscript numbers indicate the number of atoms of that element in a unit or molecule of the mineral, and parentheses indicate groups called radicals, such as that for the hydroxyl (OH) or hydroxide $(OH)_2$. The metallic component of a formula, or a semimetal or other group that acts like a metal in the formula, is placed first. Some elements appear in either relationship.

The common mineral-forming elements and their symbols are:

Aluminum . . . . Al
Antimony . . . . Sb
Arsenic . . . . As
Barium . . . . Ba
Beryllium . . . . Be
Bismuth . . . . Bi
Boron . . . . B
Bromine . . . . Br
Cadmium . . . . Cd
Calcium . . . . Ca
Carbon C
Cerium . . . . Ce
Cesium . . . . Cs
Chlorine Cl
Cobalt . . . . Co
Copper . . . . Cu
Fluorine . . . . F
Gallium . . . . Ga
Germanium . . . . Ge
Gold . . . . Au
Hydrogen . . . . H
Indium . . . . In
Iodine I
Iron . . . . Fe
Lead . . . . Pb
Lithium Li
Magnesium . . . . Mg
Manganese . . . . Mn
Mercury . . . . Hg
Molybdenum . . . . Mo
Nickel . . . . Ni
Nitrogen . . . . N
Oxygen . . . . O
Palladium . . . . Pd
Phosphorus . . . . P
Platinum . . . . Pt
Potassium . . . . K
Rhodium . . . . Rh
Selenium . . . . Se
Silicon . . . . Si
Silver . . . . Ag
Sodium . . . . Na
Strontium . . . . Sr
Sulfur . . . . S
Tantalum . . . . Ta
Tellurium . . . . Te
Thallium . . . . Tl
Thorium . . . . Th
Tin . . . . Sn
Titanium . . . . Ti
Tungsten . . . . W
Uranium . . . . U
Vanadium V
Zinc . . . . Zn
Zirconium . . . . Zr

the image it showed before it was turned. A cube, for example, on a vertical axis and turned 90 degrees, would show a square face like the one it had previously shown, and this can be repeated at 180 and 270 degrees. Thus it has four-fold symmetry around this axis. A plane or an axis must pass through a center, obviously, and as obviously, a human face has no axis or center.

Salt, galena, and fluorite belong to the isometric system, the most symmetrical. Besides these cubic forms, the system also includes such typically octahedral minerals as the spinels, as well as the garnets, which commonly take dodecahedral (twelve-sided) or more complex forms. Galena and fluorite often show small octahedral faces on the corners of the cubic body. Cuprite (copper oxide) usually forms octahedrons, but its most curious habit is to crystallize in long hairlike strands of what is called chalcotrichite, formed of tiny cubes of cuprite piled on end into red strands as fine as wool. Pyrite apparently is a conventional cube, but the contrasting striations on its sides show that two isometric forms—the cube and the pyritohedron—struggled to take command of its shape.

CHARACTERISTICS OF THE SYSTEMS

Isometric minerals are usually blocky and ball-like with such significant details as right-angled faces or faces formed of equilateral triangles.

The next system in the declining order of symmetry is the tetragonal. Its crystals resemble those of the isometric system but the cubelike forms are either stretched out or compressed, and so are the forms that resemble octahedrons, and these usually have extra terminal faces. Crystals show right angles, but the sides differ in length, and triangular faces may no longer be equilateral.

Anatase and zircon are common pyramidal forms, and rutile is an almost cubic prism. They show four-fold axial symmetry as they are turned.

The hexagonal system includes the familiar quartz, and, like quartz, many of its members have six-sided or triangular cross sections. Beryl is a good example of the six-sided prism type. Apatite, with the same prismatic form, displays multifaced terminations. Some calcite crystals resemble quartz, while others appear as the familiar rhomb into which the mineral cleaves so easily. Calcite, however, is protean in its many crystal varieties. Tourmaline, another hexagonal mineral, is interesting for the hemimorphic or unlike terminations that its many-colored crystals show.

Quartz, like pyrite, betrays an inner complexity by striations on the prism faces of the crystal. Although it appears to be six-sided, the termination is in reality formed of two rhombs, each showing three faces alternately.

The orthorhombic system includes several common minerals such as barite, celestite, marcasite, and topaz. Barite is commonly bladed with knifelike edges, but blocky crystals are not rare. Marcasite, likewise, is usually tabular with sharp edges; celestite often appears as long or flattened prisms, and topaz is usually squarish in cross section with multiple terminal faces. In tetragonal crystals, the length of two sides of a crystal are the same, the third side is shorter or longer; in orthorhombic crystals, the three dimensions all differ in length but faces meet at right angles. Thus it resembles in its simplest form a sawed-off two-by-four timber.

Monoclinic minerals are considerably less symmetrical to the eye than the preceding classes, for they appear to have a slanting profile which is easily seen in crystals of orthoclase feldspar and gypsum. The rock-forming pyroxenes and azurite belong here. Right angles are less common in this system.

Triclinic minerals, such as albite feldspar and rhodonite, are often thin and lacking in right-angled faces, because in this system all dimensions and angles reach the extreme of difference. Axinite with its knife-edged crystals is a good example of the system's unconventionality.

CHALLENGES AND ODDITIES

This highly simplified review of the crystal systems only hints at the challenges and complexities of the subject. Furthermore, crystal identification goes beyond theory, for few crystals assume the ideal shape. Corresponding faces do not grow equally; extra faces appear and must be explained. It is difficult to recognize, without study, quartz in the quartzoids such as are found at the Herkimer "diamond" localities in New York, or the Pecos river crystals from New Mexico which lack any prism faces at all. A few quartz crystals even assume an almost cubic disguise.

There are other hurdles. Often one mineral will replace another, but it will keep the form of the re-

1

2

3

4

5

6

7

8

9

An aragonite twin from Sicily with the characteristic pseudohexagonal form. Aragonite crystallizes in the orthorhombic system.

placed mineral instead of assuming its own characteristic form. Such puzzlers are called pseudomorphs (false forms). Brassy pyrite, as a common example, is replaced in this way by limonite, which keeps the pyrite form but in a reddish brown disguise. Azurite, likewise, loses its blue color but not its shape when malachite, a more stable copper carbonate, replaces it.

There are other pitfalls in recognition, such as twinning, which was previously discussed, and the slight differences in angles that may cause one to assign a crystal to the wrong system. This appears in a study of the monoclinic and triclinic feldspars and in the trifling differences of angles that distinguish the tetragonal mineral, chalcopyrite, from the isometric tetrahedrite. Fortunately, the former is brassy yellow and the latter gray to black.

The minerals illustrated are listed together with their crystal systems.
TRICLINIC: albite **1** from Saint Gotthard, Switzerland.
MONOCLINIC: orthoclase **2** from Madagascar.
ORTHORHOMBIC: sulfur **3** from Floristella, Sicily.
TETRAGONAL: wulfenite **4** from Mexico; scheelite **5** from Darwin, California.
HEXAGONAL: dioptase **6** from Tsumeb, Southwest Africa; calcite **7** from Sardinia; beryl **8** from Minas Gerais, Brazil.
ISOMETRIC: pyrite **9** from Rio Marina, Elba.

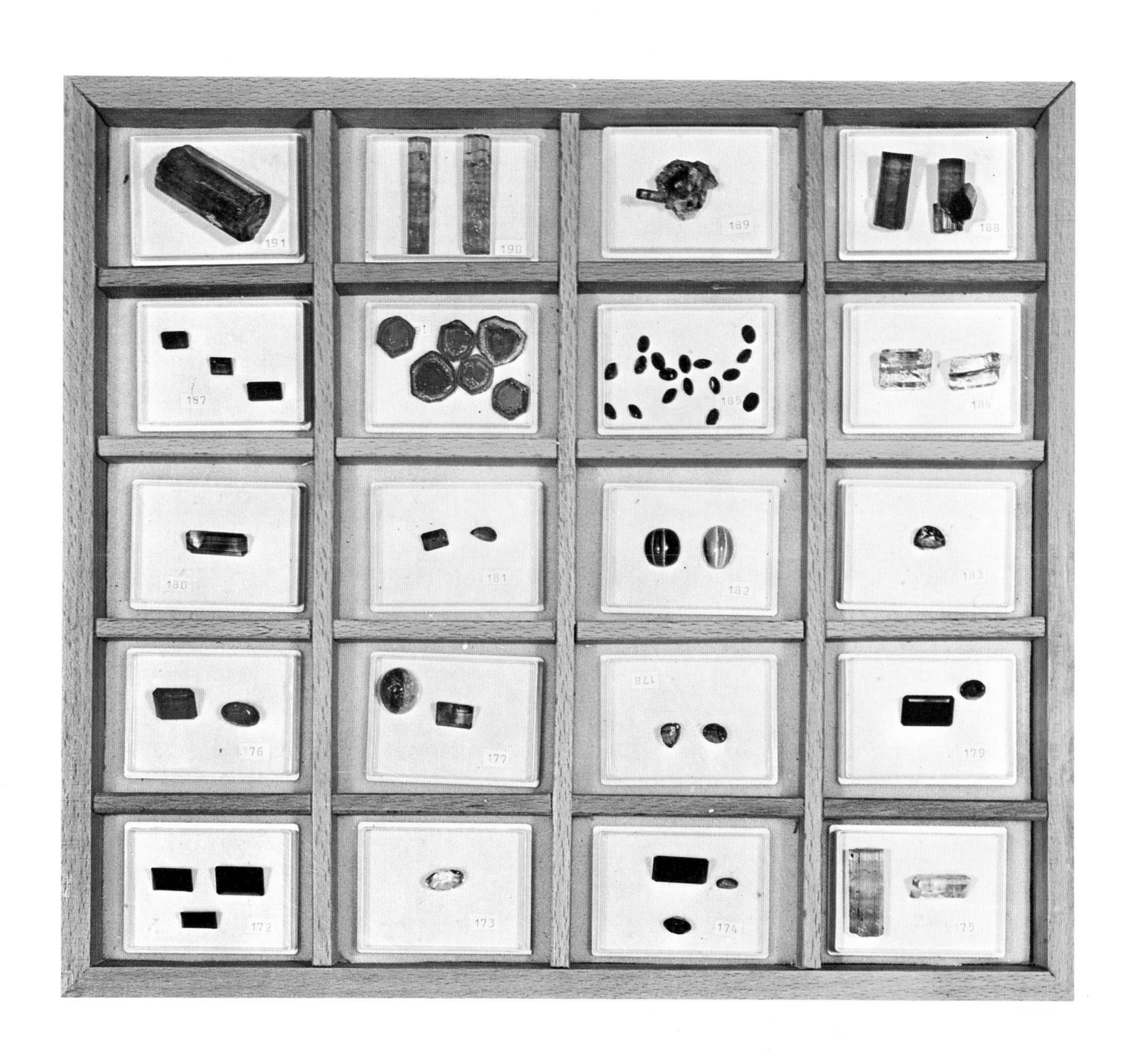
191
190
189
188
187
185
184
180
181
182
183
176
177
178
179
172
173
174
175

nplexity, the amateur should master stallography as he can. It is one ele- ning a working knowledge that will identify most common minerals by d of knowledge rubs off on the ama- idles and owns minerals, fixing in his characteristic habits of such a vari- as calcite.

intance with the physical properties vill rely heavily on superficial qualities r and luster, and on simple tests for eavage, and specific gravity.

ON BY COLOR

most obvious characteristic, but un- not the most reliable. For some min- as azurite and crocoite, it is infallible, ers, such as tourmaline with its rainbow ues, it is meaningless. Even salt can be e, or violet as well as the familiar white.

ecular structure of many minerals is enough so that elements foreign to the chemical formula of the mineral can find places within its basic cells. As was shown in a previous chapter on artificial minerals, the introduction of chrome alum into an alum solution causes brightly hued crystals to form instead of white ones. Likewise, chromium atoms force their way into the molecules of corundum, which is aluminum oxide, and take places held by aluminum atoms. In so doing they create the beautiful ruby. In beryl, they cause the green of emerald. Similarly, trace invaders of corundum, presumably titanium, create the blue gem that we call sapphire. Iron is a common intruder into the crystal lattices of minerals, coloring them blue, reddish, brown and black.

In some minerals, color depends on more complicated phenomena. A typical example of this is the blue or deep violet of specimens of rock salt from various areas. Other examples are the colors of amethyst and diamond. Exact chemical analysis does not reveal significant traces of impurities in specimens of this type.

Explanations of colors that fade or change completely as a result of such physical factors as heat or radiation involve modern physical theories of solids and can't be dealt with here. But speaking generally, this phenomenon probably results from imperfections in the crystal lattice which are "stabilized" by the presence of certain impurities. The imperfections of the lattice may have been caused by chemical and physical conditions present during the growth of the crystal or have developed from prolonged radiation.

Cleavage is a more consistent property than color because it arises from planes of weak cohesion in the crystal structure itself. It can be likened to the grain of wood that splits along the fibers but not across them.

Minerals differ greatly in this property. Quartz, for example, has little or no cleavage, while mica

Tourmaline crystals, rough, sliced cross sections and polished cabochons and faceted stones. This mineral occurs in many colors, including green, yellow, blue, red, violet, and combinations of two or more colors on one crystal.

owes its usefulness to its ability to cleave into thin sheets. Cleavage is usually described as perfect, for such a mineral as mica, and related terms are used for the varying degrees of facility with which a mineral cleaves. Cleavage may be brilliant, as in mica or selenite, or pearly as in many of the feldspars. It is a property that is especially helpful in identifying calcite, with its perfect rhombohedral cleavage; fluorite with its easy octahedral cleavage; topaz, which cleaves parallel to the base of the prism, and tourmaline, which develops characteristic cleavage cracks across the prism.

Like cleavage, fracture is too destructive to be a test, but it is often a useful identification clue in a mineral. The quartz materials develop what is called conchoidal fractures, shell-like concave breaks, and so do the corundum gems, such as sapphire and ruby, and glassy materials such as obsidian. Jade, however, and similarly fibrous minerals break with a jagged, hackly fracture that is highly distinctive.

SPECIFIC GRAVITY

At some time, you may come across a specimen of small, colorless crystals whose structure reminds you of quartz—but you can't be sure. At another time, fragments of clear crystal, rather shapeless but still good enough to cut into semiprecious stones, may turn up. A mineral dealer is unable to identify these. Or perhaps you may own an attractive cut gem, pure yellow and transparent. You certainly won't wish to try any destructive experiments on such a piece, but whether it is a topaz or heat-treated amethyst remains to be settled. Many of these questions can be resolved by measuring the specific gravity. Specific gravity (Sp. G) is the comparison of the weight of the specimen with the weight of an equivalent volume of water. It varies considerably from one mineral to another; thus one of the most reliable ways to identify a specimen is by measuring its specific gravity.

There are two principal methods for determining the specific gravity of a mineral, and each has certain advantages. The first method makes direct use of a scale, the second determines specific gravity by means of heavy liquids.

SCALES AND SPECIFIC GRAVITY

As mentioned above, finding the specific gravity of a mineral means determining the ratio between its weight and its volume. The specimen is first weighed in air. Then, according to the principle of Archimedes, which states that any object immersed in liquid is subject to a vertical thrust equal to the weight of the volume of the liquid displaced (a volume which equals that of the object), you immerse the crystal in water and weigh it again. It will weigh less than in the air, and from the difference between its weight in air, represented by w, and in water, by w^1, the specific gravity is calculated by this formula:

$$\text{Sp. G} = \frac{w}{w - w^1}$$

It is not difficult to determine the specific gravity of a mineral with a scale such as druggists use or such as is used in chemical laboratories to weigh out reagents. To one arm of such a scale tie a thin thread, place the specimen on the pan, and deter-

MINERAL LUSTER

The luster of a mineral is the appearance of its surface by reflected light. If a mineral has a brilliant metallic look, it is said to have metallic luster. Some oxides, like hematite, have metallic luster in their natural state. Other minerals have a nonmetallic luster which is usually described by a qualifying adjective. If the luster has the appearance of glass, as quartz does, it is called vitreous. If a mineral looks as though it is covered with a film of oil, as with nephelite, it is said to have oily or greasy luster, and when a mineral is so brilliant that it shines like a diamond, it is said to have adamantine luster. Some fibrous minerals have silky luster, and others such as sphalerite are resinous.

A laboratory scale used to determine the specific gravity of a mineral. To use it, tie a thin thread to one arm of the scale. (1) Weigh the mineral before attaching it to the thread to get its weight in air. Then attach the mineral to the thread. Next, place a support on the weighing pan straddling the pan, and on the support place a cup filled with water. Place the specimen in the water, but don't let it touch the bottom of the cup. Then weigh the mineral again. This will give you the weight of the mineral in water (2). From this you can compute the specific gravity.

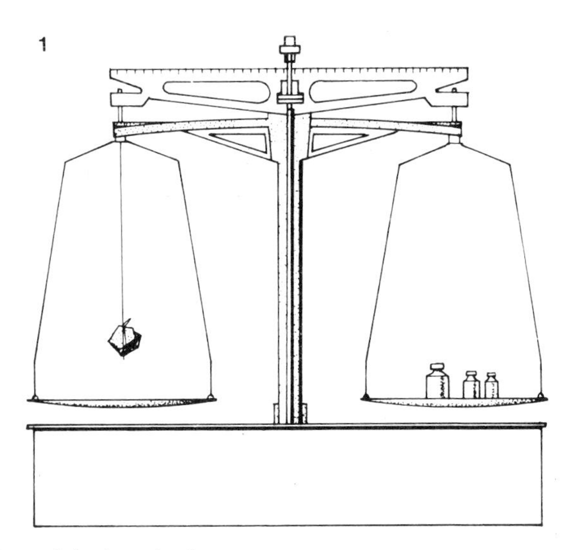

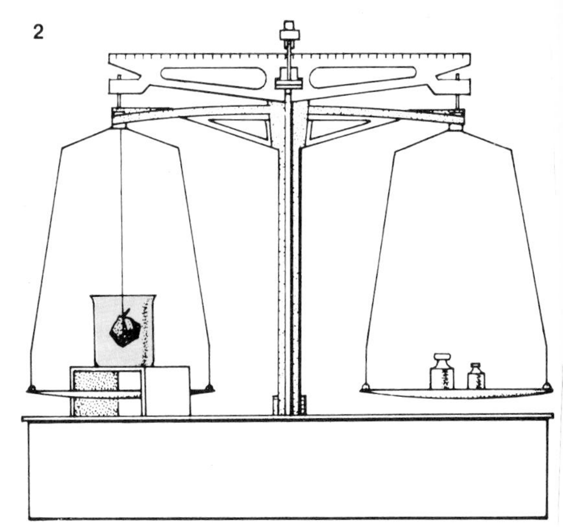

mine its weight by placing counterweights on the other pan until the two pans balance. Then tie the specimen by the thread and straddle the weighing pan with a support on the side where the specimen hangs. On this support place a cup filled with water. Immerse the specimen, still hanging by the thread, in the water and weigh it again.

A simple homemade balance will also give satisfactory results. It consists of a yardstick pivoted freely on a forked upright with about one-fifth of its length on the weighing side, and balanced by a weight attached to the top of the short end of the beam from which hang two small pans, the bottom one immersed in a beaker of water. The specimen is weighed in air by placing it in the upper pan and balancing the beam by a straddling weight on the long end of the beam. Reading is taken and then the process is repeated with the specimen in the lower pan in water.

Suppose the question is to determine whether a large crystal is quartz or topaz. In air it weighs 3.28 ounces, in water 2.34 ounces. Dividing the weight in air by the difference, .94, gives 3.5, which is the specific gravity of topaz. That of quartz is 2.65.

THE SPECIFIC GRAVITY OF VARIOUS MINERALS

1.71	boracite
2.56–9	orthoclase
2.6–8	scapolite
2.65	quartz
2.67–90	beryl
2.71	calcite
2.8–3.0	datolite
	dolomite
2.86	**bromoform**
3.0	phenacite
	danburite
	aragonite
3.0–3	tourmaline
3.2	spodumene
	fluorite
3.3	**methylene iodide**
3.50–3	diamond
3.5–6	topaz
3.6–4.0	spinel
3.6–65	grossular garnet
3.6–7	strontianite
3.8–9	andradite garnet
3.95–4.4	almandine garnet
4.0–1	corundum
4.1–2	spessartite garnet
5.02	pyrite
5.3	hematite
6.55	cerussite
7.04–20	pyromorphite
	mimetite
8.1	cinnabar
8.95	copper
9.7–8	bismuth
10–11	silver
14–19	platinum
15–19	gold

The entries in boldface type are heavy liquids used for measuring specific gravity.

THE HEAVY LIQUID METHOD

It is difficult to determine the specific gravity of a small specimen with the scale. Fortunately, there is a simpler and more responsive way. It utilizes the fact that even a small crystal floats or sinks if the liquid in which it is immersed is heavier or lighter than the mineral in question. You must take care that the crystal is clean and that there are no air bubbles in the liquid to carry the specimen up to the surface. In either event, the measurement would be inaccurate. Suitable liquids are not always available, and they are rather expensive. For example, there is no liquid for sale with a specific gravity higher than 4, and that is why this method isn't used for heavy minerals. You can get bromoform (specific gravity about 2.86), however, and trichloroethylene, which is lighter, and dilute the bromoform to the desired specific gravity. You can buy methylene iodide (CH_2I_2), which has a specific gravity of 3.3 and is one of the heaviest liquids known, but it is expensive. Thoulet and Clerici solutions are toxic and dangerous; use of them is inadvisable.

As a first experiment, prepare a liquid having the same specific gravity as quartz (2.65). This is useful whenever you wish to determine whether a mineral is quartz. To make this liquid, add trichloroethylene to bromoform, drop by drop, stirring well. Then add fragments of quartz, and when they no longer float but hover in balance, your test liquid is ready.

In this same way, you can make up a series of liquids of different specific gravities. Store these carefully and use them to solve identification problems. Note that tourmaline sinks in bromoform, while pink beryl (easy to mistake for tourmaline) hovers in balance. Topaz sinks in methylene iodide and so on. You'll find the heavy liquid method a useful tool for identifying minerals.

HARDNESS

Hardness is one of the easiest mineral properties to determine. It requires neither expensive equipment nor profound scientific knowledge. By using

Octahedrons of Illinois fluorite obtained by cleavage from specimens of different colors.

CLEAVAGE

If you drop a piece of glass, it will break and the fragments will show irregular surfaces. On the other hand, if you break a calcite crystal, the fractures will occur along plane surfaces. The property of a crystal that causes it to part along plane surfaces is called cleavage.

Cleavage is not common to all minerals, but those that have it are usually qualified with a descriptive adjective indicating whether the cleavage occurs more or less easily. The range is from the almost perfect cleavage of mica to the almost nonexistent cleavage of quartz. Often the cleavage shows up as cracks impossible to see with the naked eye but easy to see through a microscope. These cracks are called cleavage traces and are important in the identification process. For instance, the angles that cleavage traces make with each other help to distinguish pyroxenes from amphiboles. Both of these are important mineral groups.

The hardnesses of some minerals.

1	**talc**
1–2	graphite
2	**gypsum**
2.5	FINGERNAIL
2.5	rock salt
2.5–3.0	gold
2.5–3.0	silver
2.5–3.0	copper
3	**calcite**
3.5–4.0	dolomite
4	**fluorite**
4	aragonite
4	BRONZE
5	**apatite**
5.5	GLASS, ORDINARY STEEL
6	**orthoclase**
6.5	TEMPERED STEEL
6–7.0	zircon
7	**quartz**
7.5	tourmaline
8	**topaz**
8	beryl
9	**corundum**
10	**diamond**

The names in bold are those of the minerals in the Mohs scale as shown in the picture. The capitalized names not in bold are not minerals.

MOHS SCALE

Hardness is measured by scratching one mineral with another. For example, you can say that quartz is harder than calcite because a point of quartz will scratch a calcite crystal, but not vice versa. This method has been employed to make up a graduated scale known as the Mohs scale. This scale is composed of ten minerals, in order of increasing hardness; each one is marked with a number from one to ten. Talc, which is the softest and hence the first in the scale, is said to be of Hardness 1; diamond, which is the hardest and the last in the scale, is of Hardness 10. The ten minerals are: talc, gypsum, calcite, fluorite, apatite, orthoclase, quartz, topaz, corundum, and diamond.

These ten numbers are for reference only. The difference in hardness between one number and the next is not uniform. For instance, the difference in hardness between a diamond (Hardness 10) and corundum (Hardness 9) is greater than the difference in hardness between corundum and talc (Hardness 1).

a little care, you can test a mineral for hardness right in the field. This makes it possible to tell calcite from quartz immediately, and to identify other minerals, too.

HARDNESS AND FRAGILITY

Hardness as defined in mineralogy is not synonymous with resistance to mechanical stress. Diamonds, for example, are so hard that they will scratch all other minerals, but contrary to popular belief they are not tough. You can break a diamond with an edged tool. This property is utilized in shaping rough diamonds by cleaving them. Like diamonds, several other gem minerals are hard but comparatively fragile, such as topaz and spodumene.

Chemistry enters into the degree of hardness for, in general, compounds of the heavy metals such as silver and copper are soft, but compounds of iron, nickel, and cobalt are relatively hard. The hard minerals are usually oxides, such as corundum, or the silicates such as garnet and most of the gem minerals.

Many minerals differ slightly in hardness in different directions of the crystal structure. One of the most striking examples of this appears in kyanite, which has about the same hardness as apatite in one direction but is harder than quartz in another. This property is also taken advantage of in scratching one diamond with another preparatory to cleaving it into shape for cutting as a gem.

Care is needed in testing for hardness, because carelessness can lead to serious errors. It might embarrass you to find that a specimen you have taken to be corundum when tested appears to be softer than quartz. What has happened is that the quartz fragment has crumbled when scratched across the harder corundum, leaving a powdery, whitish streak. You would decide that the specimen has been scratched and was not corundum unless you examined it carefully. Wash the dust off the supposed scratch every time you test for hardness. Then examine the specimen carefully through a good lens to see whether a scratch has actually been made. That is the only way to be sure.

Whenever possible, use metal points instead of the points on test minerals that may crumble and lead even an expert to a mistaken identification. For instance, copper is about equal to calcite in hardness, and the blade of a good penknife approaches 5 or 5.5 on the Mohs' scale. The steel in a file is even harder—about 6.5. Test the hardness of your metal tools on mineral specimens, and then use the points to test other minerals.

Testing for hardness can damage a fine crystal irreparably. By bearing down with the point of your testing tool you can scratch a facet or break the crystal. So even when you're positive that the mineral can't be scratched, it is unwise to test cut stones or fine crystals for hardness this way. If you feel you must, choose an inconspicuous area for the test. When you have small crystals or one single crystal, skip the hardness test and use other means to make your identifications.

STREAK TESTS ON PORCELAIN

The color of the dust that powders off when a dark-colored or black mineral is rubbed on an unglazed porcelain surface is characteristic. This streak test is a means of identification. Streak plates are available, made of the same material that is used in certain industrial appliances and for chemical laboratory apparatus.

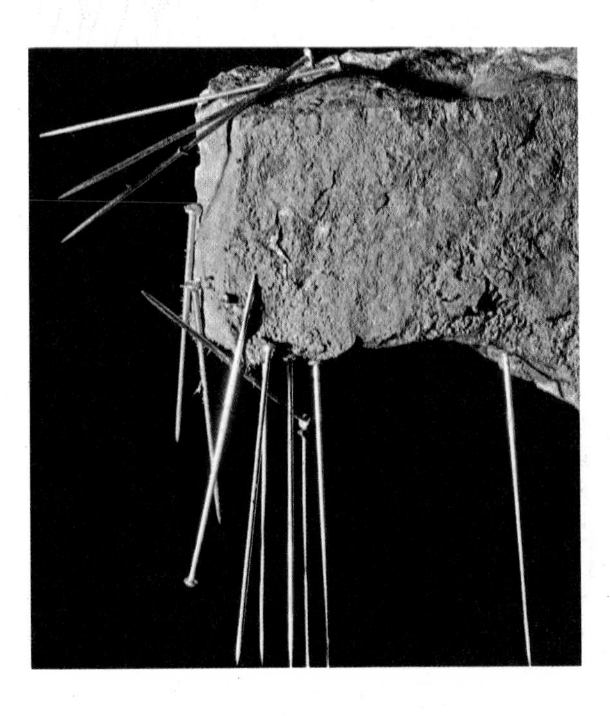

Magnetite from Cape Calamita on the island of Elba acts as a magnet, holding filings and bits of iron such as these pins. All magnetite is attracted by a magnet, but it doesn't always pull like a magnet. When it does pull, it is said to have become a permanent magnet. A classic example is offered by specimens from Cape Calamita.

To evaluate the evidence produced by a streak, notice that sphalerite (so dark it's almost black) leaves a white streak or at most a light brownish one. Its dust is white or whitish. On the other hand, tetrahedrite, often found in association with sphalerite, with crystals like sphalerite, usually leaves a streak that is almost black.

The streak is more accurate than other tests in identifying hematite (iron oxide), which appears either in beautiful crystals or in black masses with a metallic appearance. This mineral's red streak is quite unusual, because other minerals with a metallic look don't leave red streaks. There is one variety of Alpine hematite called *iron rose* on which the streak test won't work. This is a splendid crystal formation shaped like a rose and found near the Saint Gotthard Pass. Some roses are not hematite but ilmenite (oxide of iron and titanium), similar in appearance and crystal structure to hematite. They produce a black streak. It would be useful to be able to distinguish between these two minerals by means of streaks, but unfortunately all iron roses produce black streaks, including the hematite ones, because Alpine hematite always contains a considerable quantity of titanium oxide.

MAGNETIC PROPERTIES

Some minerals are magnetic, a property that can provide useful clues toward identification for the collector.

Magnetite is particularly easy to identify this way because it is attracted by an ordinary magnet. In this respect it differs from most other minerals. Cubanite, like magnetite, is strongly magnetic. It is a rare sulfide of iron and copper. Because of its strong magnetism it can be distinguished from other sulfides, especially pyrrhotite (iron sulfide), which it resembles and which is less magnetic.

In addition to these strongly magnetic minerals there are some that are not attracted by an ordinary magnet but can nevertheless cause a magnetized needle to oscillate. You can get an idea of the magnetism of this kind of mineral from pyrrhotite, ilmenite, and hematite. A test for magnetism on some specimens whose identity is known will provide enough experience to recognize these minerals.

Susceptibility to magnetic attraction is, of course, common to many other minerals, among them monazite and xenotime, which are phosphates of the rare earths. It manifests itself much more weakly in them than in the minerals that have been mentioned and can be perceived only by the use of strong electromagnets.

ELECTRICAL PROPERTIES

These properties are rarely useful in mineral identification but are mentioned here briefly because they are interesting and do have practical applications.

When some minerals are heated or compressed they become electrified, that is, they develop a positive charge at one end and a negative charge at the other. Those that become electrified by heating are called pyroelectric (from the Greek *pyros,* meaning "fire"); the others, electrified by compression, are called piezoelectric (from the Greek *piezo,* meaning "to compress"). Some minerals, such as tourmaline, can be either pyroelectric or piezoelectric.

Quartz is a typical piezoelectric mineral. Thin wafers of quartz are used to control the frequency of oscillation of electronic circuits, such as in broadcasting. The ultrasonic waves compress the sheet of quartz. Pierre and Jacques Curie discovered the piezoelectrical effect about 1880 while working with quartz.

Specimen of celestite, a fluorescent mineral, seen in normal light (top) and in ultraviolet light.

FLUORESCENCE AND PHOSPHORESCENCE

A mineralogical museum or a private collection often offers an impressive display in its darkened cases. Specimens in the cases glow, showing such distinctive colors as the red of calcite, the greenish-yellow of willemite and some of the uranium minerals, the orange of sodalite, the blue-violet of fluorite, and so on. The cases aren't really dark; they just look that way. They are lighted by ultraviolet rays invisible to human eyes. Some minerals absorb ultraviolet rays and emit visible light. This phenomenon is called fluorescence. It differs from phosphorescence in requiring constant ultraviolet light for its effect. Phosphorescence lingers on after the activating light has been removed.

With an ultraviolet lamp (also called black light) you can do some interesting experiments. For example, you can verify the existence of minerals that are both fluorescent and phosphorescent. Some well-crystallized forms of selenite (gypsum) such as those that come from Wiesloch in Baden, Germany, exposed to ultraviolet rays, glow and emit a beautiful white light.

If, after being exposed to ultraviolet rays, the crystal is placed in darkness, it will continue to emit light, but this time a beautiful lemon yellow light instead of white. A similar effect can be obtained from some varieties of aragonite which give off a rosy fluorescent light but a white light when phosphorescent.

Specimens containing calcite (white), willemite (red), and franklinite (black) from Franklin, New Jersey. When irradiated with ultraviolet light, two of the minerals change color. Calcite becomes red; willemite becomes green, but franklinite remains black.

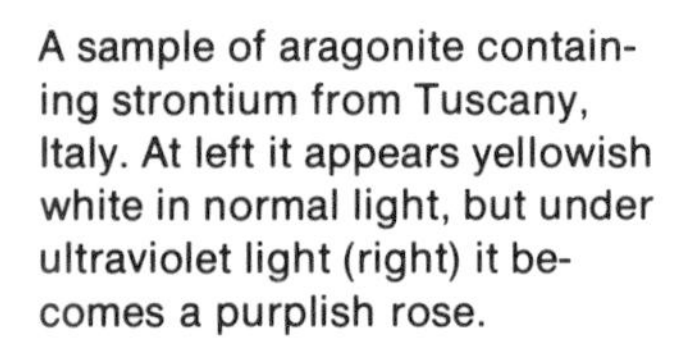

A sample of aragonite containing strontium from Tuscany, Italy. At left it appears yellowish white in normal light, but under ultraviolet light (right) it becomes a purplish rose.

Some minerals respond only to the longwave ultraviolet light, others to shortwave ultraviolet. Hackmanite from Ontario, Canada, glows orange, and when the exciting light is turned off, it glows with a bluish phosphorescence. Willemite from Franklin, New Jersey, fluoresces yellow-green by shortwave, and phosphoresces in some specimens the same color, often for several hours. Calcite from Miles, Texas, fluoresces pink under longwave, and blue under shortwave. It is also phosphorescent after exposure to shortwave ultraviolet light.

THE ULTRAVIOLET LAMP

The cheapest type of ultraviolet lamp contains a bulb in front of which is placed a filter made of a special glass that cuts off most visible light and allows ultraviolet rays to pass through. However, the shortwave ultraviolet rays are almost completely blocked out by the glass screen, which is opaque to light rays of less than 3,500 A.U.

Mercury vapor lamps are decidedly better. Mercury when vaporized in a vacuum tube has a strong emission of rays ranging from 3,660 A.U. (ultraviolet long waves on the border of visibility) to 2,530 A.U. (ultraviolet shortwaves). They can be controlled so that one wavelength predominates. Usually, shortwave lamps are more expensive than long-wave lamps because they have to be made with a window with a quartz base that is transparent to shortwave ultraviolet.

With such lamps, you will find that some specimens such as fluorite and ruby are more fluorescent in long-wave than shortwave light. Others are

SHORTWAVES AND LONGWAVES

Ultraviolet rays are not all the same. This is also true of ordinary daylight, which is made up of rays of various colors and different wavelengths. Daylight wavelengths range from about 7,000 A.U. to 4,000 A.U. (A.U. stands for Angstrom unit, which is a ten-millionth of a millimeter), while ultraviolet rays usually range from 4,000 A.U. to 2,000 A.U. Long ultraviolet rays are those whose wavelengths lie not far below the boundary of visible daylight (3,200 to 4,000 A.U.), while short ultraviolet rays are those from 2,000 A.U. to 3,200 A.U.

fluorescent in shortwave light, such as scheelite and benitoite. Still others (autunite, aragonite, etc.) are fluorescent in both long- and shortwave light. Museums put both types of light into their cases and then arrange the specimens so that each is under the kind of light that will produce the most brilliant show of color.

DIAGNOSIS WITH ULTRAVIOLET LIGHT

Offhand, you might think that fluorescence is an intrinsic property of a mineral. But this is not always so. Take fluorite as an example. It's the mineral in which fluorescence was first discovered and which gave its name to the phenomenon. Although fluorite crystals are often fluorescent (usually a beautiful blue-violet) the fluorescence shows up with greater or lesser intensity depending on where the specimen came from. In some cases, there is no fluorescence at all, as in many specimens from southern Illinois. Occasionally, when there is fluorescence, it is in colors other than blue-violet, such as cream, green, or brown. Even calcite, which usually shows a fine red fluorescence, can show other colors, among them white, blue, or green—or it can be unresponsive.

Fortunately, there are minerals in which fluorescence is an intrinsic property and an aid to identification. It occurs in such uranium minerals as autunite. This has a beautiful yellowish green fluorescence which distinguishes it from other uranium minerals such as torbernite.

Fluorescence is often helpful in establishing identity, because out of a group of specimens of the same color it pinpoints one as different from the rest. This could easily be overlooked if you were examining the specimens carefully in daylight. This applies to such minerals as scheelite, which is inconspicuous in the rock by daylight, and to two rare minerals recently discovered in California. These are walstromite (silicate of calcium and barium) and pabstite (a silicate of barium and tin). Although these two varieties were inconspicuous in appearance, they were recognized as unusual by amateur mineralogists because of their fluorescence.

Why is it that one specimen of a mineral is fluorescent but another is not? And why does the color of the fluorescence change from one specimen to another? The theory is complex, but usually in minerals not possessing intrinsic fluorescence this property is related to the presence, in small amounts, of activating elements such as the rare earth metals for fluorite, or manganese for calcite and aragonite. Certain localities, rich in manganese ores, are famous for the extraordinary fluorescence of the specimens found there. The colors are all bright, but even within each mineral the color of the reaction to ultraviolet light is not always the same. This is because the minerals have been activated to varying degrees by the manganese. Specimens of this type from Franklin, New Jersey, and Langban, Sweden, are chameleons of fluorescence and are avidly sought by collectors.

17

RADIOACTIVITY IN MINERALS

Among the specimens that the amateur will find most interesting are radioactive minerals. In addition to their radioactivity, they have several other characteristics worth noting, including exotic chemical composition. In pegmatite specimens, you'll find not only uranium and thorium but other rare metals, such as tantalum, niobium, zirconium, hafnium, and others. There are some fifteen metals that compose the radioactive minerals, and among these are the rare earth metals. They are difficult to tell apart, and all have strange properties which chemists have investigated for more than a century.

In addition to the presence of uranium and thorium which cause their radioactivity, these minerals contain traces of about twenty isotypes that are strongly radioactive and result from the decomposition of uranium and thorium. The best known of these isotypes is the famous radium (Ra^{226}), first isolated from pitchblende. Research that started with its discovery led to the splitting of the atom, which is still of paramount interest today. Collectors prize a good specimen of pitchblende, especially one like the one that the Curies studied from Joachimsthal, Czechoslovakia.

More recently we have seen a world scramble for uranium because of the efforts of the great powers to get control of atomic materials. They are needed for both military and industrial purposes, and this great demand has opened up new sources of these minerals.

For the collector who likes spectacular specimens, the uranium minerals are fascinating because of their superb colors—especially those from the Congo.

HOW RADIOACTIVITY IS DETECTED

Radioactivity in a mineral is a property that is quite easy to recognize, even in the field. Geiger-Müller counters and scintillometers make possible a quick check of an area so that radioactive mineral deposits can be located.

These instruments look alike, but they are based on different principles. Both are portable and consist of a tube or probe that contains the part of the instrument directly sensitive to rays. This is joined by a cable to the indicator, graduated to give an approximate reading of the radioactivity present. In addition, the presence of radioactivity is made evident to eye and ear by flashing lights or cracklings in loudspeakers or headphones.

These instruments, especially the more expensive ones, are protected against humidity encountered in damp places. This can cause temporary or even permanent damage to the electric circuits.

HOW TO FIND INTERESTING SPECIMENS

There are expensive instruments to detect radioactivity so well designed that they can be used in the

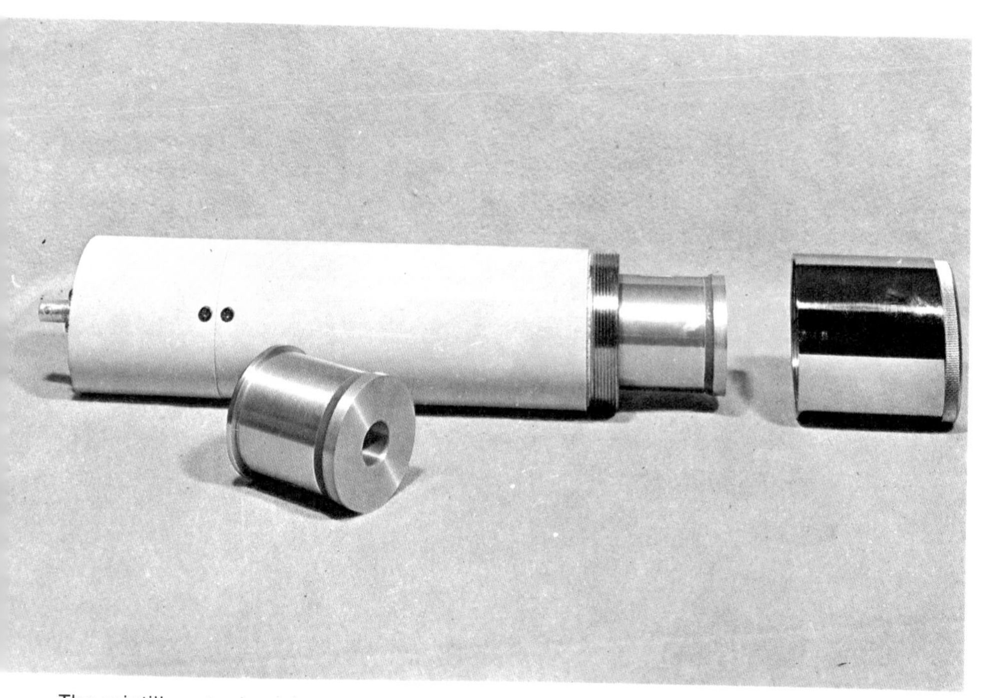

The scintillometer is an instrument that quickly indicates the radioactivity of its surroundings. It consists of a protective metal cap (at right) and a body that contains a crystal of sodium iodide and a photomultiplying device which amplifies the impulses generated in the crystal. This instrument can be attached to another apparatus that will transform the signals generated into sound or light.

field under any conditions. They can cost several hundred dollars, but most amateurs use Geiger counters or scintillometers that cost far less.

Bear in mind that these instruments are chiefly useful to locate radioactive deposits rather than mineralogical specimens. But, they can be really helpful in locating highly radioactive specimens clumped together somewhere within a rock mass which is itself not radioactive. Pitchblende (uranium oxide) occurs in pegmatites with gummite (hydrous uranium oxides) in Mitchell County, North Carolina, in the Ruggles mine, Grafton, New Hampshire, and in fine crystals at Wilberforce, Ontario, in Canada. Most uranium, however, is mined from vein deposits of these minerals, such as those at Great Bear Lake, in Canada's Northwest Territories, or from secondary minerals, such as the Colorado plateau's carnotite in sandstone.

A Geiger counter or a scintillometer makes it evident that radioactivity exists everywhere, not just in uranium mines or in places where there are radioactive specimens. No matter where you use one of these instruments, you'll never get a reading of zero. Atmospheric radioactivity is partly caused by cosmic rays which bombard us continually from space. A not unimportant factor is that many rocks themselves are faintly radioactive, especially pegmatites.

Before you start looking for specimens, it is advisable to get some idea of how much radioactivity there is around you. Take readings in several spots, being sure to count the number of impulses you get in a two- or three-minute span. Unless you do this your results will be misleading, as radioactivity fluctuates in intensity, a fact you can easily verify. After taking this background reading, walk slowly around the area looking for a spot that's highly radioactive. Because it is difficult to determine which one of a pile of rocks is the "hot" one, try removing them one by one until you find the one you're after. Sometimes, however, radioactivity doesn't come from one good specimen, but from a number of insignificant-looking specimens which have a few granules of radioactive minerals dispersed through them. Therefore you can't eliminate the possibility that the radioactivity will gradually disappear as you discard one stone after another.

THE SPINTHARISCOPE

The Geiger counter and the scintillometer have been suggested as useful tools in identifying radioactive minerals. If these instruments are too expensive, radioactivity can be detected with an instrument that you can make yourself—the spinthariscope. This instrument takes advantage of the fact that radioactive isotopes emit alpha rays, easily absorbed by matter. The fact that these rays are easily absorbed also means that they can stop and discharge all their energy in a split second. A screen coated with a luminescent substance when exposed to alpha rays theoretically should produce visible light. It is visible because, while the particles are minute, the energy of each one is so high that it produces a flash of light on the luminescent screen.

The spinthariscope was invented by the English physicist Sir William Crookes in the early part of this century. It consists of a luminiscent screen and a lens. To make the screen, take a photographic glass negative and bleach it by treating it with a solution of tincture of iodine, then with sodium thiosulfate, and finally washing it under running water for at least an hour, being careful not to damage the layer of gelatin.

Then, while the gelatin is still damp, dust it with a thin coating of luminescent powder. Be careful that the gelatin doesn't engulf the luminescent

ALPHA, BETA, AND GAMMA RAYS

Three basic types of radiation have been recognized ever since radioactive substances were first studied. These are called alpha rays (α), beta rays (β) and gamma rays (γ) after the first three letters of the Greek alphabet.

Alpha rays are nuclei of helium atoms (so they have a positive charge) emitted at enormous velocity. They are easily stopped, even by a sheet of paper.

Beta rays are electrons (with negative charge) emitted at great speed (up to 99.8 percent of that of light). In contrast to alpha rays, which are stopped by trifling obstacles, beta rays can penetrate about a tenth of an inch of brass, and a sheet of lead about half as thick.

Gamma rays are electromagnetic radiations of the same nature as light. They have short wavelengths (from a thousand to a hundred thousand times less than daylight), and have properties similar to X-rays, with which they are often confused. The wavelength of gamma rays, however, is usually shorter than that of X-rays.

What is especially characteristic of gamma rays is their enormous power of penetration. Those with the longest wavelength (the so-called "soft" gamma rays) can penetrate a half inch of lead, while the harder ones can penetrate more than an inch of lead. A Geiger counter will demonstrate that the rays emitted by a piece of radioactive mineral (for instance, high-grade pitchblende) can easily go through walls. Gamma rays have a wavelength typical of the isotope that emitted them, and this makes it possible to identify the type of radioactive material present in a mineral.

A spinthariscope can be used to determine whether a mineral is radioactive. The spinthariscope is made up of a black cylinder at one end of which is a lens and at the other end a sensitive screen. This cylinder is placed over a container whose cover is pierced, as in the illustration above. Inside the container is the specimen. Or, a suitable support can be constructed, so that the distance between the spinthariscope and the mineral can be regulated. The specimen should not be more than 2/5 inch away from the sensitive screen, as in drawing at right.

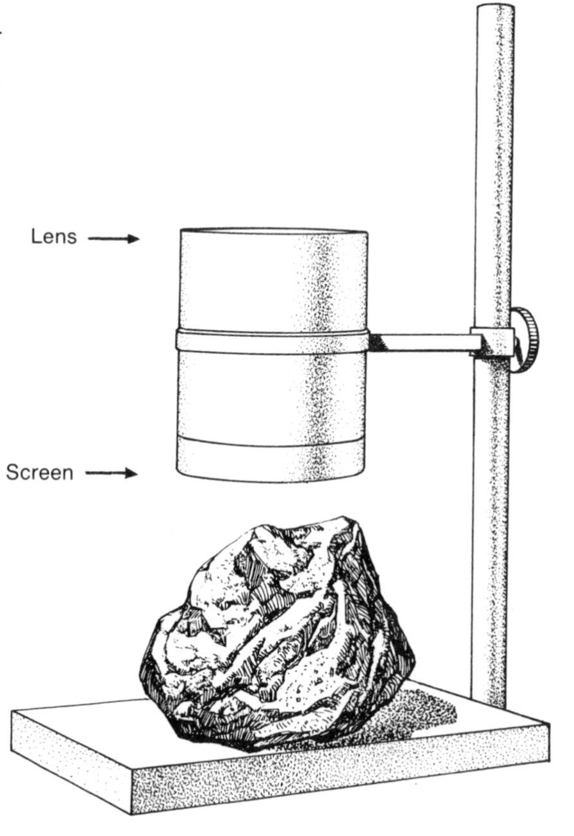

powder. If it does, the alpha rays will be stopped and won't glow. In preparing the screen, be careful not to get the luminescent coating too thick: the screen should remain sufficiently transparent so you can see through it.

As to the choice of luminescent substance, you'll find several commercial varieties of zinc sulfide that are luminescent. Not all are suitable because some are also slightly phosphorescent, and even the faint light they give off could nullify the full effect of a particle striking the screen. The preferred substance is that used on the sensitive part of yellow screens in radiological apparatus. If you can get a piece of one of these screens, you can scrape off the surface and save the rest to make several spinthariscopes. To complete your spinthariscope, put a lens with weak magnification (8 to 10 power is more than enough) over the screen, which is turned face down, and fix the lens at a distance that will bring the sensitive part of the screen into focus.

Place the specimen with the radioactive material immediately below the screen but not more than 2/5 inch away from the sensitive part. Otherwise, most of the alpha rays will be absorbed by the air.

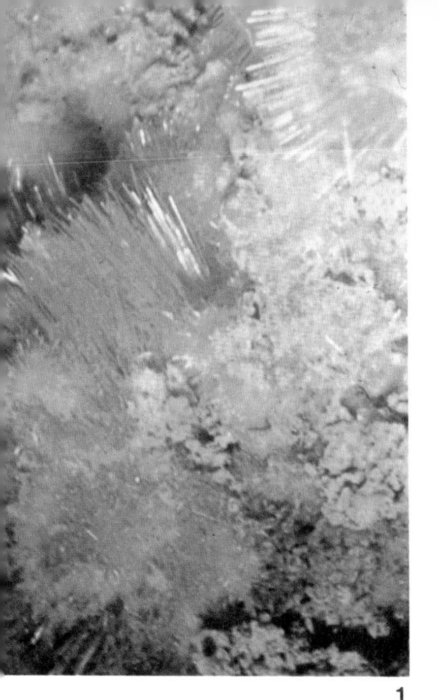

1

2

3

4

Take the apparatus and specimen into a completely dark room and look through the lens. At first, you won't see anything—but don't be discouraged. Wait about fifteen minutes until your eyes adjust to the darkness; then you will see a fascinating spectacle. The whole screen will be alive with little glowing spots, each one caused by the impact of a single alpha particle.

ADVANTAGES AND DISADVANTAGES OF THE SPINTHARISCOPE

The chief disadvantage of the spinthariscope is that it is of no use in the field to pick out the specimen that you're after from a pile of rocks. Furthermore, to use the instrument you must have enough patience to wait while your eyes adjust to darkness.

On the other hand, there are several obvious advantages. It doesn't cost much. It is sensitive and can clearly show the impact of even one particle. Keep in mind that some radioactive specimens consist of one thin crystal or a yellow powder on a matrix that is only feebly or not at all radioactive. In such cases, even with the best Geiger counter or scintillometer, it is difficult to register this localized radioactivity, which can easily be confused with the general radioactivity in the atmosphere. But the spinthariscope is sensitive only to alpha rays, so that the mineral's radioactivity registers without interference from the atmosphere. This makes it possible to determine beyond a doubt whether the specimen being examined is really radioactive.

When using the spinthariscope, be careful not to let the specimens rub against the screen. If you're careless, the screen will become contaminated by traces of radioactive substances and will no longer be useful.

Examples of radioactive minerals.
1 Cuprosklodowskite
2 Sklodowskite in yellow, needle-shaped crystals
3 Yellowish-green autunite in tabular crystals
4 Orange-colored gummite, produced by oxidation of uranium, from Grafton, New Hampshire.

18

OBSERVING CRYSTALS THROUGH A BINOCULAR MICROSCOPE

The binocular microscope is indispensable in examining small crystals, which may be all that you have found on a collecting trip. There are many kinds of microscopes, but not all are useful for your purposes. The binocular microscope allows you to use both eyes and gives a stereoscopic, three-dimensional view of the specimen. This makes the shape of the crystals more clearly evident.

It's a good idea to use the microscope to examine any specimen composed of tiny crystals of various minerals. You could discover something new and interesting. For example, under the microscope a specimen from Saint Gotthard, Switzerland, that looked like anatase accompanied by a cluster of other crystals turned out to be a little crystal of xenotime, a phosphate of the rare earth metal yttrium, which is considerably rarer.

If you look at this piece of gneiss (right) through a microscope, you will see at the point marked a magnificent monazite crystal, a fraction of an inch high.

Other rare phosphates, of which there are scores, and perhaps as many more yet unidentified, appear in all their perfection of form under the microscope lens. In the United States these are found in the pegmatites of Palermo, New Hampshire, those of the Black Hills in South Dakota, and in Alabama. Likewise, the quarries near King's Mountain, North Carolina, and Saint Hilaire, in Quebec, Canada, have yielded to the mineralogist fantastic suites of crystals of new minerals indistinguishable by the unaided eye.

There is another way of using a binocular microscope which is both interesting and instructive and has served to extend its use by amateurs. That is the examination of micromounts—miniature specimens of well-shaped and brilliant crystals, often in bright colors, either alone or in a proportionately small rocky matrix.

THE WORLD OF MICROMOUNTS

The micromounter has the world of minerals within his grasp, for few regions of our earth are so poor that they do not yield him beautiful specimens that he could perhaps not afford or that never occur in cabinet size.

A recent list of micromount specimens for sale by a dealer, most of them from the United States, was made up of nearly 300 entries, such as yellow adamite from Utah, as well as from Durango, Mexico; artinite, a powder-puff mineral, from California; such choice copper minerals as brochantite, caledonite, cuprite, dioptase, malachite, and rosasite from Arizona, as well as several from New Mexico and Mexico; gold from California, Colorado and Washington; and minerals from Japan, Australia, Greenland, Switzerland, Canada, France, southwest Africa, Germany, Romania, Zambia, Greece, Morocco, and Norway. Of special interest to advanced collectors were the rare cubanite from Brazil, pentagonite and erionite, rare species from zeolite areas in Washington and Oregon, and wermlandite, known only in a handful of tiny specimens from one locality in Sweden.

One previously mentioned locality, Saint Hilaire in Canada, has become a mecca for micromounters since such strangely named minerals as serandite, pimite, catapleiite, acmite, polylithionite, ancylite, and the more common tetrahedrite and a host of others have come on the market from collectors and dealers.

Franklin, New Jersey, the source of the highly fluorescent calcite, willemite, and other minerals, also is the source of hundreds of minerals, many of them unique or known only elsewhere in Scandinavia, and also rarely or never found except as microscopic crystals.

Collectors have risked their lives to secure the lovely minerals of the Alpine regions of Switzerland and Italy. Alpine apatite, for example, shows elongated prismatic crystals that are flat on

THE CHOICE OF A MICROSCOPE

For micromount study, it is essential to choose a good microscope so that the image of the crystals will remain sharp even at relatively high magnification, although most viewing will be done at 15 to 40 times magnification.

The quality of a microscope must not be judged by the degree of magnification it is capable of but by the sharpness of the image. There are commercial binocular microscopes on the market which give remarkable magnification, but the image is cloudy. Often, too, colors become so distorted that you can't be sure of the color of the mineral you're examining. Obviously, such equipment isn't worth buying.

A good way to test a microscope is to increase the magnification and see whether additional details come into sight, or whether the image becomes somewhat cloudy. It's advisable to avoid lenses with adjustable magnification (zoom lenses) because, for micromount purposes, they don't provide results comparable to those obtained with ordinary lenses except in very expensive equipment.

1

2

3

4

All of these beautiful crystals were photographed through a microscope. All are about $^{1}/_{25}$ inch in size.

1 Xenotime from Saint Gotthard, Switzerland
2 Azurite from Tsumeb, South West Africa
3 Rutilated quartz from Saint Gotthard
4 Crocoite from Tasmania

5

6

7

8

9

10

5 Pyromorphite from Sardinia
6 Wulfenite from Arizona
7 Cuprite
8 Goyazite, from Binn Valley, Switzerland
9 Artinite from St. Vincent, Aosta, Italy
10 Aurichalcite

top from one locality, pointed ones from another, while a third offers tabular crystals. Alpine danburite is especially of interest for the many faces on its crystals, unlike those from Mexico. Milarite's little hexagons are another scarce and desirable treasure.

Many secondary varieties are formed by the oxidation of minerals present in metal-bearing veins in the upper part of deposits. Cuprite is one—beautiful red crystalline cubes that are sharply defined and often elongated in a characteristic way. From the Congo come fantastically colored secondary minerals of uranium. These range from green (torbernite, cuprosklodowskite) through all shades of yellow (schoepite, soddyite, renardite, fourmarierite). These minerals are the pride of collectors fortunate enough to own any of them.

There are splendid microspecimens among more common minerals, however, such as cerussite, azurite, linarite, aurichalcite, wulfenite, and vanadinite. A large collection could be made of the many occurrences around the world of just one of these minerals.

THE REASONS FOR COLLECTING MICROMOUNTS

There are many reasons that micromounts are so attractive to collectors. First, there is the well-known fact that the small natural crystals are usually the most perfect. They're more plentiful in the field, and they can be bought reasonably because mineral dealers, when processing large specimens, often have small pieces left over. These fragments may not interest them especially, so a timely visit to a dealer can often yield a surprisingly good harvest.

Collecting small specimens, like micromounts or another slightly larger type called thumbnails, is growing rapidly. The specimens cost so little that they quickly offset the price of the microscope, and the collection takes up little space. A fairly small case will easily hold three or four thousand specimens, which could represent a thousand or more different minerals, some of them rare and all interesting.

19

CHEMICAL ANALYSIS OF MINERALS

The chemical analysis of minerals as treated in this chapter presents some problems of explanation and understanding, but it is included for those who have progressed beyond the rudiments and wish to deepen their knowledge of this wonderful hobby.

To determine the nature of a mineral you must know its composition, which is to identify its chemical elements and the amount of each of them. For example, celestite (strontium sulfate) and barite (barium sulfate) have similar crystals. The easiest way to tell them apart is to find out whether the mineral contains strontium or barium. To make identification even surer, you can test to see whether a sulfate ion is present. This will positively identify the specimen. Similarly, if you're testing a gray mineral with a metallic appearance (common to many metal-bearing minerals), determine whether it contains silver, copper, or lead. This will give a clue as to what you're dealing with.

Chemical analysis is one of the surest ways to establish the composition of a mineral. To recognize the presence of a certain element you can rely on typical chemical reactions which are produced by adding specific substances. These reactions produce a characteristic color in a liquid, or perhaps a sublimate, or they produce precipitates that separate from the solution. For example, nickel salts in solution yield a scarlet precipitate when you add a chemical called dimethylglyoxime.

For the tests you need a test tube, a few drops of solution of the metal salts, plus a few drops of the reagents. Note that to achieve a reaction the metal salts and the reagents must be dissolved.

When you see these reactions you may suppose that every element is easily identified by doing the appropriate test. Unfortunately, this isn't so, as the characteristic reaction of a metal may be disturbed by the presence of other metals.

For example, with potassium ferrocyanide iron produces a blue precipitate, while copper with the same reagent yields a brown one. If the mineral contains both of these metals you get a blackish precipitate in which it is impossible to distinguish the components.

Generally, the best thing to do is to separate the different metals and then proceed to identify them. The usual way to separate metals is to create conditions under which some metals dissolve in the solution, while others present remain undissolved.

CHARACTERISTIC REACTIONS OF SOME METALS

Element	*Reagent*	*Characteristic Reaction*
Arsenic, as sodium arsenate	Solution of ammonium molybdate in nitric acid, brought to a boil	Solution turns yellow with precipitation of yellow crystals
Bismuth, in solution as the nitrate	Stannous chloride solution to which is added, drop by drop, sodium hydroxide until the solution is clear	Black precipitate forms
Chromium, in solution as potassium bichromate	Dilute sulfuric acid, ether, and hydrogen peroxide	Blue color which is absorbed by the ether
Cobalt, in solution as the nitrate	Ammonium thiocyanate in concentrated solution, a little amyl alcohol	Magnificent blue color, which is absorbed by the alcohol
Copper, in solution as the sulfate	Ammonia in excess	Intense blue color
Iron, in solution as ferrous chloride	Potassium ferrocyanide	Intense blue precipitate
Lead, in solution as the nitrate	Solution of potassium bichromate	Intense yellow precipitate
Mercury, in solution as mercuric chloride	Solution of stannous chloride	White precipitate that turns gray rapidly
Or, Mercury, in solution as mercuric chloride	Potassium iodide solution drop by drop	Lively red precipitate that will redissolve on adding more iodide
Silver, in solution as the nitrate	Solution of sodium chloride (salt) or dilute hydrochloric acid	White precipitate that turns violet slowly on exposure to light

1 Test for silver. In the test tube on the right, silver chloride is precipitated. If an excess of ammonia is added, the precipitate goes into solution as in the test tube on the left.
2 Test for arsenic.
3 Test for bismuth. Adding a solution of bismuth nitrate **3A** to stannous chloride and sodium hydroxide produces a black precipitate **3B.**
4 Test for cobalt. Adding ammonium thiocyanate **4A** to a solution of cobalt nitrate forms a complex blue thiocyanate **4B.**
5 Test for mercury.
6 Test for iron.

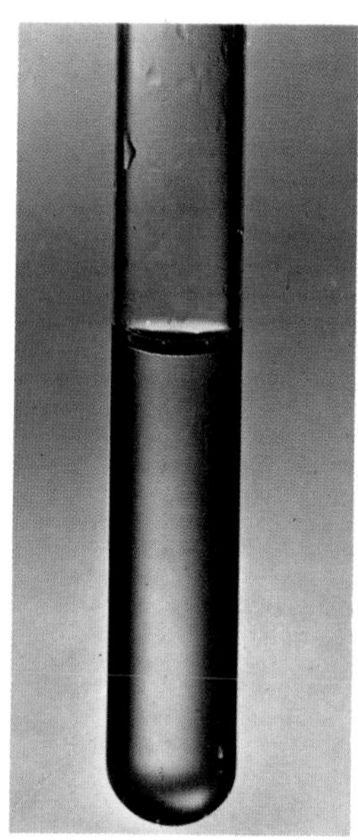
4A

1
ACIDO CLORIDRICO DIL.
AMMONIO IDRATO
2
3A
3B
4B
5
Ort
POTASSIO IODURO
6

For example, if you add an excess of ammonia to a solution containing salts of iron and copper, the copper will dissolve, while the iron remains undissolved, forming a gelatinous mass of hydroxides. The iron can then be separated easily from the copper by filtration.

For filtration you will need a glass funnel and a piece of round filter paper. Fold the paper four times and insert it in the funnel, as illustrated. Be sure to sprinkle a few drops of water on the paper so it will adhere to the funnel. Then pour the solution through the filter, taking care not to let any of it spill over. It will be helpful to use a glass rod while doing this. After the solution has all dripped through, sprinkle a few drops of water on the filter, letting these drip through completely. By doing this both the precipitate and the filter itself will be washed free of any traces of the soluble substances which you wish to remove.

AN EXAMPLE OF A CHEMICAL ANALYSIS OF METALS TO IDENTIFY MINERAL SULFIDES

A great many minerals have a metallic appearance. Among these are native metals which are more or less pure, such as gold, silver, mercury, and others. More frequently, however, minerals with a metallic appearance (often quite brittle) are chemical combinations of a metal or metals with sulfur. These are the sulfides, such as pyrite, pyrrhotite, galena, and so on. There are also chemical combinations with arsenic (arsenides such as smaltite and niccolite) and some with sulfur, arsenic, and antimony (for the most part these are the sulfosalts such as tetrahedrite, bournonite, and enargite). Because such minerals from various mines make attractive specimens, you will have the problem of identifying them, or, at the very least, of finding out something about their composition.

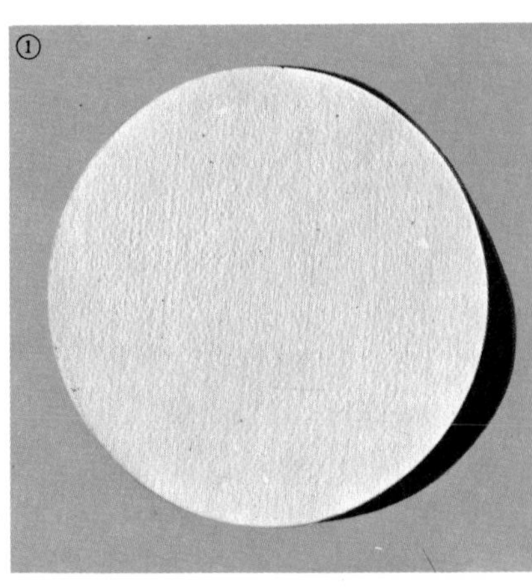

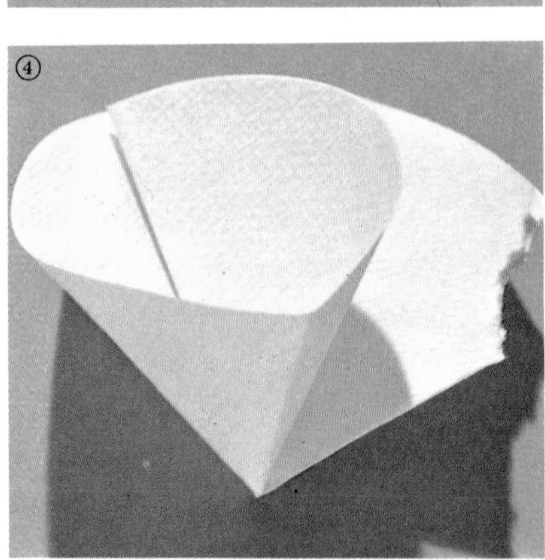

To make a cone filter, take a piece of round filter paper **1**, fold it into four parts **2, 3,** and then open it. Tear off a small piece as indicated in **4;** this will make it adhere better to the funnel. Before filtering, sprinkle a little distilled water on the paper cone.

For this purpose follow the technique described in the accompanying diagram. The analysis described is far from complete, nor is it valid in all instances. If it were, the procedure would be much more complicated. The elements considered are those that appear most frequently in these minerals. A few points are worth emphasizing:

Of all the operations described, the first—dissolving the specimen—is the most critical. Minerals often are hard to dissolve; even the most powerful acids won't break them down. When dealing with sulfides and sulfosalts, use just enough concentrated nitric acid to dissolve the specimen.

There's no point in using a large specimen for chemical analysis, as you could easily ruin it. Besides, it is wiser not to handle large quantities of acid. All you need is a fragment about the size of a couple of grains of rice and enough nitric acid to cover the bottom of the test tube. Heat the bottom of the test tube slowly, turning the tube as it heats and being careful not to spill any of the acid. Remove the test tube from the flame every now and then and shake it slightly to allow the brown fumes to escape. Usually, it is useless to continue heating after a reaction sets in. Sometimes the reaction does not occur, which indicates that the method outlined here is not suitable for that mineral.

For those who wish to avoid the risk of contact with dangerous substances such as concentrated nitric acid, the following procedure is suggested: obtain solutions of nitrates of various metals, and begin with the steps described in the diagram on

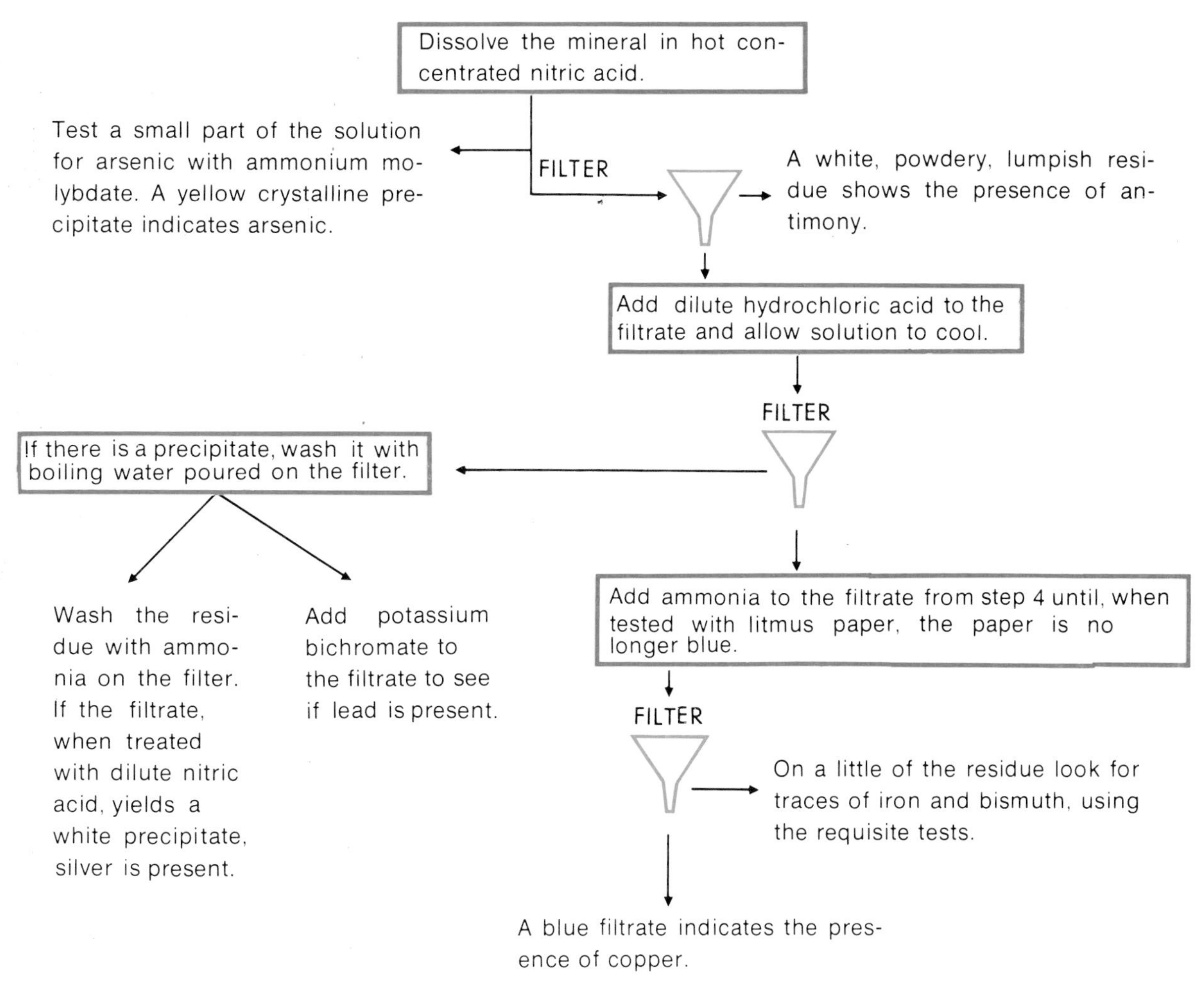

N.B. The reactions are those described in the table on page 114.

page 117 from the point at which dilute hydrochloric acid is added.

REACTIONS OF NEGATIVE IONS

Often present in minerals are chemical ion groups such as the carbonates, phosphates, sulfates, and chlorides. To carry out tests on these negative ions, boil finely ground powder of the mineral in a concentrated solution of sodium carbonate for half an hour. Filter and, using the filtrate, perform the tests described in the accompanying diagram. Some minerals are not affected by sodium carbonate. In such instances, the tests could fail even though you're using minerals that really do contain the ions you're trying to identify. With carbonates, you'll have to test the mineral as it is because the excess of soda that you add obviously furnishes a great quantity of carbonates and would disguise the reaction.

SPECTROSCOPIC ANALYSIS

Chemical analysis isn't the only method for identifying the metals in a specimen. Centuries ago it was observed that salts of various metals colored a flame in typical ways, and this observation is the basis for the colors in fireworks. The atoms of metals, when suitably activated by electrical charges at high temperatures, emit light made up of well-defined colors.

For example, a pinch of kitchen salt (sodium chloride) on the end of a wire (or, better yet, on a strip of stainless steel, which is easier to clean after use) when put into a flame, will cause it to emit an intensely yellow light, similar to that of the lamps used to light city streets (which are sodium vapor lamps). If instead of sodium chloride other salts are used, you will get other colors.

The light of a colored flame can be analyzed with a spectroscope. This instrument breaks up light into its basic colors and makes possible precise identification of the metals that produce these colors. A small direct-view spectroscope, which is not expensive, will be good enough for your purposes. When you look at the flame through this instrument, be careful to adjust the opening slit properly. If it's too narrow, it will cut down the luminosity so much that the glow will be feeble; and if you open it too wide, the lines will run together. Through the adjusted opening you'll see several brightly colored lines against a dark background. These lines are characteristic of the metal you're observing and make up what is known as its spectrum.

Alongside these lines, broader lines or bands will often appear. These are less well defined and are really aggregates of lines so close together that it's difficult to tell them apart. These bands are sometimes spectra produced by molecules and not by atoms of the individual metals, which is why they can vary from specimen to specimen. (For the best examples of this, look at calcium and barium minerals.)

After a little practice it will be possible to identify the various substances, especially if you compare them with specimens that have already been identified.

With a spectroscope, you can make several in-

CHARACTERISTIC REACTIONS OF SOME NEGATIVE IONS

Negative Ion	Reagent	Characteristic Reaction
Carbonates (calcium carbonate)	Hydrochloric acid or dilute nitric acid	More or less well-marked effervescence, in some varieties only obtainable when heated, or with concentrated acid
Phosphates (sodium phosphate)	Solution of ammonium molybdate in nitric acid (see arsenic page 114) slightly warmed	Yellow crystalline precipitate
Sulfates (sodium sulfate)	Barium chloride or nitrate	White crystalline precipitate, insoluble in acids
Chlorides (sodium chloride)	Silver nitrate	White precipitate, insoluble in acids

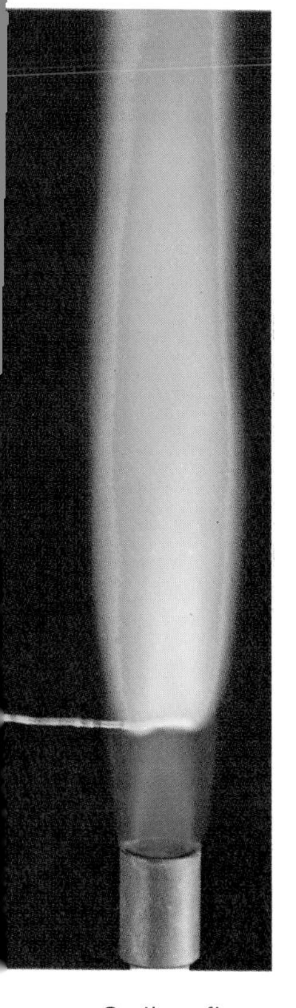

Sodium flame

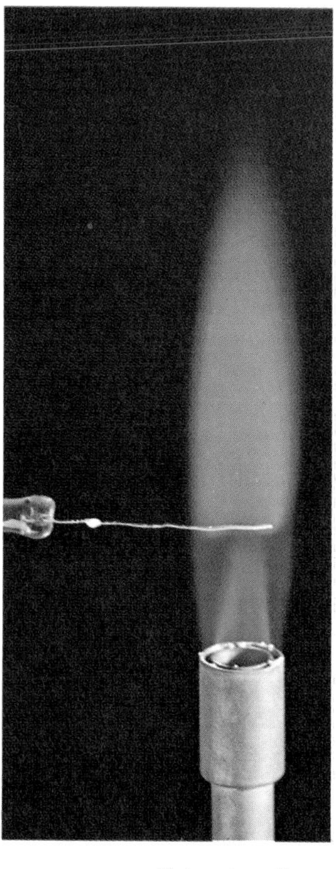

Potassium flame

COLORED FLAMES AND SPECTRA OF SOME METALS

Substance	Flame	Spectrum
Sodium salts	Bright yellow	Brilliant yellow line, separated out only with a powerful instrument
Potassium salts	Violet flame (the color is often blurred by sodium impurities)	A rather faint red line and a bluish violet line. These can be seen only with a powerful instrument
Cesium salts	Rosy violet	Beautiful double blue line
Lithium salts	Bright red	Vivid red line
Calcium salts (chloride)	Flame with scattered traces of bright red	Bands of red, orange, and light green, some of them typical of chlorides
Calcium salts (sulfate)	Brick red	Bands of red, orange, and green
Strontium salts	Flame with scattering of bright red	Several red and orange bands, and an intense blue line
Barium salts	Greenish yellow	Several bands, the brightest of which is green

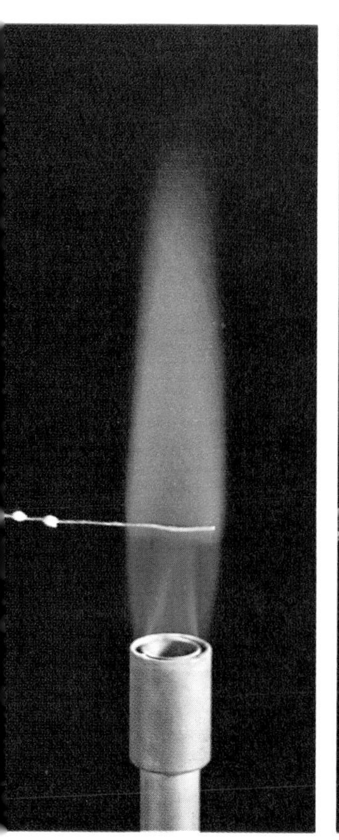

Lithium flame

Calcium flame

Strontium flame

Barium flame

teresting scientific observations. For instance, if you look at the light from a lamp through it, you will see a rainbow. This is because lamplight is a combination of all colors, graduating from red to orange to yellow to green up to violet and going through innumerable shades. This is called a continuous spectrum.

Next, look through it at the light from a fluorescent light fixture. Some intensely bright lines will stand out against a rainbow background similar to the continuous spectrum of an ordinary lamp. You will see two yellow lines, two light green ones and one bluish-indigo—the spectrum of mercury. Fluorescent tubes contain mercury vapor which, when activated by electric current, emits a spectrum rich in ultraviolet light. The fluorescent substance with which the inside of the tube is coated absorbs the ultraviolet rays and transforms them into visible light. The practically continuous spectrum in the background comes from this light.

It is even more interesting to examine sunlight through the spectroscope. You will see innumerable black lines (some intense and some faint) on a continuous background. These black lines are called Fraunhofer lines, after the physicist who discovered them. They are evidence of hydrogen and metals (sodium, magnesium, iron, calcium, etc.) present in the sun's atmosphere. By a curious phenomenon, these black lines correspond to the brilliant lines formed by the same elements when you activate them in the flame. In this case, the spectrum is inverted, more or less like the relation of a negative of a photograph to the positive print.

If all metals emit spectra, you may wonder why they don't all color flame. Actually, colored flames are produced only by elements described in the table on page 119, and by a few others which are quite rare—gallium, indium, thallium, radium, and rubidium.

The temperature of the gas flame isn't high enough to volatilize all components of the nonresponsive metals, and even when it is, as with mercury, it doesn't always activate the atoms sufficiently to make them emit their typical lines.

Many elements do not show a spectrum unless exposed to intense heat, something like the 3000 degrees C. of an electric arc light. Under such conditions, all the components become volatilized (that is, evaporate) and practically all of them emit their spectra. This produces a great number of lines so that for identification large and expensive apparatus is needed, quite beyond the means and skill of the average collector.

To obtain colored flames it has already been pointed out that substances must be volatilized. Bear in mind, however, that chemicals and minerals containing calcium, strontium, barium, and other metals listed in the table aren't always sufficiently volatilized to produce a spectrum in a flame. For example, calcium oxide, which is formed by heating calcium carbonate (calcite and aragonite), is a refractory substance. In a flame it shines with an intense white light without volatilizing. It is necessary to transform the oxide into a volatile compound, such as a chloride.

To do this, take a clean piece of wire. Heat a little of the substance on the tip to red heat and dip it into dilute hydrochloric acid. Then look at the flame through the spectroscope. With many substances this treatment produces satisfactory results. But refractory minerals such as phosphates, sulfates, and silicates of calcium, strontium, and barium will have to be broken down. To do this, boil a bit of the finely powdered mineral for at least half an hour in a concentrated solution of sodium carbonate (washing soda) in distilled water. Tap water won't do as it always contains an appreciable quantity of calcium. The breaking down process works even better if you dissolve the soda along with the mineral. Filter the solution and wash the residue left on the filter carefully several times with distilled water to remove as much of the sodium as possible. If you don't do this, it will throw off your observations by blocking out the colors of the other metals. Finally, moisten the residue with dilute hydrochloric acid and examine it in the flame.

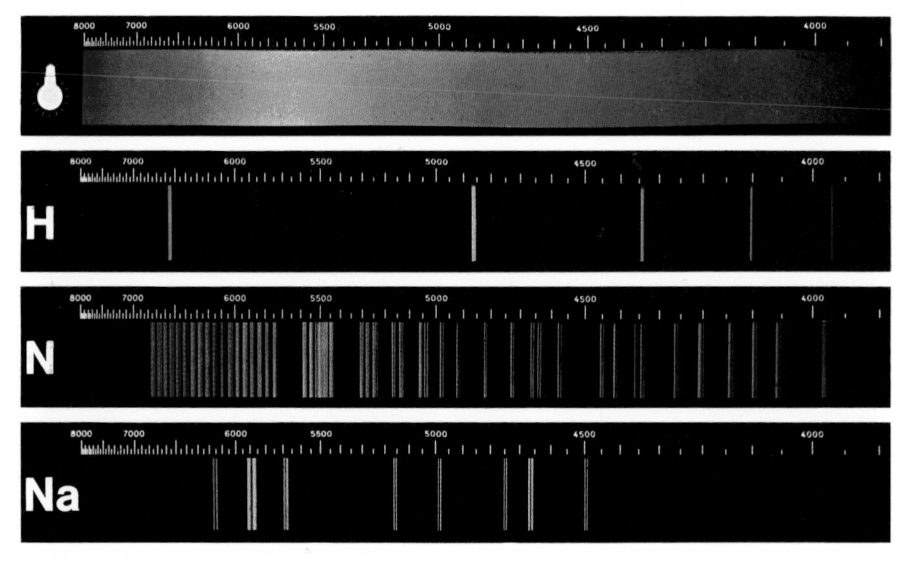

Some spectra observed in the spectroscope. Starting from the top is the continuous spectrum of a lamp, then those of hydrogen, nitrogen, and sodium (identified by their chemical symbols).

20

TABLE FOR RECOGNIZING MINERALS

To facilitate identification of specimens, a table is appended here giving typical, easily recognized data about common minerals. In the table, minerals are grouped according to color (their most striking characteristic). Each mineral color is then classified again according to luster, and under each type of luster minerals are arranged in ascending order of hardness. For each mineral, the specific gravity and the streak color (on unglazed porcelain) are also given. These tables are not an infallible means of identifying minerals. Often you'll have to resort to the chemical analyses previously described. But the tables will help to narrow the area of research.

COLOR RED

Luster	*Hardness*	*Specific Gravity*	*Streak*	*Name*
Adamantine	2.0–2.5	8.1	Scarlet	**Cinnabar**
Adamantine	2.0–2.5	5.55	Red	**Proustite**
Adamantine	2.5–3.0	6.5–7.1	Yellowish	**Vanadinite**
Adamantine	2.5–3.0	6.0	Yellow-orange	**Crocoite**
Adamantine	2.5–3.0	6.5–7.0	Yellowish	**Wulfenite**
Adamantine	3.5–4.0	3.9–4.1	Yellowish	**Sphalerite**
Adamantine	3.5–4.0	6.14	Red	**Cuprite**
Adamantine	4.0–4.5	5.68	Yellowish-orange	**Zincite**
Adamantine	6.0–6.5	4.2–4.25	Light brown	**Rutile**
Waxy	7.0	2.6–2.64	Light brown	**Chalcedony**
Metallic	2.5	5.85	Purplish red	**Pyrargyrite**
Metallic	2.5–3.0	8.95	Copper red	**Copper**
Metallic	3.0	5.07	Gray-white	**Bornite**
Metallic	5.0–5.5	7.78	Blackish brown	**Niccolite**
Resinous	1.5–2.0	3.56	Orange-red	**Realgar**
Earthy	6.5	5.3	Brick red	**Hematite**
Glassy	5.5–6.5	1.99–2.25	White	**Opal**
Glassy	6.5–7.5	3.15–4.30	White	**Garnet**
Glassy	7.0	2.65	White	**Quartz**
Glassy	8.0	3.58–3.98	White	**Spinel**
Glassy	9.0	4.0–4.1	White	**Corundum**
Glassy	6.5–7.0	3.2–3.3	White	**Axinite**

COLOR ROSE

Luster	*Hardness*	*Specific Gravity*	*Streak*	*Name*
Adamantine	10	3.50–3.53	White	**Diamond**
Glassy	1.5–2.5	3.06	Rose	**Erythrite**
Glassy	2.0–2.5	2.8–2.9	White	**Muscovite**
Glassy	2.5–3.0	2.8–2.9	White	**Lepidolite**
Glassy	3.0–3.25	2.71	White	**Calcite**
Glassy	3.5–4.0	2.8–3.0	White	**Dolomite**
Glassy	3.5–4.0	3.4–3.6	White	**Rhodocrosite**
Glassy	3.5–4.0	2.1–2.2	White	**Stilbite**
Glassy	3.5–5.0	3.0–3.1	White	**Margarite**
Glassy	3.0–4.0	2.2	White	**Heulandite**
Glassy	4	3.18	White	**Fluorite**
Glassy	4.0–4.5	4.0–4.5	White	**Smithsonite**
Glassy	4.0–5.0	2.05–2.15	White	**Chabazite**
Glassy	4.5–5.0	2.3–2.4	White	**Apophyllite**
Glassy	5.5–6.0	2.2–2.3	White	**Sodalite**
Glassy	5.5–6.5	1.99–2.25	White	**Opal**
Glassy	6	2.6–2.8	White	**Scapolite**
Glassy	6	3.5–3.7	White	**Rhodonite**
Glassy	6	3.25–3.37	White	**Zoisite**
Glassy	6	2.56–2.59	White	**Orthoclase**
Glassy	6	3.0–3.1	White	**Amblygdonite**
Glassy	6.5–7.0	3.25–3.36	White	**Jadeite**
Glassy	6.5–7.5	3.15–4.30	White	**Garnet**
Glassy	6.5–7.5	3.1–3.2	White	**Spodumene**
Glassy	7.0	3.3–3.4	White	**Dumortierite**

COLOR VIOLET

Luster	*Hardness*	*Specific Gravity*	*Streak*	*Name*
Glassy	2.5–3.0	2.8–2.9	White	**Lepidolite**
Glassy	4	3.18	White	**Fluorite**
Glassy	5	3.1–3.2	White	**Apatite**
Glassy	5.0–6.0	3.0–3.3	White	**Tremolite**
Glassy	5.0–6.0	2.6–2.8	White	**Scapolite**
Glassy	6.5–7.5	3.15–4.30	White	**Garnet**
Glassy	6.5–7.0	3.25–3.36	White	**Jadeite**
Glassy	6.5–7.0	3.2–3.3	White	**Axinite**
Glassy	7	2.65	White	**Quartz**
Glassy	7	3.3–3.4	White	**Dumortierite**
Glassy	7.5–8.0	3.58–3.98	White	**Spinel**
Glassy	9.0	4.0–4.1	White	**Corundum**

COLOR YELLOW

Luster	*Hardness*	*Specific Gravity*	*Streak*	*Name*
Adamantine	3.0	6.5–7.0	White	**Wulfenite**
Adamantine	3.5–4.0	3.9–4.1	Yellowish white	**Sphalerite**
Adamantine	5.0–5.5	3.4–3.55	White	**Titanite**
Adamantine	10	3.5–3.53	White	**Diamond**
Greasy	5.0–5.5	3.6–4.0	Brownish white	**Limonite**
Pearly	2.2	2.08–2.17	Yellowish	**Copiapite**
Resinous	1.5–2.0	3.49	Pale yellow	**Orpiment**
Resinous	1.5–2.5	2.07	White	**Sulfur**
Resinous	3.0–3.5	4.9–5.0	Yellow-orange	**Greenockite**
Silky	7.0	2.65	White	**Tigereye**
Earthy	Soft	4.0–5.0	White	**Carnotite**
Glassy	2.0–2.5	3.1–3.2	Yellowish	**Autunite**
Glassy	3.0–3.25	2.71	White	**Calcite**
Glassy	4	2.95–3.0	White	**Aragonite**
Glassy	4	3.18	White	**Fluorite**
Glassy	4.0–4.5	4.0–4.5	White	**Smithsonite**
Glassy	5.5	3.89–4.19	White	**Willemite**
Glassy	5.0–6.0	1.99–2.25	White	**Opal**
Glassy	6	2.42–2.5	White	**Cancrinite**
Glassy	6	2.6–2.8	White	**Scapolite**
Glassy	6.0–6.5	3.1–3.2	Almost white	**Chondrodite**
Glassy	6.5–7.0	3.1–3.2	White	**Spodumene**
Glassy	6.5–7.0	3.2–3.3	White	**Axinite**
Glassy	7	2.65	White	**Quartz**
Glassy	8	2.66–2.83	White	**Beryl**
Glassy	8	3.5–3.6	White	**Topaz**
Glassy	8.5	3.71–3.75	White	**Chrysoberyl**
Glassy	9.0	4.0–4.1	White	**Corundum**

COLOR BRASSY GOLD

Luster	*Hardness*	*Specific Gravity*	*Streak*	*Name*
Metallic	2.5–3.0	15–19	Golden	**Gold**
Metallic	3.0–3.5	5.5	Greenish black	**Millerite**
Metallic	3.5–4.0	4.1–4.3	Greenish black	**Chalcopyrite**
Metallic	6.0–6.5	5.02	Greenish black	**Pyrite**
Metallic	6.0–6.5	4.89	Greenish black	**Marcasite**

COLOR BROWN

Luster	*Hardness*	*Specific Gravity*	*Streak*	*Name*
Adamantine	2.5–3.0	6.88	White	**Vanadinite**
Adamantine	3.5–4.0	7.04	White	**Pyromorphite**
Adamantine	6.0–7.0	6.8–7.1	Almost white	**Cassiterite**
Adamantine	7.5	3.94–4.71	White	**Zircon**
Waxy	2.0–2.5	5.55	Grayish white	**Cerargyrite**
Metallic	4	4.6–4.65	Black	**Pyrrhotite**
Metallic	6.0–6.5	4.20–4.25	Light brown	**Rutile**
Resinous	5.0–5.5	3.4–3.55	Pale yellow	**Titanite**
Resinous	5.0–5.5	4.6–5.4	White	**Monazite**
Earthy	5.5–6.5	5.3	Reddish brown	**Hematite**
Glassy	2.5–3.0	2.8–3.4	Reddish brown	**Phlogopite**
Glassy	2.5–3.0	2.8–3.4	Reddish brown	**Biotite**
Glassy	3.5–4.0	3.8–3.9	Reddish brown	**Siderite**
Glassy	3.0–3.5	6.2	Orangy brownish red	**Descloisite**
Glassy	5.0–5.5	3.3–4.3	Brownish yellow	**Goethite**
Glassy	5.0–5.5	3.6–4.0	Brownish yellow	**Limonite**
Glassy	4.0–4.5	4.0–4.5	White	**Smithsonite**
Glassy	5	3.1–3.2	White	**Apatite**
Glassy	5.5	3.9–4.2	White	**Willemite**
Glassy	6	3.25–3.37	White	**Zoisite**
Glassy	6.0–6.5	3.1–3.2	White	**Chondrodite**
Glassy	6.5	3.3–3.6	White	**Vesuvianite**
Glassy	6.5–7.0	3.2–3.3	White	**Axinite**
Glassy	7	2.65	White	**Quartz**
Glassy	7.0–7.5	3.0–3.3	White	**Tourmaline**
Glassy	7.0–7.5	3.7–3.8	White	**Staurolite**
Glassy	7.5	3.1–3.2	White	**Andalusite**
Glassy	8	3.5–3.6	White	**Topaz**
Glassy	8	3.58–3.98	White	**Spinel**
Glassy	9	4.0–4.1	White	**Corundum**

COLOR BLUE

Luster	*Hardness*	*Specific Gravity*	*Streak*	*Name*
Adamantine	10	3.50–3.53	White	**Diamond**
Waxy	5.0–6.0	2.6–2.9	White	**Turquoise**
Waxy	7	2.6–2.64	White	**Chalcedony**
Metallic	1.5–2.0	4.6–4.76	Blackish gray	**Covellite**
Metallic	3	5.07	Blackish gray	**Bornite**
Pearly	2	3.64	White	**Aurichalcite**
Glassy	1.5–2.0	2.68	Bluish	**Vivianite**
Glassy	2.5	2.17	White	**Halite**
Glassy	3	2.71	White	**Calcite**
Glassy	2.0–4.0	2.0–2.24	White	**Chrysocolla**
Glassy	3.0–3.5	4.3–4.6	White	**Barite**
Glassy	3.0–3.5	3.96–3.98	White	**Celestite**
Glassy	3.5–4.0	3.77	Blue	**Azurite**
Glassy	3.5–4.0	2.95–3.0	White	**Aragonite**
Glassy	4	3.18	White	**Fluorite**
Adamantine	3.5–4.0	7.04	Whitish	**Pyromorphite**
Adamantine	5.0–5.5	3.4–3.55	White	**Titanite**
Waxy	2.0–2.5	5.56	Greenish white	**Cerargyrite**
Waxy	2.0–5.0	2.5–2.6	White	**Serpentine**
Waxy	3.5–4.5	2.53–2.57	White	**Variscite**
Waxy	5.0–6.0	2.96–3.1	White	**Nephrite jade**
Waxy	5.0–6.0	2.6–2.9	White	**Turquoise**
Waxy	7	2.6–2.64	White	**Bloodstone**
Waxy	7	2.6–2.64	White	**Chrysoprase**
Greasy	1.0–1.5	2.7–2.8	White	**Talc**
Pearly	2	3.64	White	**Aurichalcite**
Pearly	2.0–2.5	3.22	Light green	**Torbernite**
Glassy	1.5–2.0	2.68	Greenish	**Vivianite**
Glassy	2.0–2.5	2.8–2.9	White	**Muscovite**
Glassy	2.0–2.5	2.7–2.9	Greenish white	**Chlorite**
Glassy	2.5–3.0	3.0	White	**Annabergite**
Glassy	3.5–4.0	3.9	Pale green	**Brochantite**
Glassy	3.5–4.0	3.6–4.05	Pale green	**Malachite**
Glassy	3.5–4.0	2.36	White	**Wavellite**
Glassy	4	3.18	White	**Fluorite**
Glassy	4.0–4.5	4.4	White	**Smithsonite**
Glassy	4.5–5.0	2.3–2.4	White	**Apophyllite**
Glassy	5	3.1–3.2	White	**Apatite**
Glassy	5	3.28–3.35	Pale green	**Dioptase**
Glassy	5.0–5.5	2.9–3.0	Pale green	**Datolite**
Glassy	5.5	3.9–4.2	Pale green	**Willemite**
Glassy	5.5	2.98	Pale green	**Brazilianite**
Glassy	5.0–6.0	3.16–3.35	White	**Actinolite**
Glassy	5.0–6.0	3.25–3.30	White	**Diopside**
Glassy	5.0–6.0	3.45–3.55	White	**Augite**
Glassy	5.0–6.0	1.99–2.25	White	**Opal**
Glassy	5.0–7.0	3.65–3.69	White	**Kyanite**
Glassy	6	2.56–2.59	White	**Microcline**
Glassy	6.0–6.5	2.80–2.95	White	**Prehnite**

Luster	*Hardness*	*Specific Gravity*	*Streak*	*Name*
Glassy	6.5	3.3–3.6	White	**Vesuvianite**
Glassy	6.0–6.5	3.4–3.6	White	**Epidote**
Glassy	6.5–7.0	3.25–3.36	White	**Jadeite**
Glassy	6.5–7.0	3.22–4.39	White	**Olivine**
Glassy	6.5–7.0	3.17–3.23	White	**Spodumene**
Glassy	6.5–7.5	3.15–4.30	White	**Garnet**
Glassy	7	2.65	White	**Aventurine**
Glassy	7.0–7.5	3.0–3.3	White	**Tourmaline**
Glassy	7.5–8.0	2.67–2.90	White	**Beryl**
Glassy	7.5–8.0	3.58–3.98	White	**Spinel**
Glassy	8.5	3.71–3.75	White	**Chrysoberyl**
Glassy	9	4.0–4.1	White	**Corundum**

COLOR SILVERY

Metallic	1.5–2.0	8.1	Gray	**Sylvanite**
Metallic	2.0–2.5	9.7–9.8	Silvery	**Bismuth**
Metallic	2.5–3.0	10.0–11.0	Silvery	**Silver**
Metallic	3.0–3.5	6.6–6.7	Silvery	**Antimony**
Metallic	4.0–4.5	14.0–19.0	Silvery	**Platinum**
Metallic	5.5	6.33	Black	**Cobaltite**
Metallic	5.5–6.0	6.1–6.9	Black	**Skutterudite**
Metallic	5.5–6.0	6.07	Black	**Arsenopyrite**
Metallic	5.5–6.0	5.7	Black	**Arsenic**

COLOR GRAY

Adamantine	3.5–4.0	3.9–4.1	Brownish	**Sphalerite**
Adamantine	5.0–5.5	3.3–4.3	Yellowish brown	**Goethite**
Adamantine	6.0–7.0	6.8–7.1	Light brown	**Cassiterite**
Adamantine	10	3.50–3.53	White	**Diamond**
Metallic	1.0–1.5	4.6–4.7	Greenish gray	**Molybdenite**
Metallic	1.0–2.0	2.1–2.2	Black	**Graphite**
Metallic	2	4.63	Grayish	**Stibnite**
Metallic	2	6.4–6.5	Lead gray	**Bismuthinite**
Metallic	2.0–2.5	7.2–7.4	Blackish gray	**Argentite**
Metallic	2.0–2.5	5.85	Purplish red	**Pyrargyrite**
Metallic	2.0–2.5	4.4–5.0	Black	**Pyrolusite**
Metallic	2.0–3.0	6.0–6.2	Black	**Polybasite**
Metallic	2.0–2.5	6.2	Black	**Stephanite**
Metallic	2.5	7.58	Lead gray	**Galena**
Metallic	2.5–3.0	5.83	Blackish gray	**Bournonite**
Metallic	2.5–3.0	5.5–5.8	Blackish gray	**Chalcocite**
Metallic	3	4.4–4.5	Blackish gray	**Enargite**
Metallic	3.5–4.0	4.9–5.1	Blackish gray	**Tetrahedrite**
Metallic	4	4.3	Faint brown	**Manganite**
Metallic	5.0–5.5	7.3	Blackish brown	**Wolframite**

Luster	Hardness	Specific Gravity	Streak	Name
Metallic	5.0–6.0	3.3–4.7	Blackish brown	**Psilomelane**
Metallic	5.0–6.0	4.7	Blackish red	**Ilmenite**
Metallic	5.5	9.0–9.7	Blackish brown	**Uraninite**
Metallic	5.5	4.1–4.9	Brown	**Chromite**
Metallic	5.5–6.5	5.3	Red-brown	**Hematite**
Metallic	6	5.2–8.0	Red-brown	**Columbite**
Metallic	6	5.18	Black	**Magnetite**
Metallic	6.0–6.5	4.2–4.25	Brown	**Rutile**
Glassy	2.5–3.0	2.8–3.4	White	**Biotite**
Glassy	5.0–6.0	3.0–3.4	Grayish white	**Hornblende**
Glassy	6.5–7.5	3.14–4.3	White	**Garnet**
Glassy	7.0–7.5	3.0–3.3	White	**Tourmaline**
Glassy	7	2.65	White	**Quartz**
Glassy	8	3.58–3.98	White	**Spinel**
Glassy	9	4.0–4.1	White	**Corundum**

COLORLESS, WHITE, AND LIGHT COLORS

Luster	Hardness	Specific Gravity	Streak	Name
Adamantine	3	6.3–6.39	White	**Anglesite**
Adamantine	3.0–3.5	6.55	White	**Cerussite**
Adamantine	3.5–4.0	7.04	White	**Pyromorphite**
Adamantine	3.5–4.0	7.24	White	**Mimetite**
Adamantine	10	3.50–3.53	White	**Diamond**
Waxy	2.0–2.5	5.55	Gray-white	**Cerargyrite**
Waxy	7	2.6–2.64	White	**Chalcedony**
Dull	1.0–3.0	2.55	Reddish white	**Bauxite**
Dull	2.0–2.5	2.6–2.63	White	**Kaolinite**
Silky	1	1.96	White	**Ulexite**
Greasy	1.0–1.5	2.7–2.8	White	**Talc**
Greasy	1.0–2.0	2.8–2.9	White	**Pyrophyllite**
Glassy	2	2.32	White	**Selenite**
Glassy	2	1.97–1.99	White	**Sylvite**
Glassy	2.0–2.5	1.71	White	**Boracite**
Glassy	2.0–2.5	1.75	White	**Epsomite**
Glassy	2.5	2.97	White	**Cryolite**
Glassy	2.5	2.17	White	**Halite**
Glassy	2.5	2.39	White	**Brucite**
Glassy	2.0–2.5	2.8–2.9	White	**Muscovite**
Glassy	2.5–4.0	2.8–2.9	White	**Lepidolite**
Glassy	3	2.71	White	**Calcite**
Glassy	3	1.91	White	**Kernite**
Glassy	3.0–3.5	4.29	White	**Witherite**
Glassy	3.0–3.5	4.3–4.6	White	**Barite**
Glassy	3.0–3.5	2.98–3.0	White	**Anhydrite**
Glassy	3.5–4.0	3.96–3.98	White	**Celestite**
Glassy	3.5–4.0	2.95–3.0	White	**Aragonite**
Glassy	3.5–4.0	2.8–3.0	White	**Dolomite**
Glassy	3.5–4.0	3.72	White	**Strontianite**

Luster	*Hardness*	*Specific Gravity*	*Streak*	*Name*
Glassy	3.5–5.0	3.0–3.12	White	**Magnesite**
Glassy	4	3.18	White	**Fluorite**
Glassy	4.0–4.5	4.0–4.5	White	**Smithsonite**
Glassy	4.0–4.5	2.42	White	**Colemanite**
Glassy	4.0–5.0	2.05–2.15	White	**Chabazite**
Glassy	4.5–5.0	2.3–2.4	White	**Apophyllite**
Glassy	4.5–5.0	3.4–3.5	White	**Hemimorphite**
Glassy	4.5–5.0	5.9–6.1	White	**Scheelite**
Glassy	5	3.1–3.2	White	**Apatite**
Glassy	5	2.7–2.8	White	**Pectolite**
Glassy	5.0–5.5	2.25	White	**Natrolite**
Glassy	5.0–5.5	2.8–2.9	White	**Wollastonite**
Glassy	5.0–5.5	2.3	White	**Analcime**
Glassy	5.0–5.5	2.8–3.0	White	**Datolite**
Glassy	5.0–6.0	1.99–2.25	White	**Opal**
Glassy	5.0–6.0	2.98–3.16	White	**Tremolite**
Glassy	5.0–6.0	3.25–3.30	White	**Diopside**
Glassy	5.0–7.0	3.65–3.69	White	**Kyanite**
Glassy	5.5	3.9	White	**Willemite**
Glassy	5.5–6.0	2.55–2.65	White	**Nephelinite**
Glassy	5.0–6.0	2.6–2.8	White	**Scapolite**
Glassy	5.5–6.0	2.28–2.30	White	**Sodalite**
Glassy	5.5–6.0	2.45–2.50	White	**Leucite**
Glassy	6	3.0–3.1	White	**Amblygdonite**
Glassy	6	2.5–2.9	White	**Feldspar**
Glassy	6.0–6.5	2.80–2.95	White	**Prehnite**
Glassy	6.0–7.0	3.23–3.24	White	**Sillimanite**
Glassy	6.5–7.0	3.17–3.23	White	**Spodumene**
Glassy	7	2.65	White	**Quartz**
Glassy	7.5	3.1–3.2	White	**Andalusite**
Glassy	7.5–8.0	2.97–3.0	White	**Phenakite**
Glassy	7.5–8.0	2.67–2.90	White	**Beryl**
Glassy	8	3.5–3.6	White	**Topaz**
Glassy	9	4.0–4.1	White	**Corundum**

Part III

GUIDE TO HUNTING LOCATIONS

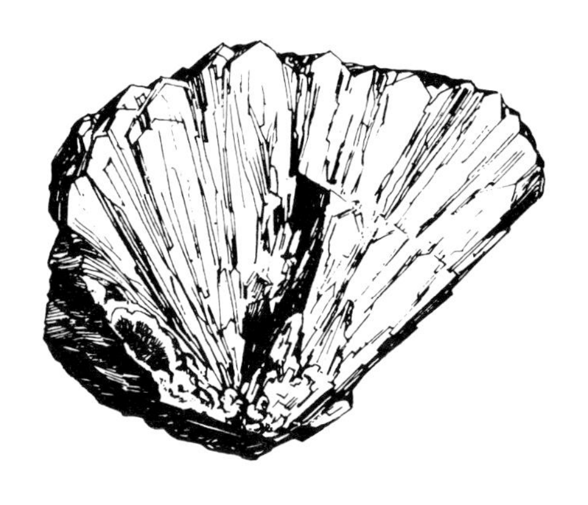

21

GUIDE TO GEM HUNTING LOCATIONS

This directory of locations in the North American continent has been made up from state and federal reports, from other published materials, from personal communications from collectors, from museum lists, and from other reliable sources. New gem locations are discovered every season; old ones become exhausted. Constant revision of such a list as this is therefore necessary. The current Rand McNally Road Atlas has been taken as the standard reference, and with few exceptions the following locations appear in it.

It is not always possible, however, to pinpoint locations, especially in the West, where the absence of man-made landmarks prevails over vast areas. Other areas have been only vaguely described or even kept secret by their discoverers to prevent commercial collectors from stripping them. A number of dormant eastern locations have been included only because mining may again be resumed at them, making possible the discovery of gems as a by-product, or because interest in them has been renewed.

Many areas have been closed, either by state or federal authorities, or by private owners who have other uses for their land or who have been annoyed by thoughtless collectors. Storm, fire, urban expansion, and road changes may occasionally make localities inaccessible. For these reasons, it is wise to inquire about locations before undertaking a long trip to them. Neither the availability of locations described in this book nor the quality of the material can be guaranteed.

MAP SYMBOLS

357 .... U.S. ROUTES	.... MINES
9 123 .... STATE ROUTES	.... AIRPORTS
.... STATE LINES	.... RAILROAD TRACKS
2 MI. DISTANCE BETWEEN POINTS	.... PARKING PLACES
.... HOUSES	.... GEM LOCATIONS
.... FACTORIES, MINE BUILDINGS, ETC	

DIRECTIONS ARE IN ABBREVIATED FORM, AS IN N FOR NORTH, NW FOR NORTHWEST, S FOR SOUTH, ETC. * DENOTES MAP

United States

Alabama

A coastal plain formed of sedimentary rocks, sand, and gravel makes up the lower half of the state. The northern half rests on sedimentary beds, rich in coal and iron, while a small wedge-shaped area of about six counties in east central Alabama offers an area of metamorphic rocks to the gem hunter.

- *Athens, Limestone County* QUARTZ NODULES: NW 18½ miles on Hwy 99 to Good Springs, then S on Hwy 26, go a mile to Dobbins Branch and collect in field downstream.
- *Blountsville, Blount County* AGATE NODULES: W 2 miles on Hwy 27 on way to Holly Pond.
- *Brookwood, Tuscaloosa County* SAGENITIC AGATE: Hwy 116 W for 4 miles, then take road N to strip mines to collect in pits. Also look for petrified wood.
- *Cedar Bluff, Cherokee County* QUARTZ: Take Hwy 9 for 3½ miles, then left ½ mile to search in fields.
- *Dadeville, Tallapoosa County* SOAPSTONE: E 12 miles at Garfield Heard farm at Dudleyville.
- *Delta, Clay County* QUARTZ, KYANITE, BERYL: NW 2½ miles at Smith Mica mine and at old Delta mine.
- *Erin, Clay County* APATITE, BERYL: To S along Gold Mine creek and to E of creek.
- *Hissop, Coosa County* BERYL: Take Crewsville road NE for a mile, then left ¾ mile to fork, take left fork to end of road at Thomas Prospect.
- *Hollis Crossroads, Cleburne County* BERYL: E 1½ miles on Hwy 431, left on SACP road 4199 for ½ mile, then left on dirt road ½ mile. Collect in pegmatite in left-hand ditch.
- *Jackson, Clarke County* SEAM AGATE: In road cuts NW on Hwy 1, 5½ and 14½ miles NW of junction with U.S. 43.
- *Leesburg, Cherokee County* AMETHYST: On Lowe farm to N. See Mrs. James Hampton in Leesburg.

- *Lineville, Clay County* TURQUOISE: In railroad cut at Erin NW on Hwy 49; and also S of Pleasant Grove church on the Hobbs farm.
- *Our Town, Tallapoosa County* EPIDOTE, QUARTZ: To E in fields and along Wind Creek.
- *Paint Rock, Jackson County* AGATE, JASPER: N on Hwy 65 to collect to N in tributaries of Paint Rock River and on Jacobs Mountain.
- *Phil Campbell, Franklin County* CARNELIAN: In gravel pits 2 miles N of town on Hwy 43.
- *Pinetucky, Randolph County* APATITE, RHODOLITE GARNET: At Jones Mica mine W of road to Milner, and with beryl to SW and NE in pegmatite mines.
- *Pyriton, Clay County* BERYL, FELDSPAR: Take road E to church, then N to first graded road and E to Lake Simon sign to turn N on logging road.
- *Quenelda, Clay County* RHODONITE: NW 2 miles on Watts farm.
- *Rockford, Coosa County* BERYL: S 5 miles on Hwy 231 to Pentonville, then W on Hwy 14 for ½ mile to fork, take right fork 1½ miles to mine at Williams Prospect.
- *Sylacauga, Talladega County* MARBLE: 1 mile W on Hwy 8, then S to quarry.
- *Talladega, Talladega County* AZURITE, MALACHITE: Go 11 miles SE near Coleta, turn left on Hwy 7, then S to where Hatchett creek crosses road. Collect ¼ mile farther S on E side of road.
- *Tuscaloosa, Tuscaloosa County* QUARTZ, PETRIFIED WOOD: NE on Hwy 116 to Girls' 4-H club camp sign, then ¼ mile more and N to Brookwood location to collect in strip mine area.
- *Wetkumpka, Elmore County* GARNET: At dam to N.
- *Winterboro, Talladega County* SOAPSTONE: In quarries.

Alaska

The largest of the states resembles the Western United States in topography. A chain of mountains borders the Pacific, including active volcanoes, separated by a basin from another mountain chain which includes Mt. McKinley, highest in North America. These mountains are formed of sedimentary rocks intruded by igneous rocks. Northeast of these ranges lies an arctic plain like the great plains of the West. South of the main plateau of Alaska lies a panhandle with many islands, and the Aleutian chain stretches west almost to Asia. The geology of Alaska is complex and is made more difficult for the gem prospector by frozen ground, vast distances, and lack of transportation.

- *Alcan Highway* SMOKY QUARTZ: Around poles on right hand side of road at Milepost 1225½.

  AGATE, BLOODSTONE: Upstream in Caribou creek at Milepost 118.
- *Anchorage* JASPER: Along Matahuska River at Milepost 72 on Glenn Highway.

  AGATE: At Fire Island, reached by cannery barge.

  AGATE NODULES: At Luster's Claim in Talkeetna mountains.

  AGATE, JASPER: In Kenai River to S.

  PETRIFIED WOOD, AGATE: In Anchor River.
- *Admiralty Island* AGATE NODULES: On beaches from Gambier Bay to Wilson Cove and near Point Gardner.
- *Fairbanks* AGATE, OBSIDIAN: To E in 40-mile area.

  FOSSIL IVORY: In gold dredge gravels.
- *Healy* AMETHYST: With agate and quartz.
- *Juneau* GRAY SAPPHIRE, STAR RUBY: In Copper River gravels.
- *Kenai* (On Cook Inlet) AGATES: At Salamatoff beach.
- *Kobuk River* DARK GREEN AND GRAY JADE: Boulders in Dahl Creek about 150 miles inland from Kotzebue Sound.
  At headwaters of creek at 5,000 ft. level.

  GRAY JADE: At Shungnak River, 14 miles W of Dahl Creek.

  GREEN JADE: Fairly free of black spots. At Jade Mountain, 30 miles NW of Dahl Creek, and in Jade Creek.
- *Kotzebue Sound* FOSSIL IVORY: In scarp on S side of sound.
- *Lake Iliamna* AGATE, BLOODSTONE: On beaches, best in spring.
- *Platinum* FOSSIL IVORY: Near Cape Newenham on Bering Sea.
- *Popof Island* CHALCEDONY PEBBLES: On beaches near Sand Point.
- *Port Heiden* AGATES: On beaches all the way to Port Moller.
- *Port Houghton* GARNET: To S with tourmaline.
- *Point Barrow* AMBER: In beach deposits.
- *Prince of Wales Island* EPIDOTE: Near Summit Lake on Green Monster Mountain.
- *Sand Point, Shumagin Islands* PETRIFIED WOOD: On NW side of Unga Island, reached by boat or plane.
- *Takeen, Marble Island, off Prince of Wales Island* MARBLE.
- *Tok Highway* NODULES: In stream at Mentasta Lodge.
- *Sitka* RHODONITE: At head of Silver Bay on Baranof Island.
- *Wrangell* AGATE NODULES: At Agony Beach, reached by plane.
  ALMANDINE GARNET (mostly specimen grade): Near mouth of Stikine River.

Arizona

The Colorado plateau, with its sandstone formations containing fossil wood and bone, extends over the northern third of Arizona. It is set off sharply from the rest of the state by an escarpment, the Mogollon Rim. South of the Rim lies a semidesert region of plains broken by low mountains, from which chalcedony minerals erode. The east central and southern areas are a major copper mining district.

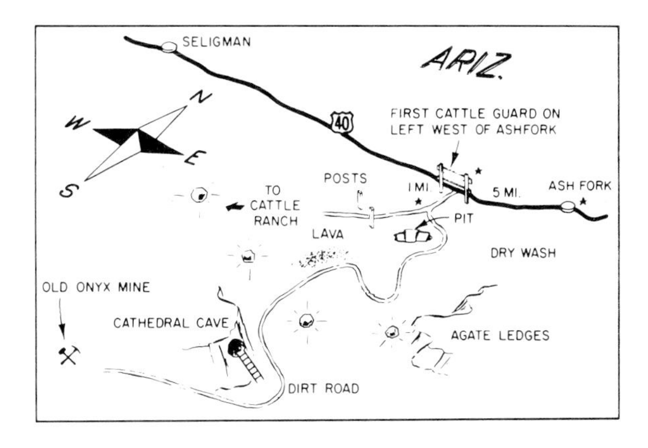

- *Ajo, Pima County* CHALCEDONY ROSES: Hwy 85 N for 20 miles, then right on road 7½ miles to far end of Black Mesa.

  CHALCEDONY: S of road.

  SHATTUCKITE: In veins at New Cornelia Mine.
- *Alpine, Apache County* MOSS AGATE: Go NW on U.S. 260 27 miles to sawmills, then E into Escudilla Mountains, and collect on N side.

  PLUME AGATE: Take national forest road NE to state line.
- *Ash Fork, Yavapai County* * AGATE: Int. 40 W for 5 miles, then left on dirt road at first cattle guard on left side of road for mile, then take left fork across a wash (which contains agate), and agate will be found along roadside where road passes under ledges from which agate is weathering. Continue to Cathedral Cave. About 500 ft. from cave entrance are ledges containing white agate spotted with colors. (Beyond cave about ¾ mile is abandoned onyx mine.)
- *Bisbee, Cochise County* SHATTUCKITE: At Shattuck Mine.
- *Boulder City (Nevada)* BLACK AGATE, BROWN JASPER: In Mohave County 3 miles SE of Hoover Dam and W ¼ mile to hill.
- *Bouse, Yuma County* SEAM AGATE: In black volcanic butte, 1 mile E of Bouse.
- *Bowie, Cochise County* FIRE AGATE: Take road N past railroad tracks, then take right fork and keep right as you go NE 21 miles toward the Peloncillo Mountain collecting area.
- *Casa Grande, Pinal County* AGATE, JASPER: South past Chuischu 12 miles. E to Wild Horse pass.
- *Cibola, Yuma County* CHALCEDONY, PETRIFIED WOOD: In river gravels 7 miles N of town.
- *Clifton, Greenlee County* * RED JASPER, VEIN AGATE, BRECCIA AGATE: Take road NE from Clifton, following San Francisco River. Cross on steel bridge, turn left and go 2 miles to Limestone Canyon on right.

  PURPLE AGATE: Three miles farther up Limestone Canyon, Mulligan Peak area to right can be reached on foot; N of peak.

  NODULES: W of peak. Similar material is also found beyond on side of Granite Mountain.

(Left) Dolomite from Traversella, north of Turin.
(Middle) Octahedral fluorite on quartz from Villa d'Ossola, Novara.
(Right) Breunnerite and quartz from Traversella, Turin.

FIRE AGATE, JASPER: At Crystal Mountain, trail to right around peak.

JASPER, BLUE AND BLACK AGATE: In nodules and boulders. Above Bobcat Canyon, cross river at Colorado Gulch and take road on right at cattle guard to Ash Spring Canyon. Found 2 miles from cattle guard.
NE of Ash Spring Canyon agate lies in foothills of Sunset Peak.
Nearer Clifton, west of the river, jasper and agate occur in Rocky Gulch and Weaver and Potter Canyons.

BLUE AGATE, CARNELIAN: N from Clifton on U.S. 666; found in first canyon to left a mile S of the Apache National Forest.

FIRE AGATE: Farther N road to left marked Upper Eagle, if followed to bottom, will lead to deposit.

OBSIDIAN NODULES (APACHE TEARS): Three miles farther N, road to right goes to Fritz ranch 16 miles.

CARNELIAN, CHALCEDONY: Continue N on U.S. 666. The 6K6 ranch sign points to this area 2 miles away.

OPALIZED WOOD: Exposed by road cuts. Farther N at Engineer Springs, 3 miles beyond Rose Peak lookout, old road to left for ½ mile.

AGATE GEODES: SE of Clifton on Hwy 75 and 4 miles up cemetery road in Wards Canyon.
S on Hwy 75, Mule Creek road leads E to Davis Ranch road, which is first road to right past tank in canyon, to dig for agate nodules.

OBSIDIAN NODULES: Continue on to state line on Mule Creek road; nodules lie scattered on hillsides.

FIRE AGATE, CARNELIAN: About 15 miles S of Clifton on Hwy 75 in the Apache Creek area E of highway. (Note: Many of these Clifton areas lie on rough roads and are on private property. Permission should be obtained to collect.)

- *Colorado City, Coconino County* PETRIFIED WOOD: S to Pipe Springs National Monument to collect on the Arizona strip.
- *Congress, Yavapai County* * PINK AGATE: Under bridge of Burro Creek which lies 47 miles NW on Hwy 93.

BLUE AGATE, JASPER: In canyon above bridge. In lava outcrop along highway E of bridge.

PASTEL ROCK: NW of Burro Creek bridge is sign to Bogle ranch. Go 12 miles E to collect.

PURPLE AGATE: A few miles NE of crossing of Signal Road at Burro Creek is a deposit of purple agate in white tufa.

OBSIDIAN NODULES, OBSIDIAN, BANDED AGATE: N of bridge 5½ miles and beyond another bridge a lava and a limestone ridge meet, forming a collecting area.

QUARTZ CRYSTALS: Found on Gypsy ranch, reached by taking Hwy 93 N to ranch sign and turning N 2 miles to diggings along road.

- *Courtland, Cochise County* TURQUOISE: At Turquoise Ridge ¾ mile NW.
- *Dragoon, Cochise County* CHALCEDONY, CHRYSOCOLLA: At Arizona Mines, 3 miles N.
- *Duncan, Greenlee County* FIRE AGATE, CHALCEDONY ROSES: SE 26 miles on Hwy 70, then take road W for 20 miles to Brister Willow Springs ranch. Follow dirt road at last cattle guard before ranch and go 3 miles to collect.

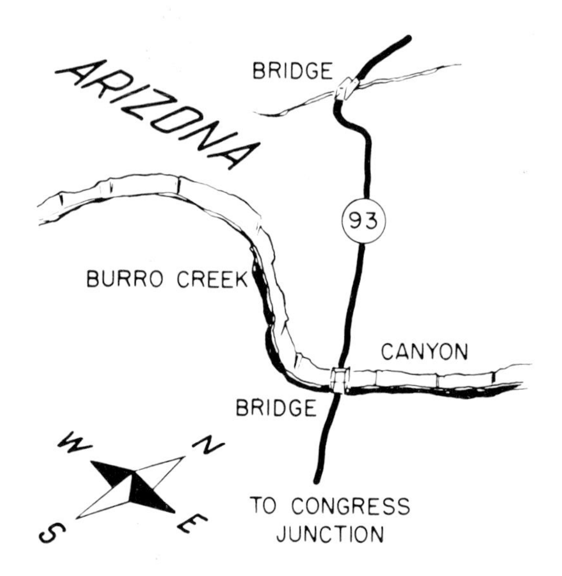

- *Florence Junction, Pinal County* CARNELIAN, CHALCEDONY ROSES: Take blacktop road W of town, go N and W for 5 miles, then N on faint road past corral.
- *Fort Defiance, Apache County* PYROPE GARNET, PERIDOT. (See Buell Park under New Mexico.)
- *Fredonia, Coconino County* PETRIFIED WOOD, AGATE: To SW in area of Pipe Spring National Monument.
- *Ganado, Apache County* PETRIFIED WOOD: At Nazlini Canyon, N of Ganado.
- *Gila Bend, Maricopa County* OBSIDIAN: Go 10½ miles S on Hwy 85, then left 36 miles on jeep road to Javelina camp to NW at base of mesa.

  GEODES IN WASH: NE at base of mesa. (Get permission from Lynn Cool in Gila Bend.)

  GEODE, AGATE: Go 24 miles S on Hwy 85, then 7 miles E on jeep road to area on W side of Hat Mountain to N in Sauceda Mountains.

  AGATE, BANDED: Go 14 miles W on U.S. 80, N on dirt road 5 miles, then NW 4 miles around red butte, where material is loose on ground.
- *Gleeson, Cochise County* TURQUOISE: E to graded road N to Courtland, then 2 miles N to dim road W around ridge.
- *Globe, Gila County* CHALCEDONY, MOSS AGATE, PINK JASPER: Go SE on Hwy 70 7 miles and take road to Coolidge Dam. Take winding road in front of dam to bridge and gravel pits for agate.
  Search in hills along big bend in river and below for agate and jasper.

  YELLOW AND BROWN ANDRADITE GARNET: Take dirt road S 10 miles E of dam to Stanley Butte, then go 1½ miles S to shack for garnets in vugs in gneiss.

  SERPENTINE, GOLDEN AND GREEN: On mine dumps at Apache town 35 miles NE on Hwy 77. Go W to the Chrysotile mine, then N to turnoff to the Phillips and other mines in the Salt River canyon.

  PERIDOT: In basalt and stream gravels S on Hwy 70.
  E on dirt road to Peridot and Tolkai (on San Carlos Indian Reservation; ask permission).

  VARIEGATED JASPER: W to Hwy 88, then 21 miles to Young Road, then N 15 miles to windmill, E to dry wash.
- *Hassayampa, Maricopa County** WHITE CHALCEDONY: Take Int. 10 to Tonopah exit, then go 3 miles S and W 5 miles to turnoff at a cattle guard onto a dirt road, then S and W $1\frac{4}{5}$ miles to a faint road S across flats to base of Saddle Mountain. White and pink chalcedony mixed with brown is found in rhyolite, and quartz crystals, and chalcedony roses.

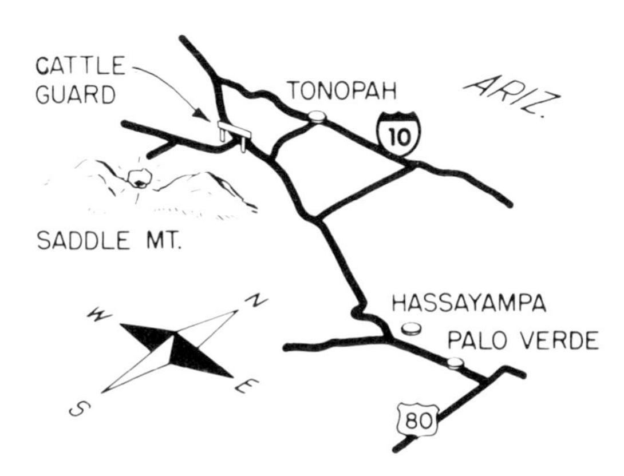

  FIRE AGATE: Is found in a cliff high on E side of the saddle between peaks of mountain, and some in the fan below peak.

  CHALCEDONY GEODES: S 8 miles on Gillespie Dam Road, then 21 miles W to Fourth of July Peak. Search in debris on S side of pass.
- *Holbrook, Navajo County* PETRIFIED WOOD: In draws and banks all around Petrified Forest National Park (no collecting in park).
  Two fee places to collect are at Dobell diggings, 19 miles from Holbrook on Hwy 180 E, and at Greer's Milky ranch. It is SE 7 miles on Hwy 180 past the National Park entrance to sign indicating ranch road.
- *House Rock, Coconino County* PETRIFIED WOOD: Along Hwy 89 to E to Marble Canyon.
- *Hyatts Camp, Maricopa County* LAZULITE: N 1¼ miles on Phoenix-Cavecreek Road.
- *Jerome, Yavapai County* PINK AGATE: N 9 miles on Perkinsville Road, deposit in place to left of road.
- *Kingman, Mohave County* TURQUOISE: In porphyry cutting schists, 15 miles NW at Ithaca Peak in Cerbat Mountains.

  AMETHYST: NE of Boulder Spring, near McConnico 4 miles SW on U.S. 66.
- *Lees Ferry, Coconino County* PETRIFIED WOOD: In Paria and Colorado Rivers.
- *Mayer, Yavapai County* BROWN AND VARIEGATED ONYX: NE of town across Big Bug Creek and to E on Hwy 69.
- *Mesa, Maricopa County* CHALCEDONY ROSES: Go 25 miles on Bush Hwy, then right on Stewart Mountain Lake Road 4 miles and turn left toward lake.

  AMETHYST: On Bush Hwy 3 miles farther to Cottonwood Ranch Road and right to end of road, then hike to Four Peaks where amethyst is found.
- *Miami, Mineral County* TURQUOISE: From miners at Castle Dome mine and at Sleeping Beauty mine.
- *Mineral Park, Mineral County* TURQUOISE: SW at Cerebras ranch.
- *Moenkopi, Coconino County* PETRIFIED WOOD: 9 miles NW at Willow Springs.

(Left) Crystals of orthoclase and smoky quartz from Baveno, Novara.
(Middle) Pyrite crystal (pyritohedron form) from Brosso, Turin.
(Right) Crystal of amethyst on siderite from Traversella, Turin.

- *Morristown, Maricopa County** JASPER, AGATE, QUARTZ CRYSTAL: Go 25 miles NE to Castle Hot Springs (where there is an excellent hotel); in area just above hotel, in creek to S, and in draws off main canyon in which stream flows.

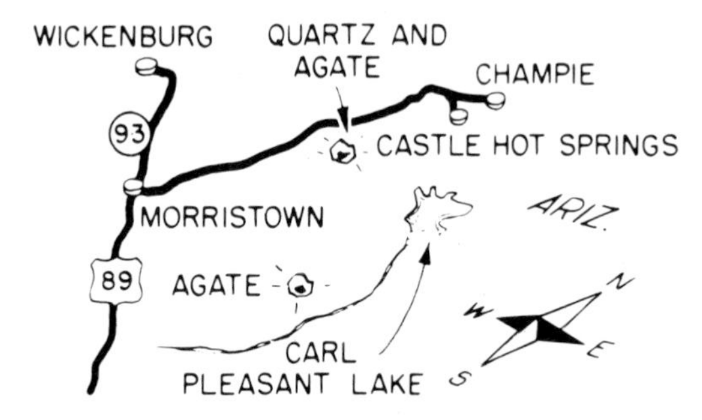

From Castle Hot Springs, Champie Ranch is reached by road N. Here, agate nodules may be collected for a fee. (Area is in rugged Bradshaw Mountains.)

- *New River, Maricopa County* RED JASPER: S in Skunk Creek.

  BLACK AND RED JASPER: In New River.
- *Oatman, Mohave County** AGATE AND NODULES: Take Kingman road NE for $5^2/_5$ miles to curve in Meadow Creek Canyon; some on slopes above canyon, but best material, including chalcedony roses, agate and sard, is just below Hwy at curve and to N of Hwy on buttes and ravines.

  FIRE AGATE: Can be collected at Sitgreaves Pass at Ed's Camp (fee).

  16 miles to NW at bend in Colorado River near Bullhead City, agate is found as float over a wide area.
- *Parker, Yuma County* CHALCEDONY: Loose on ground along Santa Fe right-of-way E of town.
- *Paulden, Yavapai County* DENDRITIC AGATE: W 3 miles along road.
- *Payson, Gila County* QUARTZ CRYSTALS: Kohl's Ranch road, take left fork for 24 miles to Diamond Point for crystals in sandstone, loose in washes.

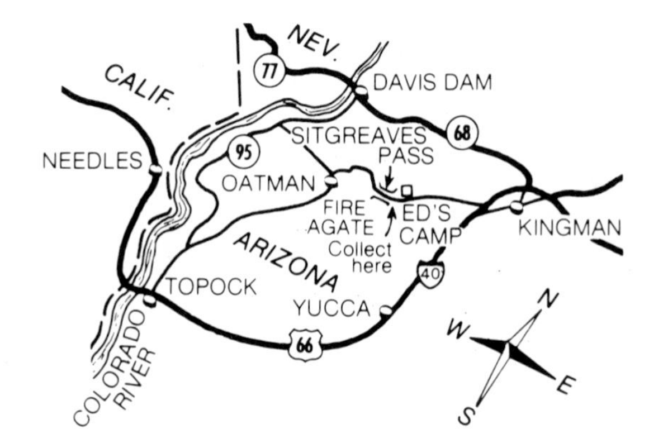

VEIN AGATE: Road W past new part of town and left to fork of North Peak and Cypress thicket roads for agate in the area between the roads.

- *Perkinsville, Yavapai County* PINK AGATE: S 5 miles on road to Jerome, collect in low hill that road cuts through.
- *Phoenix, Maricopa County* AGATE, ONYX: N 1 mile to Cavecreek road and 5 miles E to old house and Maricopa agate bed.

RED JASPER: Take Int. 17 N to Carefree road, go E 12 miles to Black Mountain ranch sign to collect opposite sign on S side of road.

AGATE: NW 35 miles NW to Agua Fria river, collect in hills across river to W of New River station.

- *Prescott, Yavapai County* RED JASPER: N on Alt. 89 to collect just N of Granite Dells.
- *Quartzsite, Yuma County* MOSS, PLUME JASPER: E 17 miles on Hwy 60 in area S of road.

QUARTZ CRYSTALS: S 9 miles on Hwy 95, then E 5½ miles to fork, and N ¼ mile to celebrated Crystal Hill area. Crystals, many containing chlorite inclusions, are dug from beds N and S of hill and in hills E of Crystal Hill, and loose on flats.

CHALCEDONY ROSES: From Crystal Hill take pipeline service road 12 miles around deep gully where pipeline is exposed, walk ½ mile S to collect.
Also 27 miles S on Hwy 95 and dig in alluvial fan E of road.

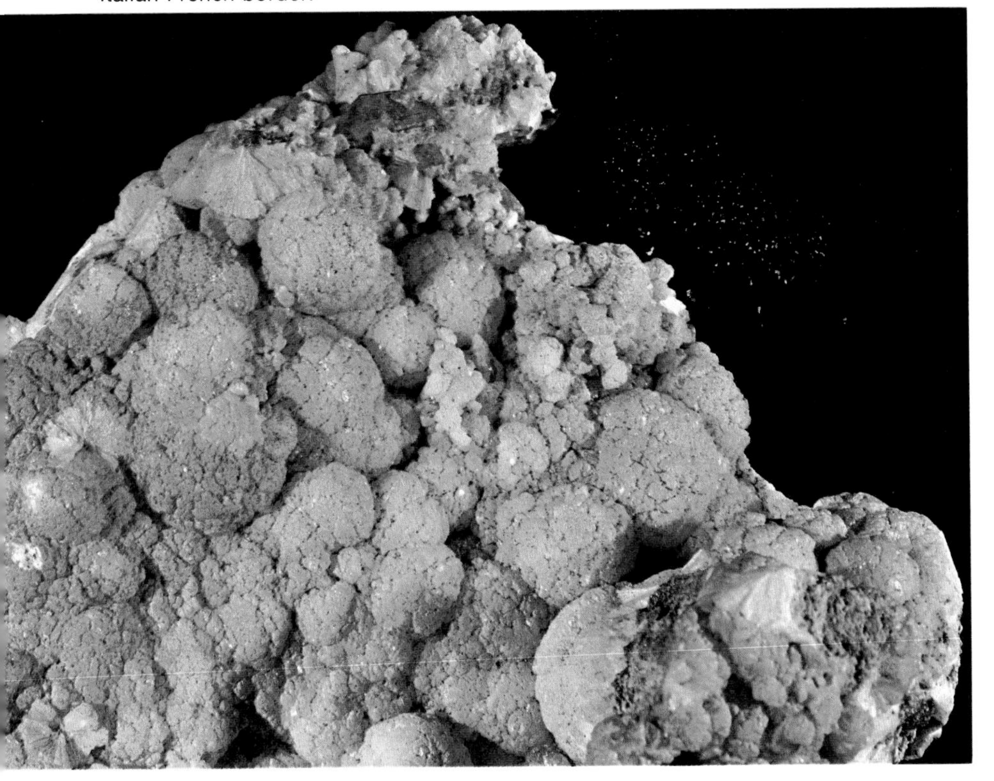

Stilbite, a zeolite, from the Miage glacier region on the Italian-French border.

FIRE AGATE: Go 19 miles S on Hwy 95 to Kofa mine sign, then E 6 miles to road S 5 miles and then W 2 miles.

GRAY AND PINK OPAL: Go 22 miles S on Hwy 95 to Cibola Road, then W 4½ miles and S a short distance to Opalite Hill.

LAZULITE: Take old highway W for 2 miles, then dirt road S to a bend to right into trees. Find poor road left under phone wires; go to last low hill, turn left over saddle, and collect in trenches in basin. There is pyrophyllite here, too.

- *Safford, Graham County* GREEN MOSS AGATE, RED AGATE, OBSIDIAN NODULES: Take Hwy 70 to Hwy 666, continue on Hwy 666 7 miles to faint road NW to chalcedony field and fire agate field NE of it (fee).

FIRE AGATE: Return to Hwy 666, go 3 miles and turn N through gate at Milepost 141½ over cattle guard for 1⅔ miles N and E of parking place.

WHITE CHALCEDONY ROSES, RED AGATE: Are found in draws in hills NW of Hwy 666.

NODULES, PALM ROOT, MOSS AGATE, RED AGATE: Continue on Hwy 666 toward Thumb Butte; collect where road passes hill.

OBSIDIAN NODULES: Scattered over hills.

AGATE, PETRIFIED WOOD, BONE: Take U.S. 70 3½ miles past U.S. 666 intersection and S to 111 ranch. Collect on hillsides a mile S.

- *St. Johns, Apache County* MOSS AGATE: In gravels to S.

AGATE, JASPER: 11 miles S on Hwy 260 at right of highway in blue sandstone.

AGATE: N 5 miles on Hwy 666; collect on both sides of road in weathered hills.

- *Salome, Yuma County* MOSS AGATE, CARNELIAN: To S in Eagle Tail Mountains.

CHRYSOCOLLA: SE 10½ miles at Socorro mine.

- *Show Low, Navajo County* RED JASPER: Along Mogollon Rim road 47 miles W.
- *Superior, Pinal County* CHALCEDONY ROSES: Go W on Hwy 60 to Florence Junction, then 2 miles on old highway to bridge, turn onto dirt road and follow under power line to hills.

OBSIDIAN NODULES: Roads W of Superior and S of Hwy 60 cut through perlite beds containing Apache tears. There are fee places to collect, such as Mike Guzeman's.

- *Topock, Mohave County* AGATE, BLACK JASPER: Go 5 miles N on road to Oatman, pebbles loose on ground.
- *Tucson, Pima County* BANDED AND MOSS AGATE: Take Int 10 N to Cortaro, left across gas pipeline to Wade Road, then right to desert roads to Little Peak area, and hike to Safford Peak.

RHYOLITE (WONDERSTONE): Near Tumamoc Hill and Sentinel Hill 2 miles SW.

- *Wickenburg, Maricopa County* CHALCEDONY ROSES, OBSIDIAN NODULES: Take Hwy 60 W to Aguila, then N on dirt road toward E end of Harcuvar Mountains to gem field.

  QUARTZ CRYSTALS, AMETHYST: Take Constellation Road NE 6 miles to cattle guard, then left ½ mile to amethyst in hills. Return to cattle guard, go S ½ mile to collect quartz crystals. Continue on Constellation Road 4 more miles to top of ridge for quartz crystals.

  QUARTZ: Take Hwy 60 22½ miles to sign for Date Creek ranch, then road to ranch house 3½ miles. Drive 2 miles to tracks right to Campfire Circle, park and go in any direction to collect.

  JASPER: NW on Hwy 93 to Santa Maria river area.

  AGATE: NW 7 miles on Hwy 93 to intersection with Hwy 71, then 4 miles NW on Hwy 71 to Alamo road. Take it 8 miles to fork, take right fork to a T, take dirt road right 7 miles to Anderson mine. Collect near mine office.
- *Woodruff, Navajo County* PETRIFIED WOOD: As chips and limb sections in area.
- *Young, Gila County* SERPENTINE (verd antique): 10 miles SE between Cherry and Canyon Creeks.

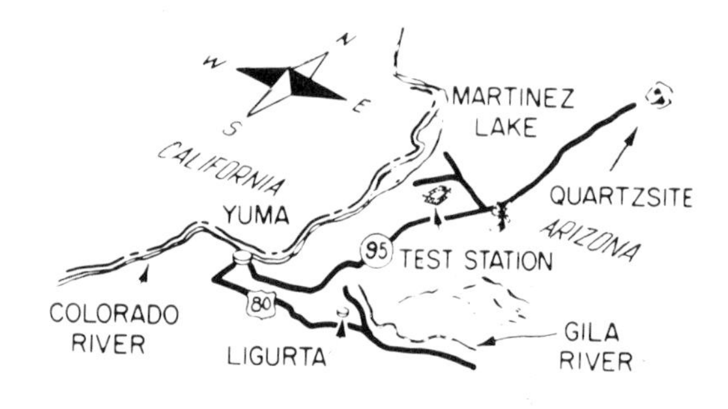

- *Yuma, Yuma County* * AGATE: E on Hwy 80 to Ligurta, then 4 miles further, go NW on dirt road and then N and E along the Muggins Mountains for 3 miles. Drive N into the foothills toward the highest peak 3¾ miles to edge of agate field, which extends a mile to the N.

  PALM ROOT SPECIMENS, JASPER, AGATE: The collecting area NE of Yuma lies in a military reservation; permission to collect should be obtained from the Yuma Test Station. The road to Martinez Lake in the Colorado river turns W from Hwy 95 at a windmill and a branch road leads to the Test Station. In the large area from a mile S of the Yuma Test Station to 10 miles N and from Hwy 95 to the Colorado river, palm root, jasper, and agate can be collected lying loose on the ground.

Arkansas

Southern and eastern Arkansas are sandy river delta and coastal plain, while the northern and western areas are rugged plateaus shared with Missouri and Oklahoma. Most of the plateaus are formed of hard sedimentary rocks, but a small area including Hot Springs and Pike counties is underlaid by crystalline rocks. This is the quartz crystal and diamond producing region.

- *Hot Springs, Garland County* QUARTZ: The area N and W of Hot Springs is famous for its crystal quartz groups found in the Ouachita Mountains, notably at Jessieville, 10 miles N on Hwy 7 at the Coleman Crystal mine (fee); at Mt. Ida, 30 miles W on Hwy 270; at the Ocus Stanley mines 10 miles SE of Mt. Ida; at High Point and Fisher Mountain (fee); and at Lewis Crystal mine (fee), Crystal Springs, 20 miles W on Hwy 270, at Crystal Mountain. Other locations are at Glenwood and Mountain Valley.
- *Malvern, Hot Springs County* NOVACULITE: On dumps along Rock Island railroad tracks near Butterfield station and in talus near Remmel Dam. Also on E side of Hot Springs mountain on bypass around Hot Springs.

  SODALITE: In old Diamond Joe syenite quarry on S side of Magnet Cove.
- *Mountain Pine, Garland County* VARISCITE: At Dug Hill, near Cedar Glades.
- *Murfreesboro, Pike County* DIAMOND: In peridotite. (See chapter on diamonds for details.) Now a state park.
- *Yellville, Marion County* SMITHSONITE: Take Hwy 14 S, turn E to Rush, collect in old mine dumps. There is agate on the mountain and in Clabber Creek. See Fred Durst at Rush as guide.

California

California's heart is a great central valley fringed with high mountains. Along the ocean rises the broken Coast range, and on the east towers the Sierra Nevada. These meet in northern California in a welter of glacier-cut valleys dominated by majestic Mt. Shasta and linked to Oregon's Cascade Mountains. In the south the Coast range and the Sierra Nevada swing together below Bakersfield to enclose the valley at that end. Below this point California's arid lands belong to the Great Basin and, like Nevada, are cut by short ranges. The Sierras tower in sheer cliffs above the narrow strip at their base, formed by the sinking of this part of the Great Basin. Within a few miles are the highest point in the continental United States, Mt. Whitney, and the lowest, Death Valley.

In the north, volcanic activity is still evident, and the abundant lavas yield obsidian to the gem hunter, while elsewhere metamorphism has created jade and serpentine. In the south, agate materials are plentiful in the arid deserts and eroded mountains, and in the coarse granites of the mountains north of San Diego are treasures of tourmaline, topaz, and beryl.

• *Acton, Los Angeles County* AGATE NODULES: W on Escondido Canyon road at Sir'Kegian gem beds, with amethyst and bloodstone.

• *Adin, Modoc County* RYOLITE (WONDERSTONE): 12 miles S on Hwy 139, then left 4 miles.

• *Alturas, Modoc County* OBSIDIAN NODULES: N 15 miles and one mile E of Davis Creek in gravel pits.

• *Amargosa, Inyo County* AGATE: S almost 8 miles on Hwy 127 to Deadman Pass Road. Collect float agate along road.

• *Amboy, San Bernardino County* * ONYX, MARBLE: E to Chambless on Hwy 66, S to phone line for 2⅓ miles and E for 2 miles, to collect in quarry to N.

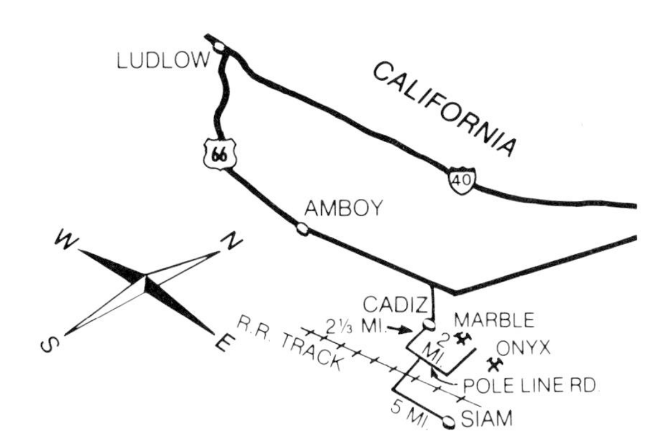

• *Applegate, Placer County* SILICIFIED ASBESTOS: At Best Bet Mine. (Fee; see Mr. Moore at Iowa Hill.)

• *Arroyo Grande, San Luis Obispo County* TRAVERTINE: Take road N to Routzahn County Park, then E along creek almost 10 miles; then hike on S side of creek to veins of travertine in hills.

• *Auburn, Nevada County* AGATE: At Pilot Hill.

• *Avenal, Kings County* PETRIFIED WOOD: Near airport.

• *Bagby, Mariposa County* JADE: N-NE 2½ miles between David Gulch and Flyaway Gulch.

• *Bagdad, San Bernardino County* OBSIDIAN: Go ½ mile E on Hwy 66, take road N across railroad tracks and take left fork to power line, then go left ⅔ mile, right under power line and take rough road to collect in hills to N and W.

AGATE: Farther along on same road.

• *Baker, San Bernardino County* * RED AND YELLOW AGATE, PETRIFIED WOOD: Take Hwy 127 N to Milepost 174, turn E 10½ miles, passing Sperry Station ruins and through canyon into open space at Sperry Wash. (Location closed to collecting at present by U.S. Bureau of Land Management.)

SAGENITIC AGATE, JASPER: Take Hwy 127 N to Salt Spring, go left on Furnace Creek Road 13 miles, and left 13 miles and N 3 miles into Owlhead Mountain collecting area.

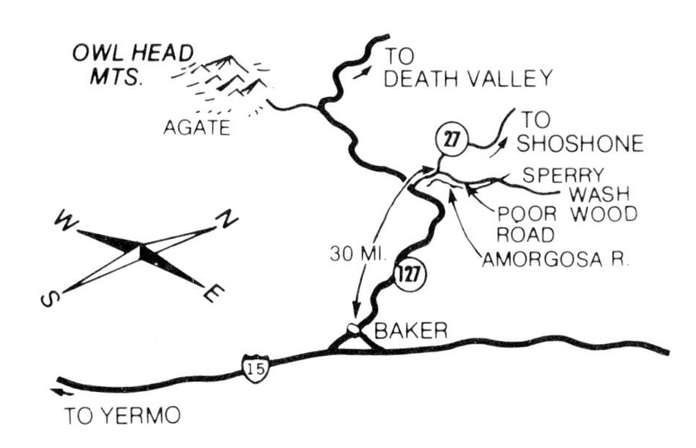

OPALITE, JASPER: Go 22 miles W on Int. 15, then S to Afton Canyon.

• *Bakersfield, Kern County* ROSE QUARTZ, AGATE: NE on Hwy 178, then W to Greenhorn Mountain Park, get permission at park office and collect 1 mile E at Little Acorn mine, and a half mile farther at Huckaby mine. Then go N and E 15½ miles to rose quartz location.

• *Bankhead Springs, San Diego County* RHODONITE: On Hwy 80 go E for 2½ miles to dirt road, and take it N to end.

• *Barstow, San Bernardino County* SAGENITIC AGATE, JASPER: E on Int. 15 to Calico road NW. Take it 1 mile, then NE on Mule Canyon road 1 mile or more to onyx diggings N of road (fee), then on 2 miles and N in Tin Can Alley road more than a mile for moss agate and sagenitic agate. Return to first fork E and go a mile to jasper and agate diggings. Return to Mule Canyon road and go E a mile to dig for palm wood.

Return to Calico road and go N 1½ miles, then N on Doran drive to the loop drive in Odessa Canyon. At its north extremity a trail goes into Green Hill for sagenitic agate.

TRAVERTINE: From Central Barstow exit take road to end, then left to Fort Irwin sign and follow signs 15 miles N to power line to dig for travertine.

CHALCEDONY NODULES: From Tiefort village in the Fort Irwin reservation Goldstone road goes W 2½ miles. Collect there.

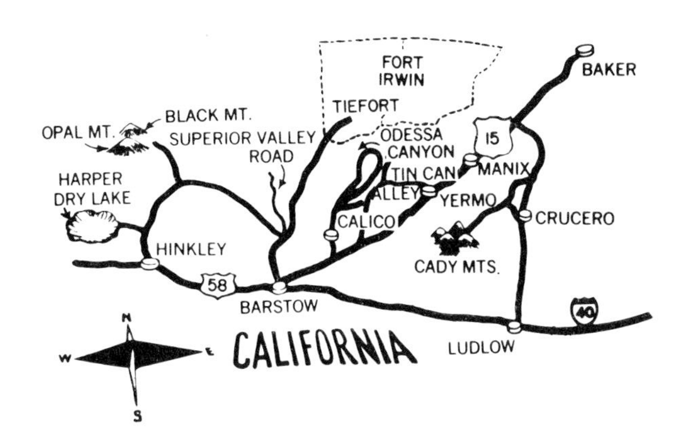

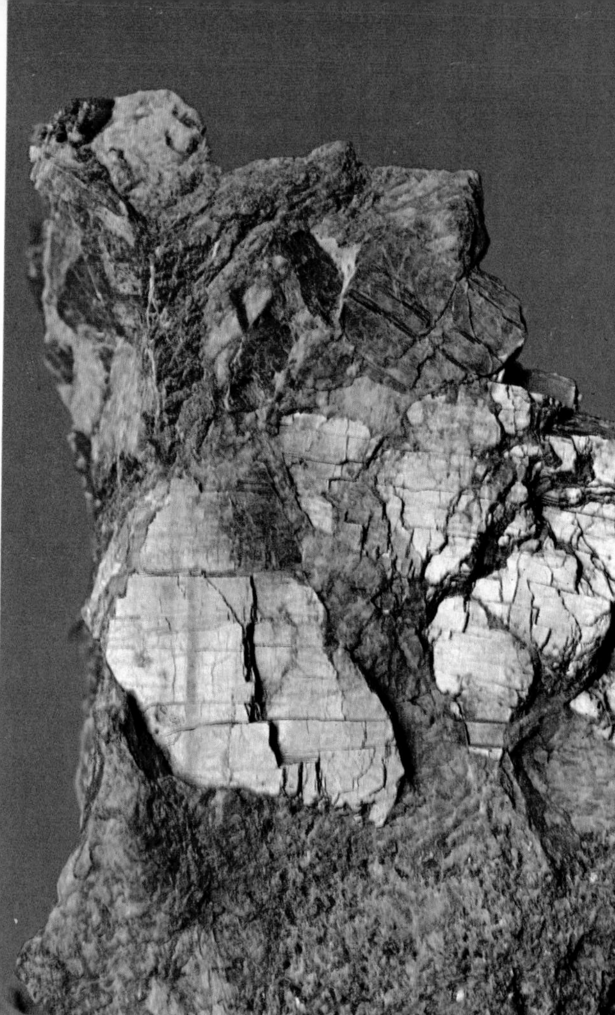

(Left) Aragonite from Borzoli, near Genoa, Italy.
(Right) Diallage, calcium-magnesium silicate, from the Bracco Pass, La Spezia, Italy.

JASPER: Take Fort Irwin road 5 miles N, then Superior Valley road 2 miles N to faint road ¼ mile E. Collect in wash and on hillsides.

JASPER, AGATE: E 2½ miles on Int. 15, then S on dirt road ⅓ mile.

PETRIFIED WOOD: E on Int 15 35 miles, turn off at Afton exit, go back a mile on N side of freeway, then N nearly 5½ miles to collect on hills and in washes.

• *Berkeley, Alameda County* IRIS AGATE NODULES: Take MacArthur Freeway to Warren Freeway, turn off at Walnut Creek, go through Caldecott Tunnel to Fish Ranch road. Park by microwave station, climb wall and go down slope to collect.

• *Bigpine, Inyo County* QUARTZ CRYSTALS: Go E through Westgard Pass, and continue 12 miles through Deep Spring Valley to cattle guard, turn left along fence and collect in rocky hills.

TURQUOISE: To E in Last Chance range almost on Nevada line. (See Roy Cummings, Big Pine.)

• *Bishop, Inyo County* OBSIDIAN: At Montgomery Pass; take Hwy 6 for 2 miles past Nevada line, then left through wash and take trail to diggings.
Return to Hwy 6 and turn right to collect at Queen Mountain.

PETRIFIED WOOD: Continue on Hwy 6 through Montgomery Pass to intersection with Hwy 10, turn right and collect in hills S of Hwy 6.

QUARTZ: In washes to W near Mt. Tom in Buttermilk area. Also N on Hwy 6 to Laws, then E into Silver Canyon in White Mountains.

• *Blythe, Riverside County* PYROLUSITE, PSILOMELANE: Take Lovelin Blvd. 21 miles NW to Inca Siding, cross tracks, turn left ¼ mile and then right for 9 miles to Arlington Mine.

AGATE: In gravel S of Hwy 60 about 8 miles W of Blythe.

• *Bodie, Mono County* LAZULITE: Mile W of Green Lake in Green Creek Canyon.

• *Bridgeport, Mono County* QUARTZ: Go N on Hwy 22, take Sweetwater road halfway to Wellington, turn right into canyon and just before reaching ranch turn left ¾ mile to collect.

• *Camarillo, Ventura County* SAGENITIC AGATE: E 3 miles on Hwy 101, turn N to county park and hike mile up private road to diggings.

• *Carlsbad, San Diego County* AGATE, JASPER PEBBLES: On beaches S to Cardiff-on-the-Sea.

• *Cedarville, Modoc County* AGATE, OPALIZED WOOD: One mile S and 4 miles W in Deep Creek area.

AGATE, PETRIFIED WOOD: W 4 miles on Hwy 299, then S to Cedar Creek. Also S 35 miles on Hwy 81 to Duck lake, then 2 miles through pass to dirt road W to Tuledad canyon. Go 2 miles more to turnoff N to steep hill and dig in ravine for agate. Petrified wood is 5 miles farther on the same road.

• *Chilcoot, Plumas County* SMOKY AND SCEPTER QUARTZ: Take Hwy 70 to U.S. 395, N on U.S. 395 7 miles and E 1½ miles to Crystal Peak (fee).

ORCHID STAR QUARTZ: Take road N for 5 miles, turn right and go NE for 8 miles; turn right and go ⅓ mile, then left less than a half mile and turn right. Park and walk uphill to left to collect.

• *Clio, Plumas County* FIRE OPAL: In ironstone 3½ miles N at Laura quartz mine.

IDOCRASE (CALIFORNITE): E 7 miles.

• *Coalinga, Fresno County** JASPER, PETRIFIED WOOD: S on Merced road to Lost Hills road to Jacolitos Canyon and continue W up canyon; look in creek bed. Chert and fossil coral are also found there.

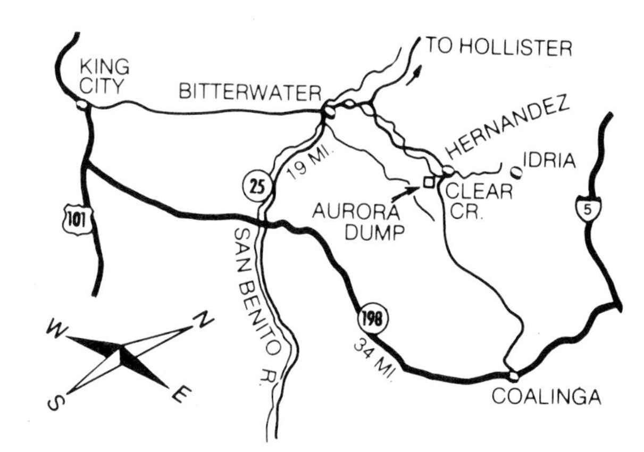

JADEITE: Take Hwy 198 W to Hwy 25, then NW to Bitterwater and on E to Hernandez. Follow Clear Creek road 3 miles to jade mine sign. The dark green jadeite, streaked with light green and white, is found as boulders in the creek and lenses in the walls of the canyon. It is also found as far south as Santa Rita peak.

SERPENTINE: On the Aurora Dump is cutting quality serpentine. (Get permission at the Idria store.)

• *Cobb, Lake County* MASSIVE QUARTZ: Hunt in road cuts on Hwy 291 and at Manke ranch, NW of Cobb.

• *Coulterville, Mariposa County* MARIPOSITE: Take Hwy 132 W for less than a mile, collect on N side of road.

(Left) Limonite from Pignone, La Spezia.
(Middle) Malachite from Libiola, Genoa.
(Right) Slender crystals of vesuvianite with red essonite garnet.

NEPHRITE JADE: At Jade King mine 2 miles S (fee) and at nearby Ming, Green Dragon and Four Jacks claims.

• *Covelo, Mendocino County* NEPHRITE JADE, JADEITE: NE 15 miles on top of Leech Lake Mountain.
Also in N fork of Eel River, where road N to Mina crosses river, at Dos Rios to SW and at Dryden ranch 6 miles E reached by Mendocino Pass road (fee).

• *Davis Creek, Modoc County* OBSIDIAN: N on Hwy 395 4 miles, then take right fork 4½ miles and E 3 miles across creek to Rainbow mine (fee). Or continue N instead of turning off, go 2 miles and collect in hills. Obsidian is also found E on the Lake City road 5 miles to second creek crossing, then hike parallel with and E of road ¼ mile to collect at base of hills. Beyond here toward Lake City 2½ miles is golden sheen obsidian in creek.

• *Desert Center, Riverside County* AGATE NODULES, SEAM AGATE: E 22 miles on Int. 10, then S on Army Road 6 miles to right fork, continue 9 miles to fork, and left to Chuckawalla Spring. Collect geodes in hills below camping place and in Augustine Pass area to W, and seam agate SE at Graham Pass.
Take Int. 10 E for 21 miles, cross Bridge 23, turn S past gravel pits for 2½ miles. Collect float agate on desert and along W side of road.

• *Earp, San Bernardino County* JASPER, AGATE: Take Wall Canyon road N for 1 mile, collect on E side of road.
Take boat S on Colorado River to collect agate and jasper pebbles on beaches and in cliffs along river, especially where Vida Wash empties into it.

• *El Centro, Imperial County* PETRIFIED WOOD, JASPER, AGATE: On Int. 8, 48 miles E, take dirt road N to old army camp to collect NE and S of camp.

• *Escondido, San Diego County* TOURMALINE, BERYL: At Mack mine. Take Hwy 6 N 16½ miles through Valley Center and Rincon reservation to red house, then right to mine.

• *Etna, Siskiyou County* MARBLE: Take Sawyers Bar road for 3 miles into mountains.

• *Eureka, Humboldt County* NEPHRITE JADE, JADEITE PEBBLES: On beaches from Patrick Point State Park, 28 miles N on U.S. 101, to Dry Lagoon, 8½ miles farther N. Also 40 miles E in Trinity River.

• *Exeter, Tulare County* ROSE QUARTZ: At Gasenberger ranch 8 miles SE.

• *Fairfield, Solano County* BANDED ALABASTER: E for 5 miles, at Tolenas quarry (fee).

• *Fallbrook, San Diego County* QUARTZ CRYSTALS: Go 2 miles NE of De Luz school, to dig in granite ledge 700 feet S of Murrieta-Fallbrook road.

• *Fresno, Fresno County* AGATE, JASPER: In Panoche Pass; take Hwy 180 W to road through Panoche hills.

• *Furnace Creek, Inyo County* TRAVERTINE: Take Hwy 190 N for 13¾ miles to abandoned quarry W of road; 1 mile E of Death Valley Monument boundary. Also collect in ravine near road ½ mile farther N. No collecting in monument.

• *Georgetown, El Dorado County* WHITE GROSSULARITE GARNET, PREHNITE, VESUVIANITE (CALIFORNITE): 2½ miles SE in serpentine along Traverse Creek.

VESUVIANITE: 4 miles S at Stifle claim on Meadow Brook road off Hwy 193 (fee).

• *Glamis, Imperial County* NODULES, PETRIFIED WOOD: Take Hwy 78 NE 12 miles, then S 4½ miles on road to Obilby, and ⅓ mile E for palm wood. Continue S 6½ miles and go E under power line 8 miles to Indian Pass for petrified wood and dumortierite. Return to Ogilby road and go 4 miles S to Gold Rock Ranch for petrified palm wood, and 5 miles farther S is road E to Bluebird mine for palm wood, kyanite, and dumortierite.
N of the intersection of the Ogilby road and Hwy 78 lies the Midway Well area. Take Hwy 78 N for 6½ miles and collect in the area of Buzzard Peak about a mile E of the road.

• *Goffs, San Bernardino County* GREEN OPAL, PETRIFIED WOOD: Take Lanfair Lane, a dirt road, 11 miles NW to Hackberry wash.

• *Goleta, Santa Barbara County* PETRIFIED WOOD, JASPER: NW on Hwy 154, then take road E on S side of Lake Cachuma, collect in hills SE of lake.

• *Grass Valley, Nevada County* PETRIFIED WOOD: E on Hwy 174 to U-Bet sign, then N 5½ miles to old house where road swings left, then go 1 mile more and N to park. Dig in area N and W of parking area.

• *Halloran Spring, San Bernardino County* TURQUOISE: In area about 10 miles N and W of Halloran Spring in dumps of old claims in the Turquoise Mountains, including Toltec.

• *Happy Camp, Siskiyou County* RHODONITE: Go 9 miles N to Mt. Thompson, collect on E side between Indian and Thompson creeks (fee).

VESUVIANITE: Take road N and then left across bridge where S fork of creek joins Indian Creek; continue mile across second bridge to ranch house, where road ends. (Get permission; hike up creek a mile.)

NEPHRITE JADE: To N at Chan jade claim on S fork of Indian Creek.
Also with serpentine 5 miles E on Hwy 96, then N past dump.

• *Hemet, Riverside County* SMOKY, ROSE QUARTZ: At Juan Diego flat; take Hwy 74 E 4 miles, then S 17 miles and turn left.

(Left) Calcite from Cavagnano, hamlet of Cuasso al Monte, Varese.
(Middle) Crystals of demantoid garnet on serpentine from Sferlun near Sondrio, Italy.
(Right) Violet fluorite on quartz from Cavagnano, a hamlet of Cuasso al Monte, Varese.

SMOKY QUARTZ, PINK BERYL: At the Williamson mine just S of Juan Diego flat at Coahuila Mountain.

•*Hinkley, San Bernardino County* * CHALCEDONY NODULES, GREEN OPAL: At Opal Mountain and Black Canyon. Go 6½ miles N and take right fork 4 miles to a left fork, continue on left fork 6½ miles into canyon, dig for nodules on Black Mountain to S; continue to summit, collect cherry opal at Opal Mountain to NE; continue left and then right for almost three miles to small white hill in Black Canyon and dig green dendritic opal.

JASPER, NODULES: N 9 miles on Hinkley road, then W a mile and N 2 miles and then 3 miles W, stay left of road 4¾ miles into valley.

•*Hornbrook, Siskiyou County* MOSS AND DENDRITIC AGATE: E 11 miles on road along Klamath River at Jenney Creek.

AGATE, PETRIFIED WOOD: N of river as far as Copco and into Oregon.

•*Independence, Inyo County* QUARTZ CRYSTALS: Take Hwy 395 N for 5⅓ miles, then new road N for 3 miles to Colosseum Road. Take that E for 1 mile, then keep generally E under power line and across old railroad for 5 miles. Go SE past national-forest sign 1½ miles, to dig at Crystal Ridge.

OPALITE: E on Mazouka Canyon road to collect at old mine on left side of canyon.

•*Indio, Riverside County* * JADE, VESUVIANITE, AGATE: Int. 10 E for 26 miles, take turnoff into Joshua Tree National Monument NE for 26 miles, then E 8½ miles to Storm Jade mine.

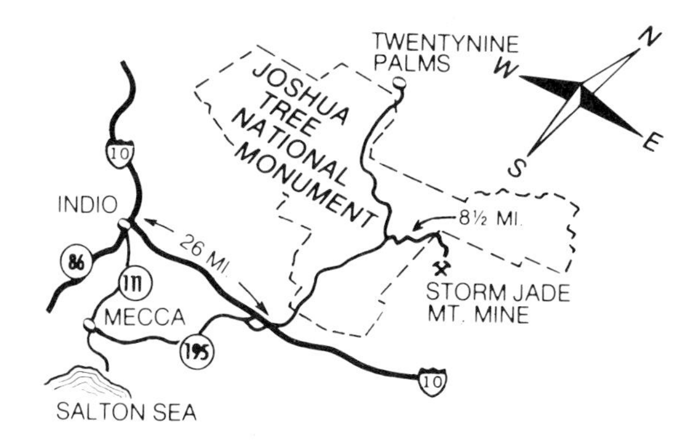

• *Inyokern, Kern County* OPALITE, RAINBOW JASPER: S on road, and as it curves toward U.S. 395, cut off S 5 miles on power line road, take road W 2 miles to collect.

• *Johannesburg, Kern County* * AGATE, BLOODSTONE: Take road N toward Westend, but take right fork skirting S end of Searles Lake 19 miles to Wingate Pass for vein agate. This road goes through a naval ordnance testing station, and special permission will be required to use it. To S is Brown Mountain, and 4 miles SE is bloodstone.

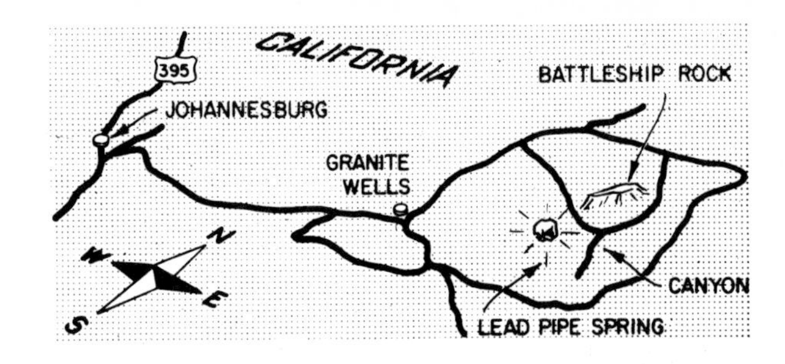

BLACK MOSS AGATE: At Sheep Spring; go N on U.S. 395 for 21½ miles, turn S where road crosses railroad tracks for 8 miles and E to Sheep Spring to collect in hills E of spring.

BLUE CHALCEDONY AND NODULES: Go E from Johannesburg on a fair road to Granite Well, then NE nearly 12 miles to road turning S that is beyond a narrow ridge visible to the S known as Battleship Rock. Curve around rock to a canyon and take a branch road into it. Leave car and find specimens in volcanic ash.

FIRE OPAL, NODULES: Farther up and higher.

SAGENITE AGATE: In nodules, lies farther up the canyon.

FIRE OPAL, BLUE AGATE NODULES: Back at canyon mouth, take road on W a short distance and turn S again to Lead Pipe Spring, where gems can be dug from red rhyolite, particularly to the SE.

JASPER, AGATE: Back near the road.

AGATE, OPAL: Back to road, next turn S goes to diggings. The road curves N shortly farther W and goes back to road to Granite Wells. (Note: Area is Naval Ordnance Testing Station. For permission to collect, write Commandant, N.O.T.S., China Lake, California 93555.)

PLUME AGATE: Take Steam Wells road E 7 miles to Brown's ranch, then 4⅔ miles N on dirt track to dry lake, keep left here less than 1 mile to collecting area.

- *Kane Spring, Imperial County* PETRIFIED WOOD: In clay hills 15 miles W.
- *Kramer, San Bernardino County* * PETRIFIED WOOD, PALM WOOD: From Kramer Junction, go 17 miles W on Hwy 58, then N past some new houses and through gap in reddish hills, keeping left at fork to large dry lake which contains best petrified wood, including palm wood.

BLOODSTONE, AGATE, PETRIFIED WOOD: Go on and keep left toward Castle Butte, where bloodstone, agate, and petrified wood can be dug on east slope and in area just NE of butte. Right fork before reaching dry lake leads to small dry lake and hills containing wood.

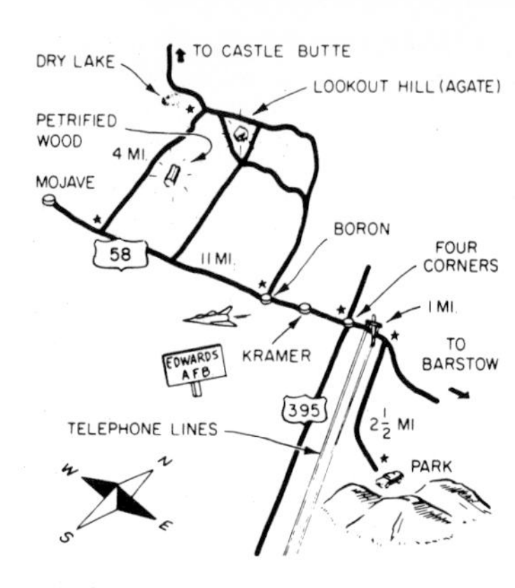

AGATE: E 1½ miles from the intersection of Hwys 395 and 58 near Kramer lie the Kramer Hills, reached by following a road that parallels telephone lines about 3 miles S of Hwy 58, turning off to the SE into the hills to park. Collect agate around parking area and to W of phone lines.

BORON WOOD: 11 miles W of Boron a road N leads to a dry lake where the noted Boron wood is dug from the soil. Some is also found on dry lake areas E of the road.

AGATE, NODULES: To the SE of this region lies Lookout Hill, high spot in the area, where agate and nodules are found.

- *LaGrange, Stanislaus County* RHODONITE: At Sturtevant ranch, 14 miles NE on Coulterville Road (fee).
- *Lake City, Modoc County* AGATE, PETRIFIED WOOD: In stream gravels from Fort Bidwell to Cedarville.
- *Lakeport, Lake County* JASPER: S on Hwy 29 to fork above Kelseyville, then take Big Valley road SW and hunt around reservoir.

OBSIDIAN: Along Bottle Rock road, 2½ miles E of Kelseyville off Hwy 29, and farther E near Soda Bay and Red Hill roads, as well as in Cold Creek.

QUARTZ (Lake County diamonds): From Hwy 29, go E to Lower Lake and take roads W and S toward Siegler Springs for 5 miles to collecting area between Perini Hill and Hoborg's Airport.

- *Lakeside, San Diego County* GARNET, EPIDOTE: Take Wiliat Canyon road NE 11 miles to Wright Canyon, go E for 1⅔ miles, then left to dig at old mine.
- *Lang, Los Angeles County* HOWLITE: At U.S. Borax and Chemical company mine.
- *Laporte, Plumas County* QUARTZ CRYSTALS: NE 22 miles at Nelson Point.
- *Lemoncove, Tulare County* ROSE QUARTZ: N 5 miles on ridge W of Dry Creek.

RHODONITE: N 3 miles on N side of ravine which is ⅓ mile NE of Kaweah river and mile E of Ward ranch.

- *Lindsay, Tulare County* CHRYSOPRASE, GREEN OPAL: SE one mile in pits on N end of Venice Hill.

  VESUVIANITE: On ridge S of Lewis creek.
- *Little Lake, Inyo County* OBSIDIAN: Go N for 2½ miles on Hwy 395 to cinder road, E into naval test station, and then 3 miles E into hills. (Open weekends; get pass at China Lake office.)
- *Littlerock, Los Angeles County* AGATE: In Agate Valley, 2 miles W of Little Rock Dam and 3 miles S near quarry.
- *Livermore, Alameda County* CITRINE QUARTZ: At Newman mine to SE near Cedar Mountain.
- *Lodoga, Colusa County* JASPER; JADE: In gravels of Stonyford creek.
- *Lompoc, Santa Barbara County* PETRIFIED WHALEBONE: At Jalama Beach, 18 miles S, with travertine.
- *Lone Pine, Inyo County* AMAZONITE: From N edge of city, turn right on road past railroad station, cross Owens River and go almost to second railroad tracks, turn S ½ mile to Kern Knob, a granite mass, and collect from seams in canyons between it and the Inyo Mountains.

  OBSIDIAN: Take U.S. 395 S 12 miles, go E 1 mile and then 2 miles S and E to road parallel to U.S. 395 to collect nodules.
- *Los Angeles, Los Angeles County* HOWLITE: Take Golden State Freeway NW to Palmdale cutoff (Hwy 14), go on old Sierra Hwy NE to Solemint Junction. Continue NE 6 miles to Davenport Road, then E for 1½ miles and N to dumps of Sterling Mine in Tick Canyon.

  AGATE: In beach gravels at El Segundo, Hermosa, and Redondo beaches.
- *Los Banos, Merced County* PLUME AGATE: S 11½ miles to Mercy Springs exit, follow power line uphill W of freeway to intersection with main power line on top of hill.
- *Los Olivos, Santa Barbara County* SAGENITIC AGATE, JASPER: Take Figueroa Mountain road 8 miles past end of pavement, then trail down hill to collect along creek.
- *Lower Lake, Lake County* CHRYSOPRASE: E 21 miles to Knoxville and S 3½ miles at Lone Pine chromite mine.

  QUARTZ ONYX: N 2 miles of Knoxville at Manhattan mine (fee.)
- *Lucerne, Lake County* GREEN TRAVERTINE: At Hitchcock ranch (fee).
- *Lucerne Valley, San Bernardino County* SERPENTINE (VERD ANTIQUE): N on Barstow Road 12 miles and W 5⅓ miles to faint road, then S 3 miles into Sidewinder Mountains.

  RHYOLITE: Go 5 miles E on Old Woman Springs Road to Camp Rock Road, then 14 miles N and NE, turning NW into East Ord mountain area near old gold mine.
- *Lucia, Monterey County* NEPHRITE JADE, RHODONITE: Farthest N location is at Limekiln Creek Beach, where jade pebbles are found with rhodonite (fee).

(Left) Fluorite from the Orobiche Alps.
(Middle) Crystallized magnesite encrusting crystals of transparent quartz, from Dosso dei Cristalli, Sondrio.
(Right) Molybdenite in a vein of quartz from Cavagnano, hamlet of Cuasso al Monte, Varese.

NEPHRITE JADE: To S on Hwy 1 at Plaskett Creek and just S of it at Jade Cove, and next cove S is another spot. Look for a new botryoidal jade and a reddish jade.
Farther S is Willow Creek Beach and Salmon Creek even farther S. Some jade is in place and some has been recovered by skin diving. (This is on a military reservation and blasting and camping are prohibited.)

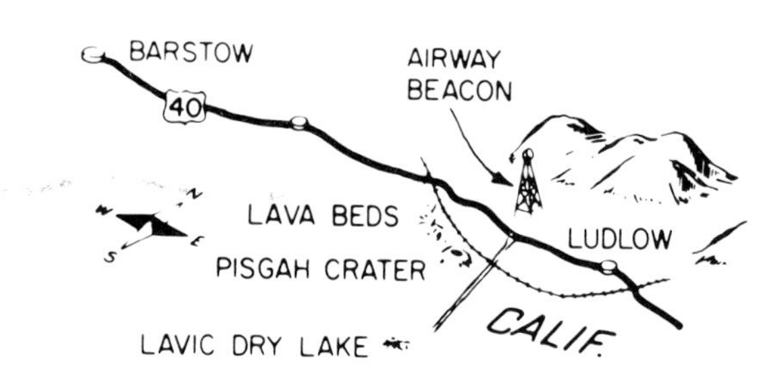

• *Ludlow, San Bernardino County* * Int. 40 exits are at Newberry, Hector, and Ludlow. Use them to reach old Hwy 66.

JASPER: Take Crucero Road N 7½ miles, take a jeep road SW for 12 miles into Cady Mountains. Collect in basin between Flat Top Peak and Mt. Afton, and on Mt. Afton and canyon to N.

JASPER, AGATE: Take any road N of Int. 40 between Ludlow and the airplane beacon to W and collect in hills and canyons of Cady Mountains 2 or 3 miles N of hwy.

CARNELIAN: Go 9 miles W on Int. 40 to old hwy, go S for ⅖ mile, hike in and collect on hill and slopes ½ mile W.

CHALCEDONY ROSES: Go 11 miles E on Hwy 66, take road N 3 miles and collect them along road, or go 4 more miles into hills and collect them there.

PINK CHALCEDONY: SE 12 miles to Siberia along railroad and 3½ miles W to gulch near Ash Hill.

OBSIDIAN: S of Int. 40, for ½ to 1½ miles E.

JASPER, CHALCEDONY: S of Int. 40 and between Milepost 114 and airway beacon 44-18.* Good jasper is also found at Milepost 121.

WIND-POLISHED CHALCEDONY, AGATE PEBBLES: N of Pisgah Crater, embedded in lava-formed bay. Farther W collect just W of where lava flow crosses road.

JASPER, AGATE: Farther E, at Milepost 114, turn from the road S across the railroad at Lavic Station, and on down to Lavic jasper field. (Area S of railroad is under claim.) About 3 miles farther S, the road leads to a dry lake and a military-reservation sign. Turn E here 8 miles on poor road into mountains for agate.

CHALCEDONY ROSES: E on Hwy 66 for 9¼ mile, take old road S for 1⅓ mile, then mine road W to Ash Hill, also look for carnelian and chalcedony with red spots.

• *Mammoth, Mono County* RHODOCHROSITE: Take road to Agnew Meadows camp, then Shadow Lake trail 1 mile to River trail. Go left ½ mile to ridge on left and collect in talus of the ridge.

• *Manix, San Bernardino County* YELLOW JASPER, SEAM AGATE: Take road N almost 9 miles into Spanish canyon, collect there and to right in side canyon.

AGATE, PETRIFIED PALM WOOD: Go E on old Hwy 91, collect on both sides of hwy in dry lake bed.

JASPER, PETRIFIED PALM WOOD: Take Int. 15 W for 11 miles and then road N for 6 miles to Alvord Mountains.

• *Mendota, Madera County* NODULES, PETRIFIED WOOD: Hwy 11 SW for 20 miles to ranch house, then S 3 miles into Panoche Hills. Collect E of road, and then go 3⅓ miles farther for petrified wood.

• *Mesa Grande, San Diego County* BICOLORED TOURMALINE, MORGANITE, AQUAMARINE: World famous locality for pegmatite gem minerals. On Gem Hill, 2¾ miles NW of Mesa Grande, are the Himalaya and San Diego mines.

PINK AND DARK GREEN TOURMALINE, MORGANITE AQUAMARINE, CITRINE QUARTZ: NW of Gem Hill 1½ miles at the Esmeralda mine. (This mine and those on Gem Hill are privately owned.)

• *Middletown, Lake County* QUARTZ (Lake County Diamonds): To N on road to Lower Lake and SE to area N of Pope Valley.

• *Mojave, Kern County* * PETRIFIED WOOD, AGATE, JASPER: Last Chance Canyon is a favorite collecting place. To reach it take Hwy 14 N through Red Rock Canyon for 21 miles to Cantil store, then 13½ miles N to ruins of Hart's Place. Turn E, pass Holly mine at 5

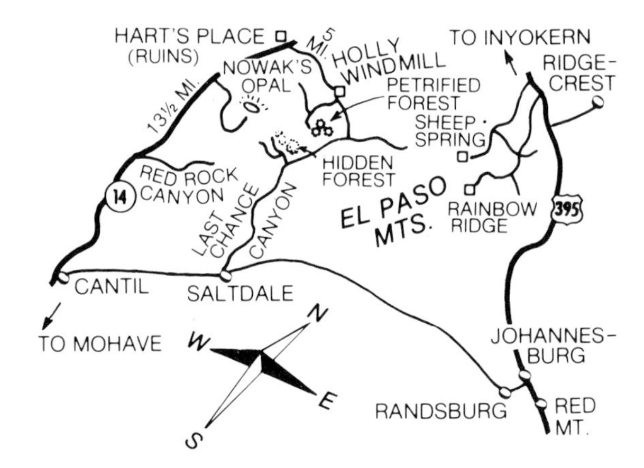

miles, go mile farther to fork, take right fork to a T, go left into Last Chance Canyon to collect in side canyons and red hills to W. Go back to T, turn S there to camp ground and through it right to a canyon often called the Hidden Forest to dig agate and jasper. There is also some collecting in Red Rock Canyon.

AGATE, JASPER, PETRIFIED PALM WOOD: E on Hwy 58 to Clay Mine Road, N almost to end of pavement (about 3 miles), then W for ¼ mile, and collect along ridge and S of ridge.

OPAL: At Leo Nowak diggings, at sign 7⅔ mi N of Randsburg road turnoff (fee).

PETRIFIED PALM WOOD: E 8 miles on Hwy 58, then S 1½ miles across railroad tracks and 1½ miles to area near butte to collect on flats and ridge.

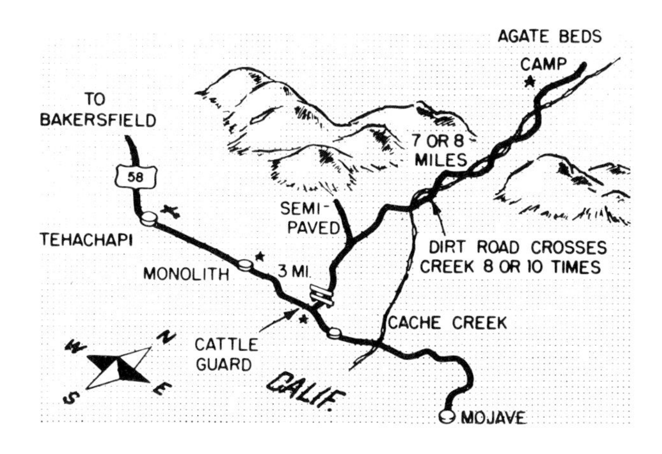

- *Mokelumne Hill, Calaveras County* QUARTZ CRYSTALS: Take Glencoe Road, turn off on road to ghost town of Jesus Maria, then to bridge and 9½ miles through Jesus Maria, park at turn, take trail to right, down slope and to left into gulch.
- *Monolith, Kern County* * MOSS AND PLUME AGATE: At Horse Canyon. Go 3 miles E on Hwy 58 to Cache Creek Road and turn N about 9 miles, keeping right. Heavy digging, and there is fee and limit on amount taken.
- *Morgan Hill, Santa Clara County* ORBICULAR JASPER: At Paradise Valley. (fee)

  MOSS AGATE, JASPER: Go NW on Hwy 101 to Cochran Road, then E to parking area near Anderson Lake at dam, and hunt along lake.
- *Moss Beach, San Mateo County* PETRIFIED WHALEBONE: On beach just N of parking area. Beach is 11 miles S of San Francisco.
- *Needles, San Bernardino County* * AGATE, CHALCEDONY ROSES, OPALITE: Hwy 95 S to Lake Havasu road, then 1½ miles farther to Turtle Mountain road. Take it 10½ miles W to Essex road NW, then take Essex road 2 miles and turn S on faint road for 2 miles to collect sagentic agate, and opalite at hill. Return to

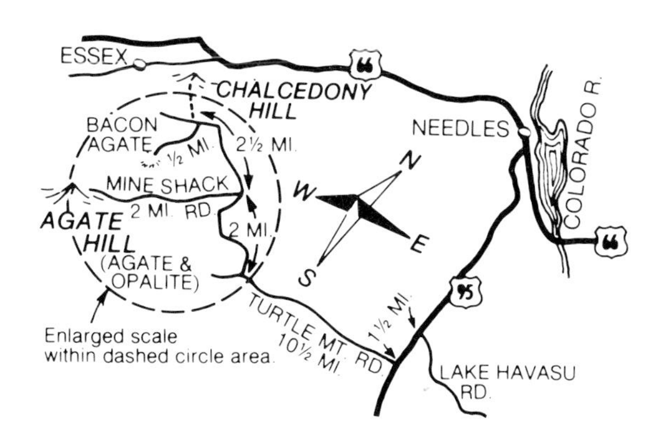

Essex road, take it NW 2 miles to butte ¼ mile N of road for chalcedony roses and fire agate. S from Essex road near this butte is road that goes ½ mile to place to collect so-called bacon agate.

  AGATE NODULES, JASPER: S on Hwy 95 23 miles to dirt road W.

  CHALCEDONY ROSES, CARNELIAN: Along the above road. Continue 11 miles, then S for chalcedony roses and agate to E and S in washes, and S and W to Mohawk Springs.

  AGATE, JASPER: S on Hwy 95 66 miles to Lake Havasu road E into Chemehuevi Mountains. Take it to powerline, then S along line to dig in hills below wash.

  BLUE-GREEN AGATE: In rhyolite on above road. (Get directions and permission, Needles Gem Society, 308 D St.)

  JASPER, CHALCEDONY ROSES: Go 39 miles S on Hwy 95, then E at milepost 270 for 2 miles to jasper field SE of knoll. Hike half mile NE across basin into canyon for chalcedony roses.
- *Nevada City, Nevada County* OPALIZED WOOD: Hwy 20 E for 5 miles, then 3 miles N to Scott Flat Lake. Collect along shore.
- *Newberry, San Bernardino County* AGATE NODULES: Use Int. 40 exit, go 2 miles S on Newberry road, keeping right to end of road. Walk ½ mile W into canyon and collect in blue-white ash in walls.
- *Newport Beach, Orange County* PETRIFIED WOOD, PETRIFIED BONE: Turn W on Cherry Street to sea cliffs, take trail to beach near Arch Rock; collect on beach and in ravines.
- *Nipomo, San Luis Obispo County* SAGENITIC AGATE: In bean fields, or at Freddi's ranch (fee).
- *Nuevo, Riverside County* GARNET, STAR QUARTZ: Go 2 miles N and take road E a mile and then S to Mountain View ranch. Also at Southern Pacific silica quarry nearby.
- *Ocotilla, Imperial County* PETRIFIED WOOD: NW on Hwy S2 for 8½ miles to collect in hills nearly on San Diego–Imperial County line.

(Left) Doubly terminated quartz from Dosso dei Cristalli, Sondrio.
(Right) Quartz and orthoclase from Cavagnano, Varese.

- *Pala, San Diego County* TOURMALINE, KUNZITE, BERYL: Famous for tourmaline are the Pala Chief mine on Pala Chief Mountain; the Tourmaline King and Tourmaline Queen mines on Tourmaline Queen Mountain. These mines and two on Hiriart Hill, 2 miles NE of Pala, the Senpe and the Vanderburg, are noted for morganite beryl. The Pala Chief, and the Katerina, Vanderburg, and San Pedro on Hiriart Hill are mines noted for kunzite. (Mines are privately owned and closed to collecting.)
- *Palmdale, Los Angeles County* AGATE NODULES: Go 5 miles S on Hwy 14, then SE to Little Rock Dam, and take jeep trail 5 miles to Agate Valley.
- *Palo Verde, Imperial County* JASPER, CARNELIAN, FIRE AGATE: S 7 miles on Hwy 78, then W at pole rack ⅔ mile to Palo Verde Pass (fee).

  AGATE, PETRIFIED WOOD: 6 miles W of town in old Colorado River terraces.
- *Palos Verdes, Los Angeles County* PETRIFIED WHALEBONE, AGATE: From Fountain square follow Pasco de Mar to bluff, then walk to beach to collect there.
- *Paradise, Butte County* QUARTZ: In pockets in quartz veins in Sawmill Peak. Some of crystals contain inclusions.
- *Petaluma, Sonoma County* NEPHRITE JADE: As lenses and veins in serpentine, SW 5 miles and on E side of Massa Hill on Vonsen ranch.

  JASPER, PETRIFIED WOOD: 5 miles N of adobe mission.
- *Pinehurst, Fresno County* QUARTZ: Take Hwy 180 into King's Canyon National Park to Camp Joaquin sign, turn right to campsite at Chimney Rock.
- *Placerville, Eldorado County* NEPHRITE JADE: Take Hwy 49 N for less than a mile, then take road right to S fork of American River. Cross bridge, turn right on dirt road along river for 2 miles, and collect in rock along river and in river.

  QUARTZ: After crossing bridge, take Rock Creek road 9½ miles to Mosquito Creek road to Pino Grande.

  ROSE QUARTZ: E 18 miles in road cut along Hwy 50.
- *Porterville, Tulare County* NEPHRITE JADE: NE 2 miles at commercial workings of Januko Brothers.

  CHRYSOPRASE, SERPENTINE: E of Plano and 1½ miles S, also 8 miles E and ½ mile S of Deer Creek.
- *Pulga, Butte County* IDOCRASE, MASSIVE GROSSULARITE GARNET: In spoil piles from gold dredging in Feather River E of town, and in outcrops ½ mile from river in hills above town to W.
- *Quincy, Plumas County* ROSE QUARTZ, RHODONITE: Take Meadow Valley road W, then N ¾ mile into hills to collect.
- *Ramona, San Diego County* * DARK GREEN TOURMALINE, AQUAMARINE, MORGANITE: Another

of the celebrated pegmatite gem-producing districts. At the ABC mine, 3½ miles NE of Ramona.

DARK GREEN TOURMALINE, TOPAZ, SPESSARTITE GARNET: At the Little Three mine, 3¾ miles NE of Ramona in the Hatfield Creek valley.

SPESSARTITE GARNET: In the Spaulding and Hercules mines.

EPIDOTE, GROSSULARITE GARNET: At McFall Mine, 7½ miles SE.

• *Randsburg, Kern County* JASPER: At Rainbow Ridge. Take U.S. 395 3 miles past intersection with Ridgecrest Road, turn S on road along power line slightly more than 5 miles and W into El Paso Mountains to collect. (Get permission: Charles Bishop, Box 354, Red Mountain, Calif. 93558.)

RHODONITE: At Main Street turn S for 7½ miles to Sunshine Mine Road. Turn here, go for 1 mile to end of pavement, continue straight on dirt road for 1 mile. In next ½ mile take two left turns, then turn right to mine dumps. Collect in vein and dumps.

FLOWER AGATE: Take Trona Road 1½ miles N, then go 6 miles E on Steam Well Road and N for 5½ miles from Brown's ranch, to collect in hills.

• *Rincon, San Diego County* TOURMALINE, AQUAMARINE, MORGANITE: At the Victor mine, 2 miles SE.

MORGANITE, AQUAMARINE: At the Clark and Mack mines.

• *Rosamund, Kern County* JASPER, PETRIFIED WOOD: Take Willow Springs road W for 3 miles, Mojave-Tropico road N for 4½ miles, and then go W ½ mile to collect in Rosamund Hills to S and E. Area is known as Gem Hill.

• *Sage, Riverside County* TOURMALINE, LEPIDOLITE: N 2½ miles on Hwy 79 and then E on dirt road to Anita mine.

• *St. Helena, Napa County* ONYX: At Erdahl ranch (fee).

• *San Diego, San Diego County* * DUMORTIERITE: Go E on Int. 8 to Alpine, take Taven Road ½ mile

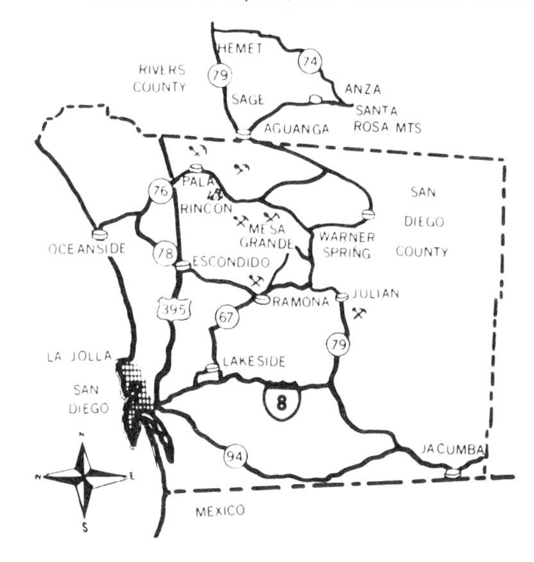

(Left) Black tourmaline on orthoclase from Cavagnano, Varese.
(Middle) Tourmaline in pegmatite from Olgiasca, Como.
(Right) Blackish zircon from Piona, Como.

to Arnold Way and go 2½ miles S to Dehesa Road and short distance SW to road S into quarry.

- *San Francisco, San Francisco County* CHALCEDONY PEBBLES, PETRIFIED WHALEBONE: At beaches at Bodega Bay, Bolinas Bay, Tomales Bay, Drakes Bay, and Duxbury Point, all in Marin County, and at Coyote Point Beach, 11½ miles S.
- *San Jose, Santa Clara County* DENDRITIC AGATE: Take Coleman Road to end at Guadalupe Mine.
- *San Miguel, San Luis Obispo County* BRECCIATED JASPER: Take Parkfield Road 17 miles, turn N for 9 miles and then go 2 miles E into Stone Canyon. (Get permission from Mrs. Hope Bagby, Hidden Valley Rancho, San Miguel.)
- *Santa Barbara, Santa Barbara County* PETRIFIED WHALEBONE: At Gaviota Beach, 32 miles W on Hwy 101; also Refugio Beach, 20 miles W.
- *Santa Cruz, Santa Cruz County* AGATE, PETRIFIED BONE: N 30 miles on Hwy 1 at Steele Beach.
- *Santa Monica, Los Angeles County* SHELL CONGLOMERATE: Go NW for 30 miles N to Coquina Beach for shells in dark matrix.
- *Siam Crossing, Riverside County* AGATE NODULES: Take old Hwy 66 6½ miles NE to Danby, then S on road across railroad tracks, and SW 7 miles along tracks in hills to E.
- *Sky Valley, Riverside County* TRAVERTINE: S on VeeBee road from Dillon road, then W ⅓ mile to deposit on slopes.
- *Susanville, Lassen County* AGATE, BLACK AND WHITE PETRIFIED WOOD: W 8 miles on Hwy 36, then S toward Stephens ranch.
  Also N on Hwy 139 11 miles, then W to collect along road.
- *Tecopa, Inyo County* PRECIOUS OPAL: Go 3½ miles W to Hwy 127, 2½ miles N on it to ruins of stage station. Collect in gray-green area in hills to W.
- *Tehachapi, Kern County* MARBLE: Take Curry Street S to Highline road, then S to Antelope Canyon Ranch to collect in quarry.
- *Tennant, Siskiyou County* OBSIDIAN: NE 4 miles from Medicine Lake at Glass Mountain.
- *Tollhouse, Fresno County* VESUVIANITE (CALIFORNITE), GROSSULARITE GARNET: On E side of Watts Valley, 1½ miles S of Hawkins School.
- *Trinidad, Humboldt County* BRECCIATED JASPER: On beach 1 miles N and S and in boulders on cliffs and at Patrick Point.
- *Trona, San Bernardino County* ONYX: N on Panamint Valley Road to summit, then 3 miles to sharp left turnoff, 2 miles to road to left and through rough country to house and around to right to Onyx Hill for Death Valley onyx (fee).
- *Ukiah, Lake County* ONYX: N on Hwy 20 for 6 miles, then left to Potter Valley and Lake Pillsbury to collect at NW side. (See Enrique Mahnke at Cobb.)
- *Upland, San Bernardino County* LAPIS LAZULI: 12 miles N in N fork of Cascade Canyon.
- *Valley Ford, Sonoma County* JASPER, AGATE: Take Hwy 1 to Bodega, then 8 miles N to Shell Beach for pebbles.
- *Valley Springs, Calaveras County* MOSS AGATE, PETRIFIED WOOD: At Marie Costa ranch 2 miles N on Paloma road (fee).

  AGATE, OPAL: E on Hwy 26 to Hwy 12, then S to Hogan reservoir road to Hooten ranch to collect in hidden valley (fee).

  BLUE DENDRITIC OPAL: Take Hwy 12 E then N a block and 2 miles to turnoff S to Snyder ranch (fee).
- *Ventucopa, Santa Barbara County* ALABASTER: S 3 miles on Hwy 33, then E through gate for a block to take steep trail up canyon. Collect in ridges on top.
- *Victorville, San Bernardino County* VERD ANTIQUE: N on Int. 15 to Bell Mountain exit, go NE 3 miles on exit road to dirt road, take it NE 7 miles, then E to quarry on mountain.
- *Vidal Junction, San Bernardino County* CHALCEDONY: Take U.S. 95 N for 10 miles, at Milepost 270 marker turn E 12 miles, passing wash to collect in Whipple mountains and farther E in gravels of Parker Dam area of Colorado River.
- *Visalia, Tulare County* SERPENTINE: E 8 miles at S end of Venice Hill, with chrysoprase.
- *Warner Springs, San Diego County* MORGANITE: At Pearson mine, 13 miles NW on Hwy 79 to Oakgrove and E to mine.

  MORGANITE, TOPAZ: At Aguanga Mountain, 10 miles NW on Hwy 79 and W to Mountain Lily mine.

  TOPAZ, BLUE-GREEN TOURMALINE: At Ware mine near summit of Aguanga Mountain.
- *Weed, Siskiyou County* AGATE: To N in Willow Creek.
- *Westmoreland, Imperial County* OBSIDIAN: To N at Obsidian Butte.
- *Westwood, Lassen County* AGATE, PETRIFIED WOOD: E on Hwy 36 to Willard Creek road S for ½ mile, collect along creek.
- *Wiley Well Area, Imperial County* * CHALCEDONY ROSES, FIRE AGATE: Take Int. 10 E from Desert Center (Riverside County) 31 miles and turn S after crossing bridge. Cross Niland Road at 8 miles and go 3 miles more to left-hand road leading into Coon Hollow in the Mule Mountains. Specimens along road.
  Road E out of Coon Hollow goes mile to fire agate and chalcedony diggings.
  Other road NE out of Hollow goes less than mile into Mule Mountains and then hike about a block to bed of white nodules.

  OBSIDIAN NODULES: About 13½ miles W of Wiley Well on the road along the power line, turn off N 1½ miles into sandy flat to hills between Big and Little Chuckawalla Mountains for nodules on stony slopes.

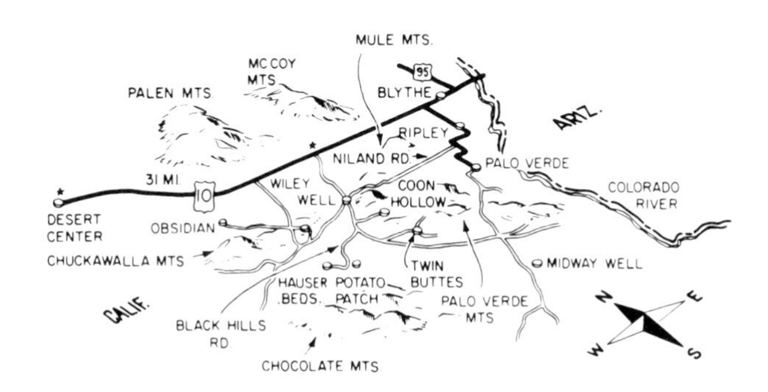

BANDED AGATE, SEAM AGATE, BLACK CHALCEDONY, FLOAT AGATE, PLUME AGATE, CHALCEDONY ROSES: In Palo Verde Mountains. Back on Wiley Well Road, go on S and then E to Twin Buttes Road which leads up a ridge and at 1½ miles it forks. Right fork leads to Twin Buttes nodule beds, a great variety of colors and materials. Left fork leads into a mountain basin where float agate, including some plume, is found. Rough road goes on toward buttes to a field of chalcedony roses. Palo Verde mountains are E of Twin Buttes. Collect seam agate there.

SEAM AGATE, GEODES, AMETHYST: Back on Wiley Well Road N almost to Coon Hollow Road but turn W on Black Hills Road. At 5⅔ miles it splits into three branches. The southernmost branch goes almost 2 miles S, then forks left between two hills where seam agate is found, and into the Potato Patch, a deposit of crystal-lined geodes, and some amethyst, now deep with the debris of digging. Branch veers to W and at 3½ miles reaches old Hauser bed and new bed a half mile farther up canyon for agate-filled geodes lying 3 to 5 ft. below surface.

CARNELIAN, RED VARIEGATED JASPER: On faint fork left nearly a mile farther on.

AGATE, CARNELIAN, JASPER: Next branch N off Black Hills Road leads 3½ miles through flats where these occur as float, and to trail up wash a half mile to blue nodule (Long Beach) bed.

Northernmost branch of Black Hills Road * goes 3 miles to fork, then left to end of passable road. Hike up wash to geode bed in side of hill.

- *Willits, Mendocino County* * JADEITE, ACTINOLITE: Take Hwy 306 E to Hearst to hunt in Eel river.

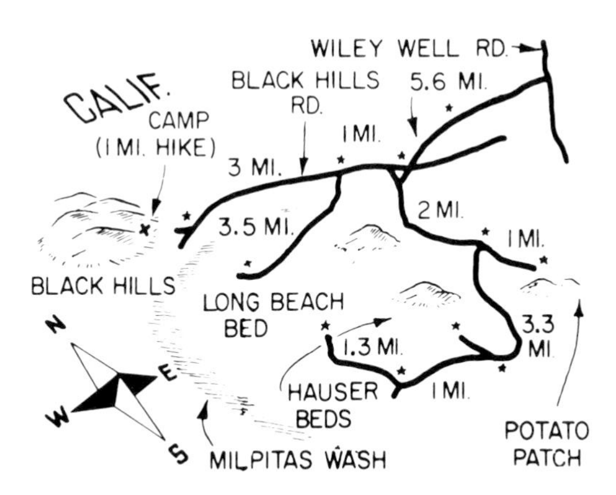

- *Willow Creek,* Humboldt County* JADE: In Trinity River; both up and down stream. Take Hwy 96 N to Orleans area, and look in Klamath River. Road parallels river for 30 miles.
- *Winterhaven, Imperial County* AGATE NODULES, CHALCEDONY ROSES: Take Imperial Dam Road 2½ miles past Laguna Dam, turn off on road across canal and toward Ferguson Lake, but keep to left on this road, cross ridge into a basin, dig on W side for nodules and on S edge for chalcedony roses. Distance from canal to basin is 10 miles.
- *Wrightwood, San Bernardino County* RHODONITE: Go mile to Heath Canyon, collect up 1,000 feet.

•*Yermo, San Bernardino County* PETRIFIED WOOD, JASPER: E on Int. 15 to Minneola exit, cross freeway and take access road N, then E a half mile to road NE. Follow it a mile under pole line and continue N a mile to roads E into hills, the Green Ash Hills in the Calico mountains.

Turn W into Mule Canyon for palm wood on the N side, and go about 2 miles to road N into Tin Can Alley a mile to collect in canyon to E for moss agate and farther N for sagenitic agate. Continuing on the Mule Canyon road will reach the Calico road SE to Int. 15. Just before junction with Calico road there is a deposit of onyx to N in hills at the Calico Silver Onyx mine (fee).

•*Yreka, Siskiyou County* * BLOODSTONE, JASPER: 18 miles NE.

Colorado

Colorado is a state of startling physical contrasts: the eastern third is part of the High Plains like Kansas and Nebraska; the midstate area is formed of massive mountain chains enclosing fertile basins; the western slope meets Utah in a welter of mesas and plateaus that comprise the wildest part of the state. Sedimentary rocks have been raised or pushed aside by the great igneous intrusions that formed the spectacular Front Range and created Colorado's mineral wealth.

•*Artesia, Moffat County* AGATE: 25 miles E on U.S. 40, then N on road between Big and Little Wolf creeks and hike mile to hill.

•*Baxterville, Rio Grande County* BLUE AND GRAY AGATE NODULES: Go SW on Hwy 160 7¾ miles beyond Wolf Creek Pass and collect in loose rock below road, but be careful; it's dangerous.

•*Bedrock, Montrose County* PETRIFIED WOOD, PETRIFIED BONE: One mile S on south bank of Dolores River.

•*Buena Vista, Chaffee County* ROSE QUARTZ: Take Hwy 24 to Trout Creek pass, collect at Clora May mine at top of hill.

•*Burlington, Kit Carson County* MOSS OPAL: In S fork of Republican River 20 miles N.

•*Canon City, Fremont County* AGATE: At Curio (Specimen) Hill, 7 miles S; loose in soil or in limestone ledge near top of ridge.

BERYL: In Mica Lode, Meyers and School section mines at Eightmile Park.

SATIN SPAR, PETRIFIED BONE, QUARTZ GEODES: 8 miles N on Shelf Road up Fourmile Creek to mouth of Felch Creek. Collect just W of Fourmile Creek.

•*Colorado Springs, El Paso County* AMAZONSTONE, SMOKY QUARTZ, WHITE TOPAZ: In pegmatites at Crystal Park, at foot of Cameron Cone, 2 miles S of Manitou Springs (use toll road on E slope of Pikes Peak). Crystals found for mile NW and SW of park, especially in Bear Creek Canyon and at Specimen Rock in canyon.

•*Creede, Mineral County* AMETHYST: N past courthouse, left on road to North Creede, at 1½ miles pass Commodore mine, take left fork to old buildings, park, return to plank bridge and climb path into dumps. Green sphalerite and wire silver are found with the amethystine quartz. The upper dump is the most productive but is unsafe.

CHALCEDONY, OPAL NODULES: Drive to W end of Rio Grande Reservoir to Trail Creek, hike S through rough country to Ute Creek. Collect along creek.

•*Del Norte, Rio Grande County* PLUME AGATE: Take Hwy 112 N for ½ mile, then left 4 miles to fork, go on to second fork and stay left to Del Norte Agate Beds sign near bridge (fee).

•*Elbert, Elbert County* PETRIFIED WOOD: In headwaters of Bijou and Kiowa Creeks, in gravels of rivers to SE, along Hwys 157 and 217, in Union Pacific railroad cut and as far S as Peyton and Calhan. Some from Peyton and Kiowa areas contains carnotite.

One specific location is N for 7½ miles from U.S. 24 to collect in a wash near a farmhouse.

•*Elizabeth, Elbert County* PETRIFIED WOOD: At Kit Carson Monument.

•*Elk Springs, Moffat County* AGATE: In gravels at SE edge of town and along Hwy 14 off U.S. 40 for a few miles.

JASPER, AGATE: Take U.S. 40 8 miles W to Hwy 16 and N 19 miles to road junction.

SPOTTED AGATE: Take dirt road from junction 6 miles to cabin.

PETRIFIED BONE: Continue W on U.S. 40 4½ miles from intersection with Hwy 16 and take trail N ½ mile, search on ridges.

AGATE, JASPER, PETRIFIED BONE: N of U.S. 40 in gravels and outcrops within two miles of highway all the way to Blue Mountain.

•*Florissant, Teller County* * AMAZONSTONE, SMOKY QUARTZ: Take Hwy 67 N to a Y fork. Take left fork 2 miles to pits and other diggings in pegmatite outcrops in the woods. From these diggings, once known as the American Gem Mines, have come spectacular gem specimens. Much of the area is under private claims. Farther along Pine creek are amazonstone diggings.

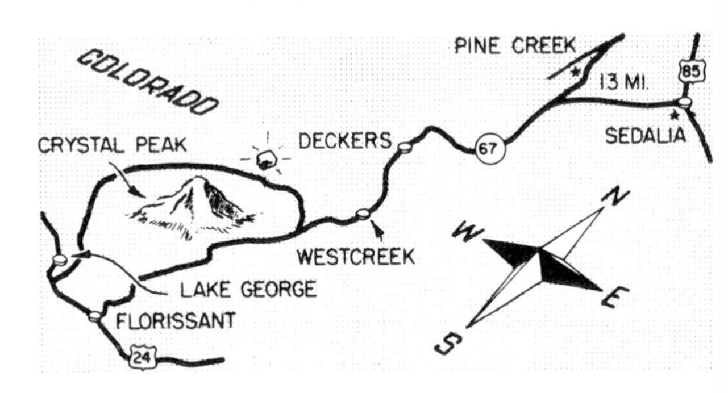

(Left) Geode of agate and amethyst from Val Giumela, Italy.
(Middle) Icositetrahedrons of analcime from Piz Sella, near Bolzano, Italy.
(Right) Apatite crystals from Valle Aurina, Bolzano.

WHITE TOPAZ, PHENACITE: Found in pegmatite near Crystal Peak, especially ½ mile NW of peak.

• *Fort Collins, Larimer County* AMETHYST: On Hwy 287 22 miles NW and W on Hwy 200 to Red Feather Lakes. Deposit is about 5 miles W on mountain at claim.

SATIN SPAR, ALABASTER: Take U.S. 287 17 miles N to quarry in Owl Canyon.

• *Fruita, Mesa County* OPALIZED WOOD: Go S on Hwy 340, cross railroad tracks and bridge, take gravel road right for 1¾ miles, stay straight at fork, and right at next fork, a half mile farther take left fork and Opal Hill is on right. Collect there.

PETRIFIED BONE: W 4 miles and S of Int. 70 at Dinosaur Ridge.

• *Glade Park, Mesa County* AGATE, OPALIZED WOOD: Take road S toward top of mesa for 8½ miles, take left fork and keep right for 3 miles; collect along road and at house ½ mile farther along road.

• *Golden, Jefferson County* AQUAMARINE, SMOKY QUARTZ: W 15 miles at Centennial Cone on Termantozzi ranch. Collect in pegmatite on N side of cone. Don't enter without permission.

• *Granby, Grand County* BLOODSTONE: On ridges in Middle Park near junction of Willow Creek and Colorado River.

• *Guffey, Park County* BLUE AGATE: At 31 Mile Mountain 8 miles W.

• *Gunnison, Gunnison County* LAPIS LAZULI, GROSSULARITE GARNET: At Italian Mountain. Take Hwy 135 19 miles N to mouth of Cement Creek. Follow creek on bad road 12 miles. Mountain is mile NE of end of road. Collect on W side of north mountain near top and just above ledges of slaty black limestone. Difficult to find without guide.

BLUE CHALCEDONY: In rhyolite in Gunnison River above Black Canyon.

AGATE: E on U.S. 50 to mile E of Sargents; take dirt road left and hunt in streams.

• *Hartsel, Park County* MOSS AGATE, PETRIFIED WOOD: Along Hwy 9 SE 1½ miles; also along U.S. 24 just W.

• *Idaho Springs, Clear Creek County* RHODOCHROSITE: At Moose Mine. Take Virginia Canyon road to Russel Gulch Road and to Willis Gulch. Mine is ½ mile below head of gulch.

ROSE QUARTZ: In pegmatite at Santa Fe Mountain prospect; 3 miles SE on ridge NE of mountain, and reached by road up Sawmill Gulch from U.S. 6.

• *Jefferson, Park County* TOPAZ, SMOKY QUARTZ: Take graded road SE into Tarryall River valley for 30 miles to Spruce Grove campground, then take trail along ridge ½ mile SE to collect in pegmatite.

• *Kalouse, Weld County* AGATE: Along Two Mile River.

• *La Junta, Otero County* FLOWER AGATE, PETRIFIED BONE: In washes and streams to S.

Augite in prismatic crystals from Buffaure, near Bolzano.

- *Leadville, Lake County* TURQUOISE: At Turquoise Chief mine, 7 miles NW just below crest of ridge between Turquoise Lake and basin to N. (Private claim.)
- *Manassa, Conejos County* TURQUOISE: At King mine (private claim). Take Hwy 142 E for 6⅔ miles; S ⅓ mile to mine dumps at bottom of hill.
- *Mt. Antero, Chaffee County* * AQUAMARINE, PHENAKITE, PHENACITE, QUARTZ: Take Hwy 162 from Nathrop up Baldwin Gulch to saddle, climb from there, or by U.S. 285 S for 3½ miles from Nathrop and taking trails up Browns Creek. It is about 6 miles and 6,000 feet up to the collecting area in pegmatite within 500 feet of top in Mt. Antero and White Mountain, and collectors are exposed to sudden storms.

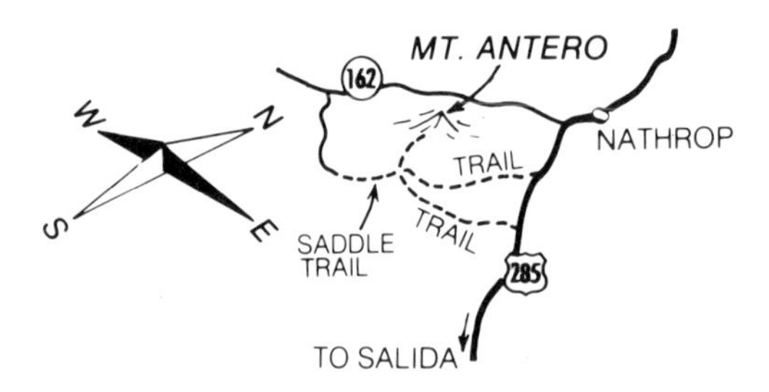

BERYL, SMOKY QUARTZ: At the California mine, 2 miles SW of Mount Antero, at 12,500 ft. and reached by either trail. Mine is on S slope of divide between Browns Creek and Baldwin Gulch, on what is known as Carbonate Mountain.

- *Nathrop, Chaffee County* SPESSARTITE GARNET, WINE-COLORED TOPAZ, OBSIDIAN NODULES: Just to N on U.S. 285 at Ruby and Sugarloaf Mountains E of river, and Dorothy Hill W of river. Stones are very small.
- *Naturita, Montrose County* PETRIFIED BONE: Take oil road W 4 miles, then S 6 miles on road toward Paradox to fork in road. Take this fork NW past Bitter Creek mine to collect dinosaur bone.
- *Ouray, Ouray County* RHODOCHROSITE: At Silver Bear mine, to S near Bear Creek Falls.
- *Parker, Douglas County* PETRIFIED PALM WOOD: One mile S.
- *Peyton, Elbert County* PETRIFIED WOOD: N on county road from gas station for 7½ miles, stop at first farmhouse on right and get permission to hunt in wash W of house.

  Continue N on road then W along gravel road for a total distance of 10 miles from Peyton, park near windmills and collect S in dry wash and pastures.
- *Rico, Dolores County* RHODOCHROSITE: At Newman Hill and Enterprise mines.
- *Saguache, Saguache County* AGATE GEODES: Take Hwy 114 W for 21 miles, then S 8½ miles and dig W of road.
- *Salida, Chaffee County* PETRIFIED WOOD, JASPER: In hills to SW on S side of U.S. 50, from Poncha Springs to Sargents.

  SAPPHIRE, GROSSULARITE GARNET, SAGENITIC QUARTZ: In schists at Calumet iron mine, in E wall of Railroad gulch. Take Hwy 291 N from Salida, right on Hwy 180 to Hwy 190, then left on Hwy 31 to gulch.
- *Sargents, Gunnison County* AGATE: 1 mile E on U.S. 50, then N on dirt road, collect in small streams that road crosses. At 7-mile point collect slag in ruins of Cosden smelter.
- *Sedalia, Douglas County* TOPAZ, SMOKY QUARTZ: In pegmatite pockets at Devils Head, just S of peak at top of ridge below highway. Take Hwy 67 SW to Rampart Range Road and S, a total of 21½ miles.

  Also across from Virgin's Bath picnic grounds.

  AMAZONSTONE, SMOKY QUARTZ: Take Hwy 67 SW 13 miles to Pine Creek store, then down Pine Creek road 2 miles to dump above stream.
- *Silverton, San Juan County* RHODONITE: On dump on N side of Sunnyside Mill at Eureka, 9 miles NE of Silverton on Hwy 110.

  At Gold Prince mine, Terry Tunnel of Sunnyside mine, and Golden Fleece mine and American Tunnel at Treasure Mountain. Buy from miners.
- *Villa Grove, Saguache County* TURQUOISE: At Hall mine (private claim). Take U.S. 285 NW 2⅔ miles, then side road 2⅔ miles W to edge of Cochetopa National Forest, and then 2 miles to cabins that are ½ mile below mine.

  CHALCEDONY, RHODOCHROSITE: N on Hwy 285 to road W to Bonanza, where road turns N walk across Kerber creek and collect in canyon. Return to road, pass ranch, and collect rhodochrosite N of Hayden's Peak.

Connecticut

A central lowland valley divides eastern Connecticut from the western part of the state. This valley is cut by ridges of trap rock, while the eastern and western uplands are broken by mountain ranges and valleys, affording exposures of crystalline rocks containing gem materials. The trap rocks of the Connecticut valley yield agate and jasper, and amethyst and prehnite in cavities.

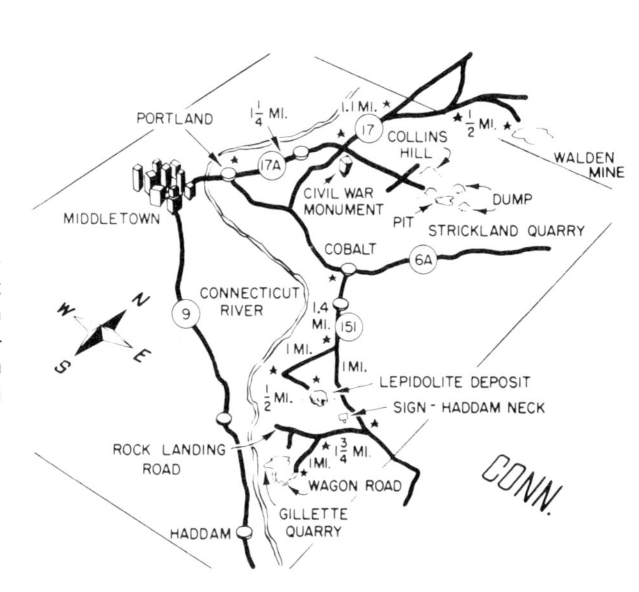

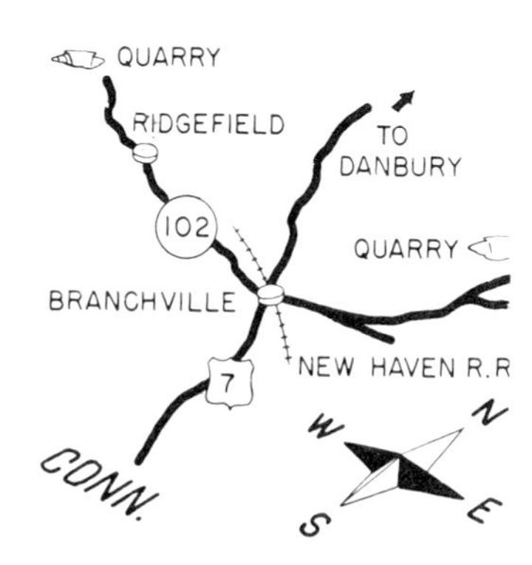

•*Branchville, Fairfield County* * GOLDEN BERYL, ROSE AND SMOKY QUARTZ, SPODUMENE: The quarry, a short distance NE of Branchville, has long been noted for these gem minerals. Work on the dumps is required to uncover fresh material, however.
West of Branchville, a short distance out of Ridgefield, is a pegmatite that has been worked, containing some beryl, as well as quartz crystals and rose quartz. It is reached by following Conn. 102 W 1½ miles from the stoplight in Ridgefield, then turning N, crossing a bridge, and taking dirt road to left just beyond bridge. Drive to end, park and hit trail ¼ mile to area of pit and dumps. Area's future is uncertain; it may be closed.

•*Canton, Hartford County* AMETHYST: Take Hwy 44 E for ¼ mile, then East Hill road N to a road left and hike to area in and near stream where quartz veins are exposed.

•*East Hampton, Middlesex County* * GOLDEN AND BROWN BERYL, ROSE QUARTZ: In Slocum Quarry. Take Hwy 196 SW to Daniel Road, then to paved road N. Continue 2 miles to fork, take left fork past farmhouse (fee).

•*East Haven, New Haven County* AMETHYST, SMOKY QUARTZ: Collect at Cinque quarry back of Weeping Willow restaurant on Laurel Street.

•*Glastonbury, Hartford County* AQUAMARINE, SMOKY QUARTZ: Take Isenglass Hill road E from Hwy 17 to Thompson Hill road. Take Old Glastonbury road ½ mile N to old truck entrance left to Simpson quarry.

N of Isenglass road on Hwy 17 about 4 miles is a road E to the dumps of the Howe quarry, a good place for beryl and other pegmatite minerals.

E on Isenglass Hill road to Thompson Hill road. Take it S to Cotton Hill road E, stop at power lines and hike N uphill to the Case quarries for good beryl and pegmatite minerals.

Guilford, New Haven County CORDIERITE: In gneiss at Hungry Horse Hill.

•*Haddam, Middlesex County* * TOURMALINE, BERYL, GARNET, AMAZONSTONE: The noted Gillette quarry is reached by taking Hwy 9 to Hwy 82 exit, across river to E Haddam, then N on Hwys 149 and 151 to Haddam Neck. A road from Haddam Neck leads to the quarry near the Connecticut river. Collect in the dumps (fee).
Nearby just off Hwy 151 is another mine notable for lepidolite. From a farmhouse as Hwy 151 veers E a dim road leads a half mile to the dump.

BERYL (GOSHENITE), SMOKY QUARTZ, TOURMALINE: Take Jail Hill road to small bridge, take left fork and go ½ mile to Turkey Hill mine sign (fee).

•*Meriden, New Haven County* AMETHYST, PREHNITE: Take Hwy 71 to road cut in Hwy 6, also quartz in reservoirs around Hubbard Park.

•*Middletown, Middlesex County* * BERYL, RUBELLITE TOURMALINE: At White Rocks Quarry.

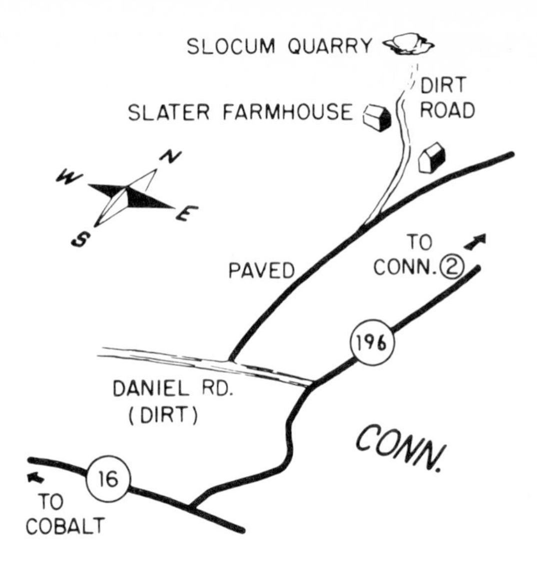

- *Milford, New Haven County* SERPENTINE (VERD ANTIQUE): Take U.S. 1 from turnpike exit 39 for 2⅓ miles NE past Hwy 152, park near thrift shop and walk W to dig.
- *Monroe, Fairfield County* ROSE QUARTZ: NE of East Village beyond old canal in feldspar quarry.
- *Morris, Litchfield County* SMOKY QUARTZ: Take path from Hwy 109 to S end of Morris reservoir, collect in quarry to W.
- *New Milford, Litchfield County* BLUE AND GOLDEN BERYL, SMOKY QUARTZ: NW 5 miles at Upper Merryll in George Roebling (Merryll) Mine.

  KYANITE: Take Hwy 67 E to Judd's Bridge, collect one mile N.
- *Old Saybrook, New London County* AGATE, MOONSTONE: Collect on beach on W side of point toward Long Island Sound.
- *Portland, Middlesex County* * BERYL, TOURMALINE, SPODUMENE, GARNET, APATITE, SMOKY QUARTZ, CITRINE: The Strickland Quarry, NE of Portland, has produced these, some in varied colors. Take Conn. 17A out of Portland to a brown Civil War monument. Turn right here and keep right until the road ends in a T. Keep straight ahead up a rough road on Collins Hill to the quarry. The pit, before it was flooded, was a choice collecting spot and the dumps have yielded many specimens to collectors.

  AQUAMARINE: SE of the Strickland quarry and W of a clearing for power lines are the Hale Walker quarries, reached by taking Collins Hill road S and a road E to the cleared strip and then N.

  TOURMALINE, BERYL: At Walden farm. Take Hwy 17 to Hwy 26, then go N 3 miles to Cotton Hill road (fee).
- *Ridgefield, Fairfield County* QUARTZ: N on Hwy 35 to Farmingville road, then E to new road, take it N and path past ball park NW to collect in exposed rock.
- *Roxbury, Litchfield County* KYANITE: From Hwy 67 and 199 junction, go N on Hwy 199 3⅔ miles, turn left and left again at a small park, then 1⅔ miles to park entrance. Park and take path left to collecting area.
- *Roxbury Falls, Litchfield County* GARNET, STAUROLITE: SE ⅘ mile from Hwy 199, turn off E on road to Green farm, garnet in dump, staurolite deposit beyond farmhouse (fee).
- *Southford, New Haven County* BERYL, ROSE QUARTZ: 1¾ miles SW in quarry.
- *Unionville, Hartford County* FELDSPAR, MOONSTONE, CORDIERITE: 1½ miles NE in road cut S of Biglow Pond.
- *Wallingford, New Haven County* AMETHYST: Exit 15 from Wilbur Cross parkway, then E to Hwy 68 and N to New Haven Traprock quarry.
- *West Redding, Fairfield County* GARNET, CLINOZOISITE: In quarry 2,000 feet from railroad station and near Simpaug turnpike.
- *West Stafford, Tolland County* QUARTZ: Hwy 190 E across brook and past firehouse to path N to Diamond Ledges.
- *Woodbury, Litchfield County* BERYL, AGATE, ROSE QUARTZ: In Flanders Quarry.

Florida

Florida is a peninsula not far above sea level but containing a diversity of natural features, ranging from the hilly area in the northwest to the coastal plain on the east, and marked by many lakes and the huge Everglades Swamp to the south. Underlain by limestone, it lacks the formations that would yield a variety of mineral or gem specimens.

- *Lake City, Columbia County* AGATE: N on Hwy 41 to White Springs; at north gate of Foster Memorial turn right, go 1¾ mile on sand road to second wooden bridge and just beyond it to cross roads. Turn right and collect in creek bed.
- *Lakeland, Polk County* CHALCEDONY, FOSSIL CORAL: On Lake Parker Beach for chalcedony and fossil coral.
  On canal near Kathleen, 7 miles NW.
- *Miami, Dade County* AGATIZED CORAL: Turn E at auditorium, cross bridge and collect in debris piles at port of Miami.
- *New Port Richey, Pasco County* AGATIZED CORAL: To S at Bailey's Bluff.
  Coral may be expected along a vast area of the coast wherever dredging brings up material from the ocean.
- *Perry, Taylor County* AGATIZED CORAL: Go 20 miles W on U.S. 98 and ¼ mile past the Oconfina River, turn ½ mile S on Hwy 14 and go E to parking place. Dig there and in river area.
- *Tampa, Hillsborough County* AGATIZED CORAL: In Hillsborough Bay off Ballast Point.

Georgia

With representative rocks of almost every geologic period exposed on the surface, it is not surprising that

(Left) Heulandite from Drio le Pale.
(Right) Natrolite in melaphyre from Piz Sella, Bolzano.

Georgia exhibits a variety of rocks and minerals. The southern half of the state is part of the coastal plain underlain by sedimentary rocks. North of this is the Piedmont Plateau and, in the extreme northeast, a highlands, both formed of crystalline rocks containing minerals of interest. The extreme northwest corner consists of ancient folded and eroded sedimentary rocks.

- *Albany, Dougherty County* RED JASPER: In Flint River.
- *Apalachee, Morgan County* AQUAMARINE: To W on Adair plantation.
- *Athens, Clarke County* GREEN BERYL: In field along Alps Road across from new airport.
- *Ball Ground, Cherokee County* RUTILATED QUARTZ, BERYL: NE 2½ miles at Cochran mine near old tenant house.

  STAUROLITE: Take Fairview Church road W to collect along Sharp Mountain creek. Also on Oscar Robertson and James Spear farms (fee).

  ALMANDINE GARNET: In prospects along Hwy 5 toward Canton.
- *Blairsville, Union County* RUBY: On S side of Track Rock Gap.

  KYANITE: S of Hwy 76 W, especially ½ mile E of Akin Mountain and 5 miles NW in Teece Creek valley a mile below highway.
- *Blue Ridge, Fannin County* STAUROLITE: Take Hwy 2 W one mile, then blacktop road left to gravel road on left, follow to second house on left and turn left to Hackney farm (fee).
- *Bremen, Haralson County* QUARTZ CRYSTALS: W 1½ miles.
- *Buford, Gwinnett County* AGATE, MOONSTONE: On Addison Lowe farm.
- *Clarkesville, Habersham County* AGATE: W 2 miles.

  RUBY WITH MARGARITE: At Alec Mountain in Piedmont Orchards, 6 miles NW by road up Beaver Dam creek.

  KYANITE: On grounds of North Georgia Vocational school, ½ mile E of grounds in gravel of small stream and in bank of Soque River, in schist belt through farms NE, and near Turnerville, and Stonepile Church.
- *Clayton, Rabun County* AMETHYST: On dump of the North Georgia Company Mine 4 miles N.
  Also at Ledbetter Mine dump, N on Hwy 23 to Rabun Gap and one mile E to S side of Black Creek.
  Also at W. T. Smith Mine at junction of road E from Clayton with Hwy 28.
  Also at Wilson farm 4 miles SE.
  Also N on Hwy 23 on mine dumps near dam at Mountain City.
  Also, take U.S. 76 W, turn N, follow Tallulah River into Towns County, then left on Upper Charlie Creek to diggings.

  KYANITE: At lower end of Burton Lake near dam.

BERYL, QUARTZ CRYSTALS: E 8 miles, at Mark Beck farm via Warwoman and Dick's Creek roads.

CORUNDUM: E to Pine Mountain, then 1½ miles NE to Laurel Creek Mine.

ROSE QUARTZ: E to road N to crossing of Walnut Fork, in dumps of Kell Mica Mine.

- *Clyattville, Lowndes County* * AGATIZED CORAL: Leave Int. 75 at Valdosta exit, turn W on Hwy 31 5 miles to Clyattville, take Main street W 1½ miles, then S on Bland's Dairy road 4 miles to the Withlacoochee river. Collecting is only possible at low-water stages.

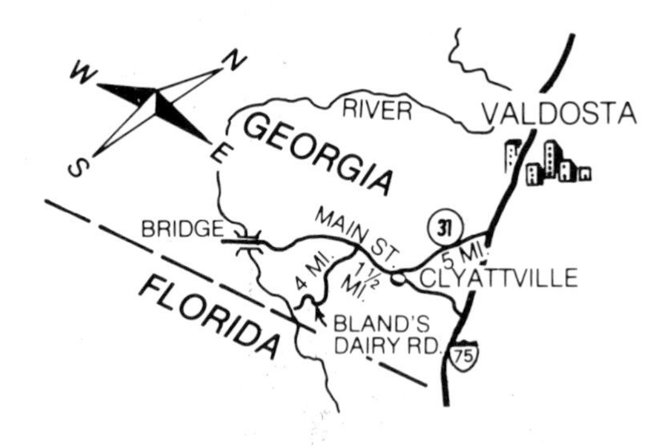

- *Columbus, Muscogee County* PETRIFIED WOOD: Near Bull and Randall Creeks.
- *Commerce, Banks County* BERYL: Along Hwy 59, 5 miles E of Jackson-Banks County line.
- *Cumming, Forsyth County* AMETHYST: E 6 miles at the I. H. Gilbert farm.
- *Dallas, Paulding County* ALMANDINE GARNET: On surface near Little Bob Copper Mine 6 miles SE.
- *Elberton, Elbert County* SMOKY QUARTZ: NE 10 miles in Chapman mine on N side of Cold Water Creek.

  AMETHYST: Take Hwy 17 5 miles NW to Deweyrose, then go 2 miles N to W. B. Perkins place.
- *Fayetteville, Fayette County* AMETHYST, RUTILATED QUARTZ: on Homer Kellin farm.
- *Greenville, Meriwether County* GARNET, TOURMALINE: Take Hwy 109 to the first millpond, then first road left of millpond to fourth house on left, the Ernest Strozier farm (fee).
- *Griffin, Spalding County* BLUE BERYL, SMOKY QUARTZ AND ROSE QUARTZ: Take Hwy 92 NW to Vaughn, and go 2 miles NE to T. J. Allen property; collect crystals in pegmatite and loose in soil.
- *Hartwell, Hart County* BERYL: Take U.S. 29 E to access road to Hartwell dam and collect in quarry to right.
- *Hiawassee, Towns County* PINK CORUNDUM: Often with smaragdite, 2 miles SW at Hog Creek Mine.
  Also at Bell Creek Mine 4 miles N at head of Chatuge Lake and in beach deposits and outcrops along Chatuge Lake, especially near Elf.
- *Hillsboro, Jasper County* BLUE QUARTZ: From Baptist church just N on Hwy 11 to dirt road 3 miles to Barron Fullerton farm. Hunt near farmhouse.
- *Hiram, Paulding County* SERPENTINE (VERD ANTIQUE), APATITE: Go W at Dunn store, follow pavement to end, take graded road ¼ mile to fork, take right fork, turn on dirt road to Verd Antique quarry, which is a mile SW of town.
- *Kingston, Bartow County* RED AND BROWN AGATE: To S along Etowah River.
- *La Grange, Troup County* BERYL, ROSE QUARTZ: Take Hwy 219 S to Cleveland Crossroads to Big Beryl (Hogg or Foley) mine (fee).
- *Lithonia, DeKalb County* EPIDOTE, THULITE: In Rock Chapel quarry and on N side of Arabia Mountain.
- *Macon, Bibb County* AGATE: At Holton Quarry, 7½ miles NW.

  BERYL: N of Calloway airport at road junction.
- *Madison, Morgan County* AMETHYST: Take U.S. 278 E to Buckhead and go 2 miles E to Ray farm.
- *Marble Springs, Chattooga County* MARBLE: In local quarries.
- *Maysville, Banks County* QUARTZ CRYSTALS: In Commerce area along railroad (see Alton Hayes in Maysville).
- *Milledgeville, Baldwin County* JASPER: At State Farm.
- *Mineral Bluff, Fannin County* STAUROLITE: Take road a mile NW on Windy Ridge, collect at Richards and Arp properties and on ridge along dirt road at end of paved road.
- *Monroe, Walton County* AQUAMARINE: On surface at Malcolm farm; take Hwy 83 SE to Blasingame, then 6½ miles on dirt road.
- *Nacoochee, White County* GREEN APATITE: In cut on N side of Hwy 17 3 miles E.
- *Monticello, Jasper County* BERYL: In pegmatite 9 miles S on J. R. Parker property.
- *Nicholson, Jackson County* BERYL: In pegmatite on W side of U.S. 441 at dirt side road just N of the town.
- *Norcross, Gwinnett County* MOONSTONE: Hwy 141 N to crossing of Chattahoochee; in pegmatite on Green farm.
- *Powder Springs, Cobb County* CORUNDUM: S 2 miles on Turner property.
- *Roswell, Fulton County* CORUNDUM: E 3½ miles.
- *Rutledge, Morgan County* CORUNDUM: Take dirt road from Hwy 12 for 2 miles SW of the Georgia railroad to collect on Bill Oxford farm.
- *Sparta, Hancock County* CHERT: Along Sinclair reservoir to W, a colorful jasper.
- *Summerville, Chattooga County* AGATE: W on Hwy 48 to fish hatchery, turn right, then right again at Baptist church sign and again at church, go ¼ mile, collect along road. Also 3 miles S on U.S. 27 over top of first ridge to collect on east slopes.

• *Sylvania, Screven County* FOSSIL AGATE: Take Hwy 301 N almost to Savannah River, turn left for 8 miles to a sharp turn, take dirt road there ½ mile, collect along road.

• *Tate, Pickens County* GOLDEN BERYL, AQUAMARINE: In pegmatite SE of Rock Creek on Ralph Cook farm near Refuge Church.

MARBLE: in quarries.

• *Thomaston, Upson County* CORUNDUM: NE 7 miles at the Kelly place.

MOONSTONE, APATITE: SE 7¼ miles and a mile NW of Waymansville on a branch of Tobler Creek, collect at the Mitchell Creek Mica mine. Also at Blount and Joe Persons mines.

AGATE: NE 6 miles at Wilmot's Ravine.

STAUROLITE, GEMMY KYANITE: SW 3½ miles on Dolly Cherry property. Take U.S. 19 S 2 miles to Shepherd school, go 1¾ miles on dirt road, turn right and go mile.

• *Toccoa, Stephens County* QUARTZ CRYSTALS: S 9 miles.

• *Warm Springs, Meriwether County* AGATE: One mile S on Southern Railroad.

ROSE QUARTZ, BERYL: 15 miles W at Pine Mountain valley.

• *Washington, Wilkes County* GREEN SPINEL: Take highway to Lincolnton and county line, take a right fork, then a left fork to Magruder Mica mine on hill to right.

• *Yatesville, Upson County* BERYL: ¼ mile E at Herron Mine and 3 miles N at Adams mine.

• *Young Harris, Towns County* CORUNDUM: On S side of Track Rock Gap reached by road S from U.S. 76 2½ miles W of Young Harris.

Hawaii

The state of Hawaii is a group of islands in the Pacific Ocean. The major islands are volcanic domes formed of basaltic lava cut by erosion into ridges and valleys, and marked in places by coral reefs. The islands show craters and other marks of former volcanic activity, and on the largest island, Hawaii, are two of the world's largest active volcanoes, Mauna Loa and Kilauea. Gem minerals are relatively few under such conditions.

• *Halemaumau, on Kilauea, Hawaii* OBSIDIAN: Droplets known as Pele's Tears.

• *Kailua, on north shore of Oahu* QUARTZ CRYSTALS: In basalt ridges, in ravines from Mount Olokanu, in washes of Keolu hills and in H & D quarry, with jasper, also jasper in Lanikai golf course washes and in Wahiawa Valley.

• *Kaneohe, on north shore of Oahu* JASPER: On ridges in Koolau range.

• *Lahaina, on south shore of Maui* BLACK CORAL: In deep water offshore.

• *Manele Bay, on SE shore of Lanai* FELDSPAR SUNSTONE: In cinder cone.

• *Olomana Peak, Oahu* BANDED AGATE: In gullies, and also in crater of West Molokai volcano.

(Left) Pectolite in botryoidal form from Tierno south of Trento.
(Middle) Quartz from Valle Aurina.
(Right) Red rutile needles in quartz from Valle Aurina.

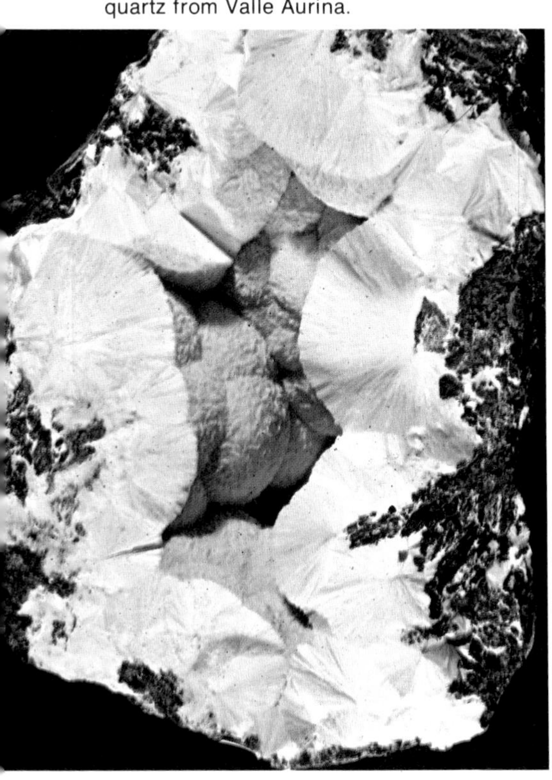

Working basalt quarry near Gambellara, east of Verona, Italy. In the quarry are beautiful basalt columns like those of the Devil's Post Pile in California and the Giant's Causeway in Ireland.

- *Puna district, on island of Hawaii* OLIVINE: In lava flow; also in green beach sands of Oahu and South Point, Hawaii.
- *Pohakea Pass, in Waianai Range,* CLEAR YELLOW LABRADORITE.

Idaho

Its diversity of geographical features, ranging from the rugged mountains of the northeast and central parts of the state to the arid wastes of the south and the basalt plateaus of the orth, makes Idaho a state rich in mineral and gem resources. The Salmon and Clearwater river regions are one of the last frontiers of collecting in the United States—a wilderness of canyons and forests.

- *Arco, Butte County* QUARTZ, AMETHYST GEODES: In Antelope Creek and Road Creek areas and Upper Lost River valley, and quartz crystals in veins in Wildhorse Canyon on E side of Hyndman Peak.

  AGATE: In lava to E and S of Hwy 93A.
- *Ashton, Fremont County* AGATE: In volcanic rocks to N and then E of U.S. 191 in Island Park Caldera.
- *Avery, Shoshone County* KYANITE, STAUROLITE: To S on divide between headwaters of the St. Joe and Clearwater rivers.
- *Avon, Latah County* GREEN BERYL: In mica mines between Deary and Princeton, especially the Levi Anderson and Muscovite mines.
- *Bliss, Gooding County* BROWN OPALIZED OAKWOOD: In volcanic ash along Clover Creek. Wood has flashes of fire opal.
- *Boise, Boise County* AQUAMARINE: To E along Middle Fork of Boise river as far as Atlanta in scattered beryl mines and prospects.
- *Bruneau, Owyhee County* PETRIFIED WOOD: W 2 miles to Hwy 51, then S 9 miles and E to collect in conglomerate formations in and around low hills.

  PURPLE AGATE: SE 8 miles to Indian Hot Springs, then S past ranch 8½ miles to collect at Indian Bathtub.
- *Burgdorf, Idaho County* CORUNDUM, QUARTZ: In placer mining dumps at mouth of Grouse Creek S of road to Warner. Also beyond Secesh Creek at Ruby Meadows in placer mining dumps.
- *Camas, Jefferson County* TOPAZ, FIRE OPAL: In rhyolite near source of E branch of tributary to S fork of Camas Creek.
- *Carey, Blaine County* MOSS AGATE: W on Muldoon Summit.
- *Cascade, Valley County* SMOKY QUARTZ: Dig in pegmatites on mountain just to N, also with agate to S and E of U.S. 55 and in placer tailings along Big Creek.
- *Challis, Custer County* * AGATE, PETRIFIED WOOD: Hwy 93 S to Hwy 93A, then 8 miles S on Hwy 93 to bridge; stay on Hwy 93 another 1½ miles to Malm Gulch, hike or take jeep trail 2½ miles E to petrified forest on ridge, or collect along the way.

  AGATE, BLACK WOOD: S on Hwy 93 through gorge, collect on hills and in valleys to right, and 2 miles on road to left collect black wood.

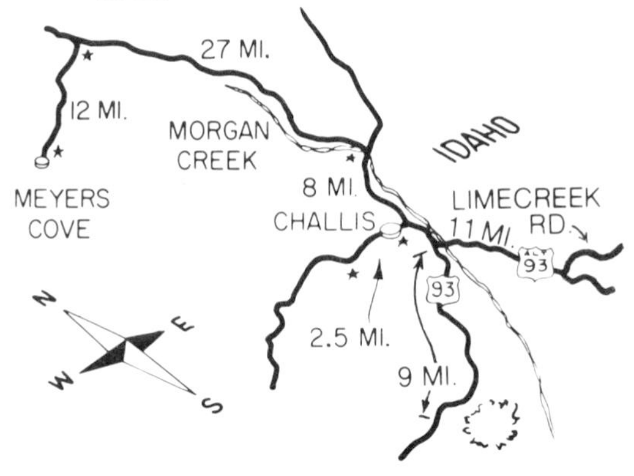

AGATE: Hwy 93 to Hwy 93A, take Hwy 93A 11 miles SE, then Lime Creek road E for 2 miles, hunt in hills.

SEAM AGATE IN VOLCANIC ASH: N of Challis about 8 miles is turnoff at Morgan Creek almost due N for 27 miles, then sharply left toward Meyers Cove. Look along road to cove.

- *Cuprum, Adams County* ANDRADITE GARNET: In limestone in contact zone where copper is mined in the Seven Devils district. Epidote is found with the garnet.
- *Deary, Latah County* GARNET: E on Hwy 8 to Helmer, hunt in Boulder Creek.
- *De Lamar, Owyhee County* PETRIFIED WOOD: To NW in Cow and Soda Creeks.
- *Emmett, Gem County* FIRE OPAL: At Black Canyon Dam. Go toward Horseshoe Bend to small pond E of road; take trail to canyon and go mile to diggings on left side.

JASPER: To S in both forks of Willow Creek E of road to Hwy 44.

- *Fernwood, Benewah County* STAR GARNET: This famous locality is now open by obtaining a federal permit to collect. The areas are reached from Fernwood by going SE on Hwy 3 along the St. Maries River. The turnoff W to Emerald Creek is 4½ miles S on Hwy 3. Take the dirt road and follow the E fork of the creek. One collecting area is along a tributary 8 miles in from the highway, the other is farther along on the E fork. Shorty's Diggin's, a concession area, is open (fee).
Purdue Creek crosses Hwy 3 a short distance N of Bovill. Take a dirt road E 1¼ mile, then hike in 3 miles along the left fork.
- *Hailey, Blaine County* JASPER, PETRIFIED WOOD: SW 5 miles to Bellevue and E to Little Wood River.
- *Homedale, Owyhee County* * (also see Adrian, Ore.) AGATE: Take Hwy 95 S 3 miles, turn right

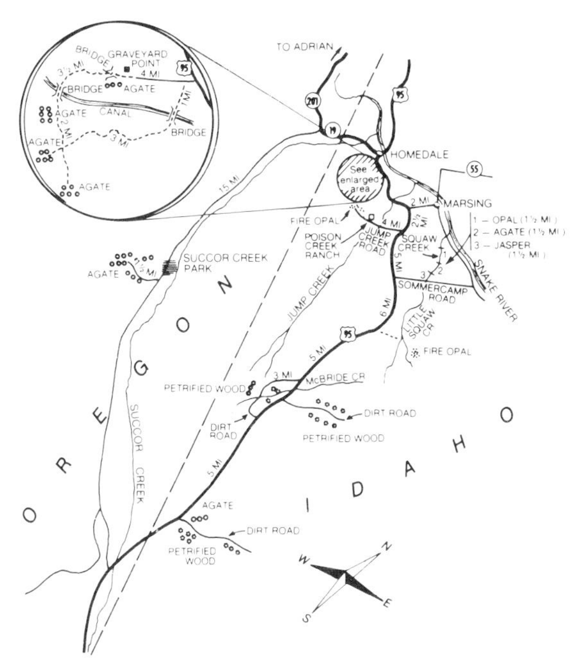

to Graveyard Point Monument, collect to W of monument near foot bridge, then continue to road bridge and S to collect S of bridge and W of road. Go on 2 miles to collect W and a mile farther to collect S of road. Latter areas can also be reached from Hwy 95 by going S a mile across canal bridge, then taking trail 3 miles W.
Succor Creek agate is reached by taking Hwy 19 in Oregon from its intersection with Hwy 201 and along the stream 15 miles, then past the state park a mile and W up the mountainside 1½ miles for agate nodules. A mile beyond is another location, and common opal is found in rhyolite back of park.

- *Idaho City, Boise County* QUARTZ, GARNET: In placer tailings and mine dumps, especially at the Gold Hill mine.

FIRE OPAL: At More's Creek.

- *Kooskia, Idaho County* PETRIFIED WOOD: Go N on Hwy 13, then NE to collect.

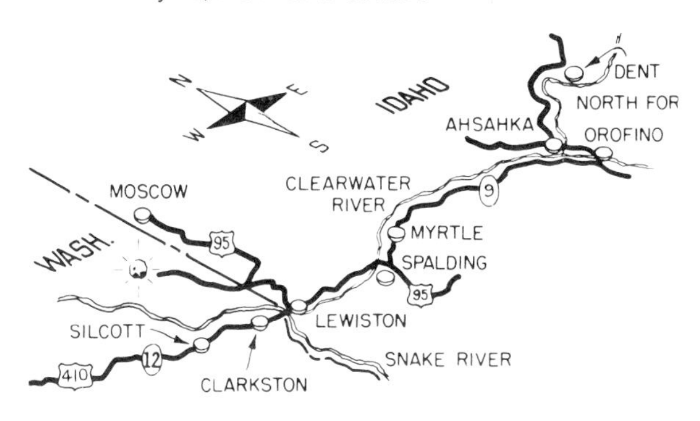

- *Lewiston, Nez Perce County* * FIRE OPAL: Just N of Lewiston a dirt road turns W from Hwy 95. Take it for 10 miles, then hike up ridge a half mile, turn right and follow along cliffs to diggings.
A mile or so farther along the dirt road and across the Snake River is a big gravel pit at Silcott. Opposite it on N side of river and 900 ft. up, caves are reached by a trail. Diggings are in caves.

BLUE AGATE: Take first gravel road left after starting up Lewiston Hill; go 9 miles to place just below pit in Snake River.

FIBROUS SILLIMANITE, AGATE: Found E and N from Lewiston in the Clearwater River and in its N fork for 50 miles. The best hunting is between the Cheerylane and Myrtle bridges and at Big Eddy above Spalding. The sillimanite is blue, yellow, green, or white pebbles.

- *Lost River, Custer County* AGATE, JASPER: On the North Fork of Lost River.
- *Mackay, Custer County* GEODES, JASPER SPOTTED WITH CHRYSOCOLLA: Found in Alder Creek mines and on ridges.
- *Marsing, Owyhee County* * PETRIFIED WOOD, AGATE, FIRE OPAL: Go W to junction of Hwy 95 and

Hwy 55, then take Hwy 95 S for 2½ miles to Jump Creek road. Follow it W to Poison Creek ranch, about 4 miles, and continue on a mile to dig fire opal.

From the Jump Creek intersection on Hwy 95 go 5 miles S and E to reach collecting area along Squaw Creek. Jasper, agate and opal are found along the creek to the NE. Farther S 6 miles along Hwy 95 is an access road NE to a fire opal area just downstream from where Little Squaw Creek enters Squaw Creek.

Five miles farther S on Hwy 95 is McBride creek. To W are dirt roads and trails to several petrified wood locations. Five miles beyond McBride Creek and E of Hwy 95 near the Oregon line is the Coal Mine Basin E of the highway. Here petrified wood and agate are found.

- *May, Lehmi County* FIRE OPAL: On W side of Pahsemeroi Valley in ledge of porphyry paralleling Panther Creek and about 6 miles from its source.
- *Montpelier, Bear Lake County* JASPER: Colored red by hematite and green by malachite at Humming Bird Mine dump in Paris Canyon.
- *Moore, Butte County* BLACK AGATE: Follow Antelope Creek canyon road 13½ miles W, then drive or walk trail left to Big Piney Mountain.
- *New Meadows, Adams County* RUBY, GARNET: Take Hwy 55 7 miles E, dirt road left, and pan or screen sands of stream at Rock Flat for small stones.

  RHODONITE: A few miles S in foothills.
- *Pierce, Clearwater County* ALMANDINE (STAR) GARNET: In streams near Headquarters 12 miles N on Hwy 11.

  SAPPHIRE, EPIDOTE: In placer tailings along Rhodes and Orofino creeks.
- *Riggins, Idaho County* GARNET: For several miles to N in Little Salmon River.
- *Rocky Bar, Elmore County* SMOKY QUARTZ, TOPAZ: N 10½ miles toward Steel Mountain, then S to trail W into Dismal Swamp. Also in placer tailings in area.
- *St. Anthony, Fremont County* YELLOW FELDSPAR (ANDESINE) CRYSTALS: At Crystal Butte, 18 miles N, where they have weathered out of lava.
- *Silver City, Owyhee County* AGATE, QUARTZ, CASSITERITE: In mine dumps in Long Gulch ¾ mile S.
- *Spencer, Clark County* FIRE OPAL: In Spencer Opal mine (fee). Write Mark Stetler, Box 113, Spencer, Ida. 83446. The Wilson & Jepperson mining company has another fee opal dig over the hill from the Stetler dig.
- *Wallace, Shoshone County* KYANITE, GARNET: Go S to Goat Mountain, collect on S side of mountain.
- *Weiser, Washington County* AGATE NODULES: W on Hwy 70 5 miles through Eaton, N on Old's Ferry Road a mile to crossroads, W 2 miles, then right up hill 5½ miles into saddle. Nodules are loose in decomposed rock.

  Also on road left from Eaton to end of road for nodules and cinnabar-colored jasper in Hog Creek area.

  BLACK AND WHITE OPALIZED WOOD: Take Hwy 95 N 13 miles to Mann's Creek guard station sign, turn W on dirt road 8½ miles to Mann's Creek and Fourth of July Creek Canyon. Dig in right bank.

  RED AGATE: U.S. 95 N 6 miles to rest area, hike 2½ miles into Sage Creek ravine, collect there.
- *White Bird, Idaho County* AGATE: S and E of U.S. 95 6 miles.
- *Yellow Pine, Valley County* WHITE OPAL (MYRICKITE): Stained red by cinnabar in mercury mine dumps.

Illinois

Most of the state consists of prairie underlain by sedimentary rocks yielding coal, oil, and glass sand and deeply buried by glacial sand and gravel. The Ozark plateau and coastal plain of the southwestern part of the state, and the unglaciated "driftless" area in the northwest corner contain fluorite, lead, and zinc mines.

- *Grand Chain, Pulaski County* BROWN JASPER: In rail cut mile to NE.
- *Hamilton, Hancock County* * BROWN JASPER: Old gravel pit.

  GEODES: In Railroad creek, East Fork of Crystal Glen Creek and other creeks to S crossed by Hwy 96.

- *Nauvoo, Hancock County* * GEODES: in creek ą mile N of Nauvoo State Park.
- *Niota, Hancock County* * GEODES: On W side of creek at second bridge 2 miles S and in

streams crossed by Hwy 96 S to Nauvoo and Hamilton. Many of the geodes are oil-filled.

- *Rosiclare, Hardin County* FLUORITE: From mines N of Cave In Rock and to W toward Golconda.
- *Warsaw, Hancock County* WATERWORN AGATE PEBBLES: In gravel pits.

GEODES: Found in area 100 miles long and 60 miles wide from eastern Iowa almost to St. Louis, especially in area N to Niota and Ft. Madison, Ia., and W to Keokuk and Kahoka, Mo. Best are in small streams. One area near Warsaw is called Geode Glen.

Indiana

Like Illinois, Indiana rests on the sedimentary rocks laid down by ancient seas, which are rich in fossils but poor in gem minerals. Where the glacial drift that covers most of the state lies on bedrock, streams sort out gold and some gem minerals such as diamond. Although most of the state is flat, resistant ridges and glacial moraines in the southern half create scenic variety.

- *Heltonville, Lawrence County* GEODES: In Salt Creek and to W toward Guthrie.
- *Martinsville, Morgan County* BROWN CHATOYANT SAPPHIRE: In gravels of Highland Creek 7 miles NW
- *Medore, Jackson County* GEODES: 5 miles W and S in creek near Jackson-Lawrence County line. Also in fields at Tunnelton.
- *Morgantown, Morgan County* SAPPHIRE, GARNET: In Gold Creek and other small streams through glacial drift and running on bedrock.
- *Salem, Washington County* GEODES: At Jim Day farm on E edge of Salem on Hwy 56. Also 10 miles N on Hwy 135 to Minnie Holstine farm. Also N on Hwy 135 to river, turn W and hunt in bottom lands.
- *Scottsburg, Scott County* PETRIFIED WOOD: in shale beds throughout county.
- *Trevlac, Brown County* QUARTZ GEODES: In Bear Creek. Streams east of Bloomington, Monroe County, and in Brown County and as far S as Washington County contain quartz-filled geodes.
  Also in Bummets creek off Hwy 46.
- *Vallonia, Jackson County* GEODES: S on Hwy 135 to Delaney Creek road, go W to right fork, take it to steel bridge and Nazarene church and on to end of pavement, then follow gravel road to bridge over creek. Collect in creek.

Iowa

Iowa is a moderately rolling prairie tableland of glacial materials resting on sedimentary rocks except in the northeast corner, which was not touched by the glaciers. Here cliffs and hills make a more rugged topography, and in the extreme west, where moundlike bluffs rise from the Missouri River's flood plain. Geodes eroding from sedimentary rocks and quartz gem materials from the glacial drift can be expected in such circumstances.

- *Bellevue, Jackson County* * CARNELIAN, BANDED AGATE, PETRIFIED WOOD: Lake Superior agates from Mississippi River gravels: Take U.S.

(Left) Analcime and fibrous white natrolite from Montecchio Maggiore, Vicenza.
(Middle) Rhombohedral calcite from Montecchio Maggiore, Vicenza.
(Right) Basalt with cavities filled with gmelinite and lined with green celadonite from Montecchio Maggiore, Vicenza.

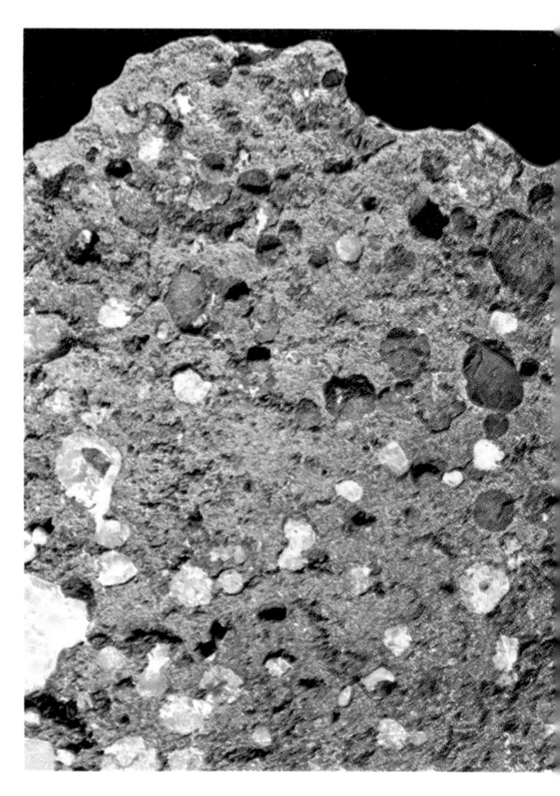

52–67 N from Bellevue ¼ mile to gravel pit, which is privately owned and is operated most of the year. Search big piles of washed gravel for specimens. Inch to 2-inch agate is large. Occasional big ones go into oversize gravel discard pile near loading dock.

Similar gravel operations can be found up and down the Mississippi River, especially at Muscatine, Burlington, at Davenport, in Block Co. gravel operation at 4th St. and River dr., near Clinton, and upstream in Wisconsin.

- *Chapin, Franklin County* GEODES: N to Sheffield along U.S. 65.
- *Donnellson, Lee County* GEODES: in gravel pit to S.
- *Des Moines, Polk County* PETRIFIED WOOD: In strip coal mines.

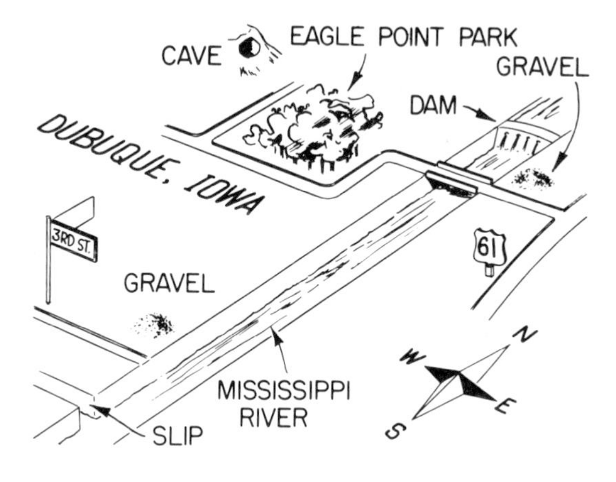

- *Dubuque, Dubuque County* * AGATE: There are two gravel operations at Dubuque: Molo Sand and Gravel Co. N of U.S. 20 bridge at E. 3d St.; the other just across the river in East Dubuque, Ill. Waterworn Lake Superior agates may be hunted in the stock piles (with permission).

  SATIN SPAR: On the bluffs above the city, just W of Y.M.C.A. camp in Eagle Point Park.

- *Farmington, Van Buren County* GEODES: In riverbanks.
- *Granger, Dallas County* GEODES: SW 3½ miles in gravel pit.
- *Iowa City, Johnson County* SILICIFIED CORAL: In stream and quarry at Coralville.
- *Keokuk, Lee County* GEODES: S on 5th Street W of Union Carbide plant, in upper shale. (Also see Warsaw, Ill.)

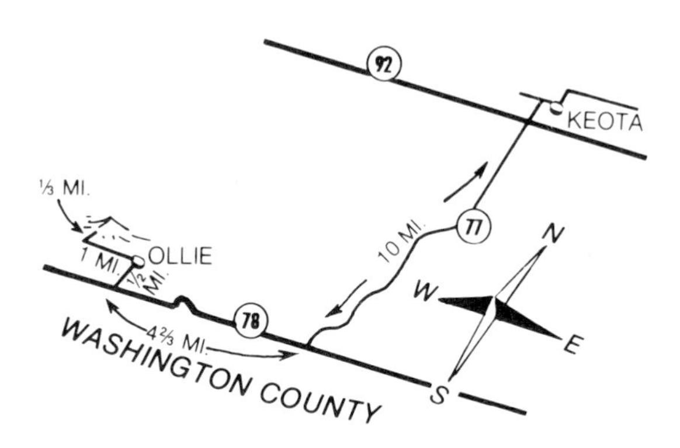

- *Keota, Washington County* * AGATE: Cold water agate at Kaser Construction Co. quarry; also at Ollie 10 miles S on Hwy 77, then W 4⅔ miles on Hwy 78 past church, N ½ mile and W 1 mile, and then N ⅓ mile to quarry.
- *Keswick, Keokuk County* AGATE: Nodules in quarry.
- *LaPorte City, Black Hawk County* AGATE: In gravel pit.
- *Mount Pleasant, Henry County* AGATE: In gravels of Big Creek and Skunk River and in pits.
- *Muscatine, Muscatine County* AGATE: In gravel pits S of town. Leave Hwys 92 and 61 at Shell station, go left past church and S to pits. Hahn's pit is 2 miles S. Acme and a third pit are 5 miles S.

  There are other pits along the shore and barges pumping gravels up and down the Mississippi River from Missouri northward.
- *Nevada, Story County* AGATE: In Indian Creek gravels to E.
- *New London, Henry County* AGATE GEODES: From water tower go due S for 8 miles, turn left to tributary of Shunk creek and collect in bed and along banks.
- *Orient, Adair County* AGATE, QUARTZ CRYSTALS, PETRIFIED WOOD: 5 miles N and E in washes and clay hillsides.
- *Red Oak, Montgomery County* CHERT (RICE AGATE): In vein in limestone of quarry just NW.
- *Sheffield, Franklin County* GEODES: In field behind quarry.
- *Shell Rock, Butler County* AGATE: Lake Superior type just N at gravel pit.
- *Steamboat Rock, Hardin County* QUARTZ GEODES: Along Iowa River

- *Vinton, Benton County* AGATE: Cold-water type. Hwy 101 N across river, take first turn right and go 4½ miles along Cedar River, then left ½ mile to gate. Get permission and walk to collecting area (fee).
- *Waterloo, Black Hawk County* GEODES: At Burton Avenue quarry and Mitchell Avenue gravel pit near Cedar River.

Kansas

Extensive sedimentary beds underlie Kansas. They contain coal, salt, and world-famous fossils. The surface is formed of sand and gravel derived from erosion of the Rockies and carried eastward by water. These deposits create the gently eastward sloping High Plains, a region where agates and other quartz materials may be expected. East of the Colorado High Plains are the Smoky Hills in the north and the Great Bend Prairie. East of them is a strip known as the Flint Hills, north to south across the state, and in the northeastern corner of Kansas is a glaciated region. The prairie surface is diversified by broad plains, isolated hills, and moderate valleys.

- *Ashland, Clark County* MOSS OPAL: To N in hills along Bluff creek.
- *Bonner Springs, Wyandotte County* QUARTZ CRYSTALS: In geodes in Lone Star Quarry.
- *Buffalo, Wilson County* AGATE: Along Verdigris River.
- *Concordia, Cloud County* PETRIFIED WOOD, AGATE: To N in glacial gravels of Old River bed.
- *El Dorado, Butler County* GEODES: In large road cut near the Butler-Greenwood County line.
- *Elkader, Logan County* AGATE: W in river terraces.
- *Ellsworth, Ellsworth County* AGATE, JASPER, PETRIFIED BONE AND WOOD: In gravels N of Kanopolis Lake.
- *Kiowa, Barber County* AGATE, JASPER: Along Medicine Lodge river to Aetna.
- *Medicine Lodge, Barber County* PETRIFIED WOOD: 10 miles S.
- *Quinter, Sheridan County* MOSS OPAL: In limestone at Saline River and S fork of the Solomon River and in outcrops on U.S. 24 from Hoxie to Hill City.
- *Ransom, Ness County* AGATE, PETRIFIED WOOD: To NE in Seybert sand pit near Smoky Hill River bridge at Hwy 283.
- *Sharon Springs, Wallace County* AGATE, PETRIFIED WOOD: in sand pit to N.
- *Topeka, Shawnee County* AGATE: Agates of the Lake Superior type in glacial moraines near city.
- *Wallace, Wallace County* OPAL: Cacholong opal with green fire 5 miles S near S branch of the Smoky Hill river; dendritic opal in Ladder Creek to S.
- *Yates Center, Woodson County* QUARTZ CRYSTALS: In granite 8 miles S.

  AMETHYST: In quartzite 4 miles W and 10 miles S.

Kentucky

Rugged eastern Kentucky belongs to the Allegheny plateau, a region of sharp ridges and deep valleys which includes extensive coalfields. The rest of the state is divided into the Mississippian plateaus and coalfields to the south and southwest and the blue-grass region of rolling hills to the north, all sloping gently to the Mississippi River. Like the Plains states, Kentucky is underlain by sedimentary rocks but is unglaciated and hence more varied in character.

- *Columbia, Adair County* GEODES: In Shamrock stone quarry.
- *Glasgow, Barren County* GEODES: In stream to E.
- *Marion, Crittendon County* FLUORITE: In mines to W with quartz crystals. Many of the mines are not operating.
- *Sandy Hook, Elliott County* PYROPE GARNET: At Isonville 6 miles SE.
- *Stanford, Lincoln County* GEODES: S 6 miles on Hwy 78 near Hall's Gap on the banks of the Green River.
- *Wickliffe, Ballard County* JASPER: In gravel pit.

Louisiana

Much of Louisiana has been built by the Mississippi River from mud and sand carried down from the north. On the west side of the river lie areas of low hills and plains becoming marshes to the south. There are agate-bearing gravel deposits in these hill, 20 to 45 miles W of the river, and petrified wood near Alexandria. No gem materials occur south of an east-west line through Baton Rouge. The east side of the river is low flood plain.

- *Alexandria, Rapides Parish* AGATE: In gravel pits and stream bars to N, such as in the Ouachita River valley near Monroe and near Pollock and Farmerville, with some petrified wood.
- *Amite, Tangipahoa Parish* AGATE: On banks of Amite River and to E in rivers and gravel pits of the Tangipahoa, Bogue Chitto, and Pearl rivers.
- *Gulfport, Harrison Parish* PETRIFIED WOOD, JASPER: In creek beds to the NW.
- *Leesville, Vernon Parish* PETRIFIED WOOD: E as far as the Red river, as far W as the Sabine river, and N as far as Shreveport.
- *Monroe, Ouachita Parish* BANDED AGATE, PETRIFIED WOOD, SILICIFIED CORAL: Scattered over wide area to south and east. To south, some of the prominent locations are Pollock, Grant Parish; Woodworth, Rapides Parish; Turkey Creek, Evangeline Parish; and, farther east, St. Francisville and Jackson, in Feliciana Parish; and Watson in nearby Livingston Parish.

  In the extreme east these materials are found near Bogalusa and Franklinton in Washington Parish; and in Tangipahoa Parish along the Tangipahoa River from Kentwood south to Independence. Most of the gem materials are found in stream gravels.

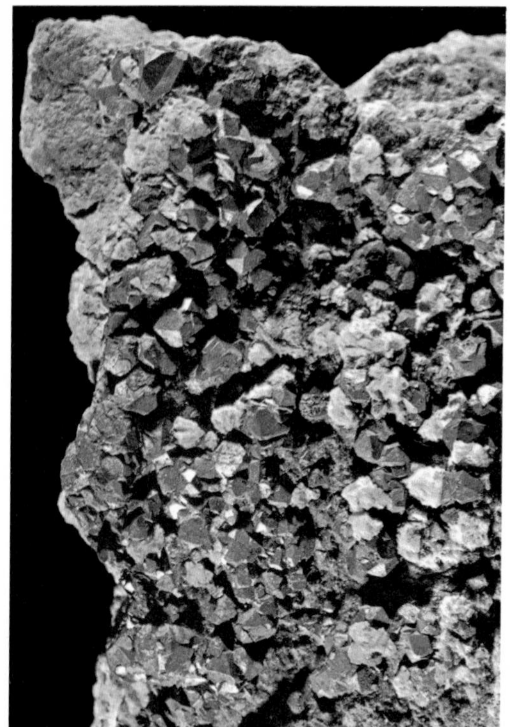

(Left) Celestite of Monteviale.
(Middle) Galena from Valle dei Mercanti, north of Verona.
(Right) Heulandite from Montecchio Maggiore, Vicenza.

Maine

Southern Maine is a rolling upland broken by hills and isolated mountains and valleys; the northern part is hilly and often swampy. Glacial action caused many lakes to form behind debris damming the normal drainage, and stripped the rocks of soil, laying bare the crystalline rocks that are the source of Maine's splendid tourmalines and other gems. Oxford County, particularly the area just northwest of Auburn, is world-famous for the many mines and quarries that have poured out mineral wealth for more than a century.

- *Albany, Oxford County* BERYL, ROSE QUARTZ, SMOKY QUARTZ: At Scribner ledge and Wardwell quarry.

  BERYL: Nearby on Lovejoy Mountain at Stearns and Guy Johnson quarries.
- *Andover, Oxford County** TOURMALINE, ROSE QUARTZ: Hwy 5 S for 7 miles to Abbot farm, drive ¾ miles NW and park; trail SW goes to Nevel and Dunton pits and farther S to Bell pit. W from parking area ¼ mile is Scotty pit and ¾ mile farther another pit, all on Halls Ridge of Plumbago Mountain. A spectacular find of tourmaline was made in the Dunton-Nevel quarry in 1973, and later the area was closed to amateur collecting.
- *Blue Hill, Hancock County* RHODONITE: 1¾ miles SW on Hwy 176 at Blue Hill manganese mine.
- *Bethel, Oxford County* BERYL, ROSE AND SMOKY QUARTZ: At the Bumpus quarry 6½ miles SE on Hwy 5. Dumps are along E side of highway.

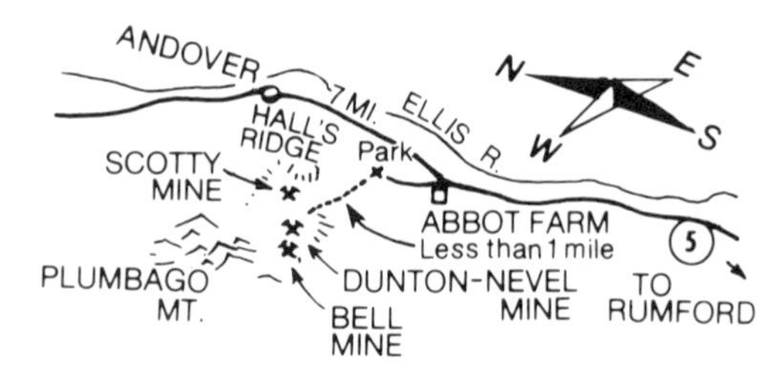

- *Brunswick, Cumberland County* BERYL: At LaChance Mine 4 miles S.
- *Buckfield, Oxford County* BERYL: At Fletcher Mine 2 miles SW on Hodgson Hill and 2½ miles SW at Robinson Dudley Mine.

  BERYL, APATITE, ROSE QUARTZ, TOURMALINE: At Paul Bennett Quarry 3 miles W on back road to Mount Mica (fee).

  BERYL: At Irish Mine 3 miles SE.
- *Byron, Oxford County* RED JASPER: In Swift River.
- *Canton, Oxford County* AMETHYST: In brook at Ragged Jack Mountain.
- *Deer Isle, Hancock County* LAVENDER GRANITE: On Moose and Crotch Islands.
- *Denmark, Oxford County* AMETHYST, SMOKY QUARTZ: In Warren Quarry on W side of Pleasant Mountain.

• *Dixfield, Oxford County* BERYL, GARNET: On south slope of Hedgehog Hill.

• *Fryeburg, Oxford County* GARNET, SMOKY QUARTZ: To S on E side of Stark Mountain at Eagle Granite Quarry.

• *Greenwood, Oxford County* * BERYL, ROSE, SMOKY AND STAR QUARTZ: Stanley Perham, of Trap Corner, was a leader in making Maine gem sources available to collectors. One of his mines, the Heikkinen mine, is reached from Greenwood by going S 500 feet, then to the Rawleigh Hayes house on Hayes Hill, and walking ¾ mile on the mine road.

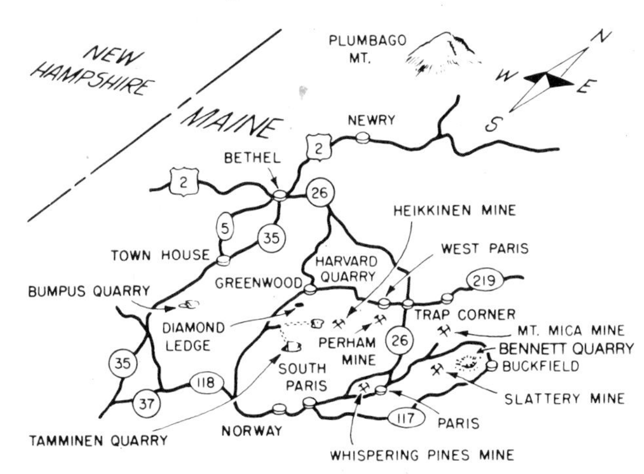

Another is the Harvard quarry, reached by driving S for 2½ miles to a crossroad below Mud Pond. Turn left 1,000 feet to a rise above Nestor Tamminen's house and walk ½ mile to mine on SW brow of Noyes Mountain. Tourmaline, beryl, and purple apatite are found here.

Nearby are the Tamminen mine and the Waisanen quarry, which yield the same gem minerals as the Harvard quarry. (Directions at the Tamminen house.)

PINK BERYL, ROSE QUARTZ: Take road W to Patch Mountain school, then N to end of road and hike to Emmons quarry. The mine is on the east face of Uncle Tom mountain. W of this quarry is the Tiger Bill quarry, noted for purple apatite, aquamarine, and golden beryl.

QUARTZ: S 1½ miles to gravel road between Hicks and Mud Pond. Hike up Noyes Mountain, which lies to left of the road from Greenwood and collect at Diamond Ledge. (Permission at Rawleigh Hayes house.)

• *Hebron, Oxford County* GREEN BERYL, TOURMALINE: N 2½ miles at quarries at Number 4 hill—the Mills, Foster Haverinen, and Mt. Marie mines.

PINK TOURMALINE, APATITE: N 2 miles to Mt. Rubellite quarry on steep ridge just north of a church.

GOLDEN AND BLUE BERYL, ROSE QUARTZ: 1½ miles N at Hibbs Mine.

• *Lisbon Falls, Sagadahoc County* BERYL, GREEN FELDSPAR, QUARTZ: E on Hwy 125 past Hwy 201 to Stoddard's Pond, then N on road past marsh to Coomb's mine.

• *Litchfield, Kennebec County* SODALITE: At Spear's Corner.

• *Machiasport, Washington County* JASPER PEBBLES: At Jasper Beach.

• *Minot, Androscoggin County* TOURMALINE, PURPLE APATITE: Hwy 121 E to Haskell's Corners, then left 2 miles to Hatch road to right to quarries on side of Mt. Apatite. There are several other quarries along Hatch road. Nearby are the Pulsifer & Wade quarries, notable for apatite and lepidolite; the Maine Feldspar mine, with pink beryl; the Littlefield quarry, which yields smoky quartz, and the Phillips mine, for amethyst and smoky quartz.

• *Mount Desert, Hancock County* AMETHYST, SMOKY QUARTZ: At Hall's Quarry.

• *Newfield, York County* VESUVIANITE: In boulders in the game preserve.

• *North Lovell, Oxford County* BLUE BERYL: 3 miles N at Chapman Hill.

• *Norway, Oxford County* TOURMALINE: At B.B No. 7 Mine at Nobles Corner 8 miles NW.

TOURMALINE, ROSE QUARTZ: N 2 miles at Tubb's Ledge.

• *Paris, Oxford County* * TOURMALINE, BERYL, SMOKY QUARTZ: Mount Mica's open pits and dumps lie 1⅓ miles E and are reached by a mine road to left up a hill. Herderite and amazonite are also found here. (Get permission from Mrs. Howard Irish in Buckfield; fee.)

SMOKY QUARTZ, AQUAMARINE: In Slattery mine. Take right turn from Paris and go a half mile to mine road. Walk 1,000 feet to dumps. (Get permission at Perham store.)

ROSE QUARTZ, CHRYSOBERYL: At Hooper's Ledge on S side of Paris Hill.

• *Pembroke, Washington County* RHYOLITE, JASPER: At Gleason Cove.

• *Perry, Washington County* AGATE: At Loring Cove to N off U.S. 1.

• *Phippsburg, Sagadohoc County* BERYL: At Thomas mine at Parker's Head.

• *Poland, Androscoggin County* GREEN TOURMALINE: In Berry quarry.

• *Roxbury, Oxford County* JASPER: At bend in Swift River around Thomas Intervale.

• *Rumford, Oxford County* TOURMALINE, LEPIDOLITE: N on Hwy 120 10 miles to Roxbury Notch, turn left on dirt road 2 miles to mine road to left, to Black Mountain quarries.

• *Sanford, York County* BROWN VESUVIANITE: In pit and on dump. Go 1½ miles E on School Street at Goodhall farm.

(Left) Mordenite from Valle Zuccanti, north of Verona.
(Middle) Natrolite from Montecchio Maggiore, Vicenza.
(Right) Natrolite in fine needle groups from Altaville, Vicenza.

- *South Paris, Oxford County* * ROSE, CITRINE, SMOKY QUARTZ: At Whispering Pines mine 6 miles S on Hwy 26 and at mine by road E.

  CITRINE QUARTZ: At Blueberry Mountain.
- *Stoneham, Oxford County* TOPAZ, PURPLE APATITE: At Lord Hill. Take Hwy 5 N to Kezar Lake, then W through Narrows and N 1⅔ miles, take left fork and go 2 miles to mine in ledge near top of hill. At Melrose quarry on Pleasant Mountain E of Lord Hill, aquamarine is found.
- *Stow, Oxford County* AMETHYST, APATITE: Hwy 113 N for 5 miles, then E on dirt road and take trail N up valley ½ mile to CTA trail. Take it E when it heads up mountain. Dig in new area over top and down on E side. Jeep trail leads to Eastman Ledge, and a trail leads beyond it over top of hill. (Get permission: Harry Eastman in Fryeburg.)
- *Topsham, Sagadahoc County* GARNET, TOURMALINE, SMOKY QUARTZ, BLUE BERYL: At quarries. Take Hwy 24 for 3 miles N; turn on left fork at Topsham Quarry Company sign; cross Cathance River and go mile to top of hill. Turn left on dirt road to Fisher (the best), Consolidated, Staples, and Willes quarries.
- *Westford, Middlesex County* CHIASTOLITE: In soil and stream at Small's Falls, Madrid twp., Franklin County.
- *West Minot, Androscoggin County* GARNET: At Pitts & Tenny mine N 1 mile on Hwy 119 to quarry on W. (Get permission at Perham store at Trap Corner.)
- *West Paris, Oxford County* * SMOKY QUARTZ, APATITE: The Perham mine is reached by taking High Street to a sign reading "Perham Mine," there a half mile up the mine road. In the open pits in feldspar are found smoky quartz crystals, sometimes with pale amethyst tints. (Get permission from Bell Mineral Company of West Paris.)
- *Winslow, Kennebec County* BLUE BERYL: In Winslow Mine.

Maryland

The easternmost part of Maryland along the line of Baltimore and Washington is coastal plain, backed up by the Piedmont plateau of crystalline rocks containing a diversity of mineral wealth, and giving way in the west to mountains and valleys of the Appalachian system, made up of sedimentary and metamorphic rocks of lesser mineral interest.

- *Baltimore, Baltimore County* SERPENTINE: In Bare Hills Serpentine quarry ½ mile N at Falls and Pimlico roads. Quarry E of Falls road is owned by the city. (Get permission from Baltimore Department of Parks.)
- *Beltsville, Prince Georges County* PETRIFIED WOOD: In stream beds to N.
- *Cape Sable, Anne Arundel County* AMBER: In sedimentary deposits on the Magothy River.
- *Cockeysville, Baltimore County* MARBLE, QUARTZ, TOURMALINE, DIOPSIDE: At H. T. Campbell quarry. Take Padonia exit off Int. 83 N of Int.

695. Collecting permitted only on Saturday mornings with advance permission.

- *Elk Mills, Cecil County* BERYL, GARNET: From U.S. 40 go N on Hwy 280 to Cherry Hill, then E on Hwy 277 to quarry on E bank of Elk Creek. Get permission.
- *Granite, Baltimore County* QUARTZ: Loose in soil on Nash farm.
- *Hancock, Washington County* QUARTZ: S on Hwy 522 to Pennsylvania Sand corporation pit.
- *Jarrettsville, Harford County* SERPENTINE: At Reed chrome mine.

  At Wilkins chrome mine 1½ miles SE along road to Cooperstown. Both mines are on private lands and collecting is discouraged.
- *Ocean City, Worcester County* QUARTZ: Crystals like Cape May "diamonds" in beach sands at Point Lookout.
- *Point of Rocks, Frederick County* BRECCIA: In abandoned quarry near Potomac river.
- *Reistertown, Baltimore County* SERPENTINE, CHALCEDONY, JASPER: Off Hwy 140 2 miles S, turn right on Nicodemus road at quarry. Get permission.
- *Rock Springs, Cecil County* SERPENTINE (WILLIAMSITE), CHALCEDONY: The area at the Maryland-Pennsylvania line offers some of the world's finest serpentine to the collector. One location for this translucent green material is the Line Pits (Lowe chrome mine) dumps north of Conowingo dam on the Susquehanna River. Hwy 222 leads N to the Pleasant Grove road to the left, then a short trail through the woods leads to the dumps. Information can be obtained from Mrs. Glenn Holdsworth, 3730 Chestnut St., Baltimore, Md. 21211 (fee).

  East of the Line Pits are scores of prospect pits and mines in the chrome serpentine deposits, including the Wood Chrome mine just N of the state line in a meander of Octoraro creek, the Jenkins or Rock Springs mine, and the Cedar Hill quarries in Pennsylvania.

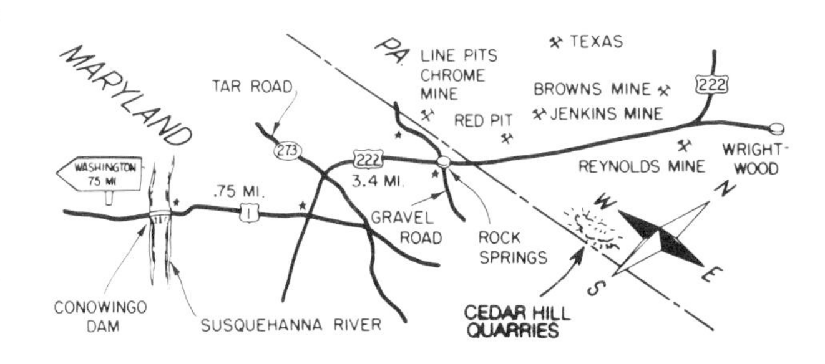

- *Rockville, Montgomery County* DIOPSIDE, GROSSULAR GARNET: NW on Hwy 28 for 3½ miles to Travilah road, then left 1 mile to Piney Meeting House road, take it left to Hunting Hill quarry to collect a rock formed of massive diopside and grossular garnet known as rodingite.

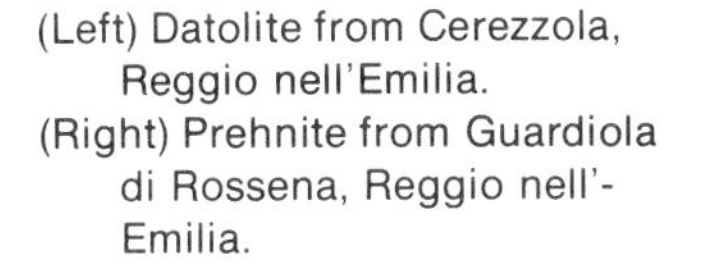
(Left) Datolite from Cerezzola, Reggio nell'Emilia.
(Right) Prehnite from Guardiola di Rossena, Reggio nell'-Emilia.

- *Simpsonville, Howard County* AMETHYST, QUARTZ CRYSTALS: In Maryland mica mine on Arrington farm.
- *Springfield, Montgomery County* JASPER: Take first road on left from school marked "Vaughn Summit" to concrete bridge. Collect under it in stream.
- *Union Bridge, Carroll County* QUARTZ CRYSTALS: SW 3 miles in Mountain View lead mine ¼ mile W of Beaver Dam Church on Beaver Dam road.
- *Westminster, Carroll County* QUARTZ CRYSTALS: N of New Windsor Road ¼ mile at Hyde limestone quarry.

Massachusetts

Massachusetts, like Connecticut, is divided into two geographical provinces by the Connecticut River. East of the river, the land falls with few elevations toward the ocean, although the underlying rocks are contorted metamorphic schists; to the west lies an Appalachian Mountain region. Most gem-producing areas lie in the Connecticut River valley or just east of it, except the Essex County area in the extreme northeast part of the state.

- *Amherst, Hampshire County* AMETHYST, PREHNITE: In Lane Traprock quarries on Hwy 116, with datolite.
- *Bolton, Worcester County* SCAPOLITE: 2¼ miles E in dumps of Bolton Lime quarry (fee).
- *Cape Cod, Barnstable County* JASPER: Pebbles on beach with epidote between Sandwich and the Plymouth County boundary.
- *Chester, Hampden County* JASPER: In W branch of Westfield river.
- *Chesterfield, Hampshire County* RHODONITE, KYANITE: N of meetinghouse 1 mile on old Searle farm.
- *Cohasset, Norfolk County* JASPER: With epidote as pebbles on shore of Massachusetts Bay.
- *Conway, Franklin County* JASPER: In Deerfield River, and in breccia in SE part of town.
- *Deerfield, Franklin County* AGATE: In Deerfield River and a mile E of Deerfield Academy.
- *Fitchburg, Worcester County* GOLDEN BERYL: In pegmatite in W side of Rollstone Hills.
- *Gay Head, Dukes County* AMBER: On shore eroding from greensand deposits.
- *Gloucester, Essex County* SMOKY QUARTZ, AMAZONSTONE: In Pomroy quarry.
- *Greenfield, Franklin County* AMETHYST, CHALCEDONY: In Cheapside quarry, S of village, with datolite and prehnite.
- *Marshfield, Plymouth County* JASPER PEBBLES: At beach.
- *Middleboro, Plymouth County* AGATE, CHALCEDONY: In vein running N from Rochester to Middleboro and SW to Fairhaven.
- *Nantucket, Nantucket County* AMBER: On sea beaches eroded from deposits of greensand.
- *Newburyport, Essex County* SERPENTINE: On turnpike 2 miles to Newbury, then first road left for 2 miles. Park, walk to Devil's Den, and look in mine dumps.
- *Pelham, Hampshire County* SERPENTINE, APATITE: At asbestos mine. 4 miles SW.
- *Pittsfield, Essex County* GREEN QUARTZ: In SE part of town.
- *Plainfield, Hampshire County* RHODONITE: In Betts manganese mine and another mine 1 mile W.
- *Rockport, Essex County* AMAZONSTONE: In the Cape Ann granite quarries.

  CITRINE QUARTZ: At Babson farm quarry.
- *Royalston, Worcester County* BLUE-GREEN BERYL: In Reynolds mine 2½ miles NE at Beryl Hill.
- *Stockbridge, Essex County* SMOKY QUARTZ: On Monument mountain 3 miles S via U.S. 7.
- *West Chesterfield, Hampshire County* SMOKY QUARTZ: W ¼ mile in road cut on Hwy 143.

  TOURMALINE: In Clark Ledge on Reed farm.

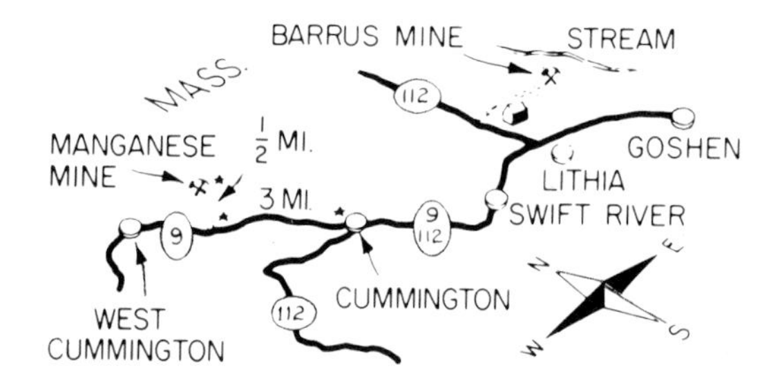

- *West Cummington, Hampshire County* * RHODONITE: The West Cummington manganese mine is ½ mile N of Hwy 9 on a mine road that leaves Hwy 9 roughly 3 miles from the fork of Hwys 9 and 112 just NW of Cummington. Rhodonite is found in the mine ore and on the dumps.

  TOURMALINE, LEPIDOLITE, CAT'S-EYE SPODUMENE: Farther E and just N of the hamlet of Lithia is the Barrus mine, the first farm N of Lithia on the right of Hwy 112. Take trail to the diggings alongside a small stream. (Obtain permission at the farmhouse to collect.)
- *Westfield, Hampden County* AMETHYST: At Lane Traprock quarry with prehnite, datolite, and serpentine with bronzite inclusions.

  SERPENTINE: In Atwater quarry.

Michigan

Lower Michigan is quite level and not much elevated above the Great Lakes, and is underlain by sedimentary deposits of limestone, salt, and gypsum. Upper Michigan, however, is a rugged land of ancient igneous and metamorphic rocks, highly contorted and containing some of the world's richest iron and copper deposits, as well as a wealth of specimen minerals.

- *Allouez, Keweenaw County* * CHRYSOCOLLA: From dump at Allouez Mine.

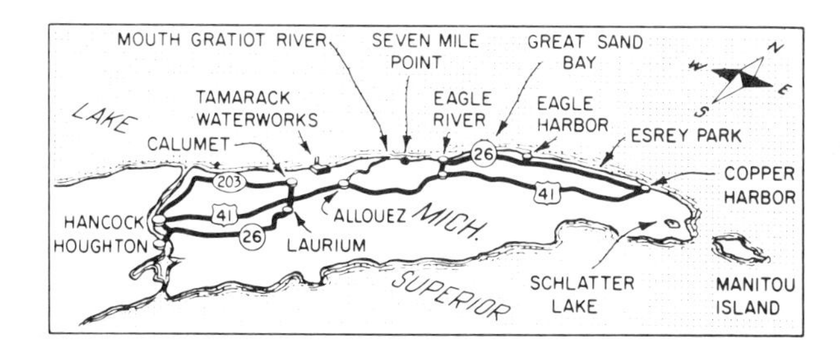

AGATE: The Keweenaw beach agate is distinctive for its pastel shades. It is rarely large and is not easy to distinguish from the other pebbles on the beach. These agates are found along the NW shore from Tamarack waterworks to the tip of the peninsula.

The best beach pickings are at Pete's Beach, reached by taking the Five Mile Point Road from Allouez to turnoff marked with sign and through woods to lake shore (fee).

At Gratiot River Beach, reached from Five Mile Point Road by turning S on very rough road.

Also on Manitou Island.

LEDGE AGATES: Larger and of a more conventional type. Found in the ledges that cross the road from Allouez to the lake shore.

Also at High Rock Bay at Keweenaw Point.

In the ledges back of Esrey Park on Agate Harbor.

Inland from Seven Mile Point and on the N side of Schlatter Lake.

PINK, GREEN THOMSONITES: Found on the Keweenaw, Pete's, and Gratiot River beaches. Also on Cedar Bay beach, from Ahmeek to thomsonite area near Eagle River.

- *Alpena, Alpena County* FOSSIL CORAL (PETOSKEY STONE): In Rockport Quarry, 11 miles NE.
- *Brighton, Livingston County* OOLITIC AGATE: E on Int. 96 to Kensington road, S ½ mile to the American Aggregate quarry.
- *Charlevoix, Charlevoix County* FOSSIL CORAL (PETOSKEY STONE): Take U.S. 31 to Bell's Bay road to Medusa quarry. Petoskey stones, a form of calcified coral, are widespread in eight counties—Benzie, Leelanau, Grand Traverse, Antrim, Charlevoix, Cheboygan, Presque Isle, and Alpena. They are most abundant along the S shore of Little Traverse bay from Petoskey to Charlevoix. They are also found in quarries along the bluffs on the shore from Petoskey to W of Charlevoix and in gravel pits S of this area, on beaches of Burt and Torch Lake, and in the area N of a line between Beulah and Manton on the S and W of Hwy 131 to Petoskey. A favorite spot is the Afton-Onaway district in Cheboygan and Presque Isle counties.
- *Copper Harbor, Keweenaw County* DATOLITE, GREEN EPIDOTE (SHOT THROUGH WITH COPPER), THOMSONITE: Datolite on Clark mine dump. Massive green epidote is found in many of these mines and makes an attractive cut stone. Thomsonite occurs in nodules and seams in the basalt.

AGATE: At northern point of peninsula, reached by taking logging road at northern end of U.S. 41 5 miles to clump of three birches at fork, and taking left fork 3 miles to

(Left) Scalenohedral calcite from Passo del Furlo, Pesaro, Italy.
(Right) Sulphur from Perticara, west of San Marino, Italy.

point. Traffic is permitted only on Sundays. Long hike to right around point leads to less picked area on Keystone Bay.

- *DeTour, Chippewa County* AGATE: Take ferry to Drummond Island. Collect on beach.
- *Grand Haven, Ottawa County* GEODES: E 12 miles in gravel pits.
- *Grandville, Kent County* ALABASTER: In gypsum quarry.
- *Ishpeming, Marquette County* JASPER, HEMATITE: The layered rock known as jaspalite is found widely but especially at Jasper Hill in Ishpeming. From U.S. 41 turn right on Hwy 28 and Division Street through the city to Jasper Street and turn right to foot of hill.

  SERPENTINE: At Verd Antique quarry. Go W along U.S. 41 to Cooper Lake Road, turn right 2½ miles, then left on Rd. 572 for less than a mile to Ropes Gold mine and hike ⅓ mile to the serpentine quarry.

  DOLOMITE: The rock known as Kona dolomite outcrops many places S of Marquette. The Lindberg quarries are reached by taking U.S. 41 to the Negaunee caution light, then right on Rd 480 SE for 7 miles to a caution light, then 1½ miles farther to the quarries.
- *Isle Royale* AMETHYSTINE AGATE: In Siskiwit Bay. On Thomsonite Beach.

  AGATE, CARNELIAN: At head of Siskiwit Bay.
  NE of McGinty Cove.
  N side of Amygdaloid Point.

  THOMSONITE: At point N of Stockly Bay.
  On main island S of Hawk Island.
  Near end of Scoville Point thomsonite has been found.

  CHLORASTROLITE: At Mott Island, Smithwick Island, Caribou Island, Rock Harbor, on S shore of Siskiwit Lake, at Scoville Point, Todd Harbor, Chippewa Harbor, and Tobin Harbor. (Isle Royale is a national park and collecting is forbidden there.)
- *Marquette, Marquette County* AGATE, JASPER: On point at N end of Presque Isle Avenue.
- *Michigamme, Marquette County* STAUROLITE: In road cut S of Lake Michigamme.
- *Mass, Ontonagon County* EPIDOTE ROCK: Green rock with copper inclusions on dumps of Mass and Minesota mines and other nearby mines.
- *Mohawk, Keweenaw County* DOMEYKITE: Several copper arsenides in white massive quartz are found in the dumps of the Mohawk, Seneca, and Ahmeek mines near towns of those names.
- *Newport, Monroe County* AMETHYSTINE QUARTZ: At Point aux Peaux.
- *Ontonagon, Ontonagon County* AGATE: On shores of Ontonagon and Gogebic counties, such as at Gull Point.
- *Oxford, Oakland County* OOLITIC AGATE: In gravel pits and also at Holly, Romeo, and Clarkston.
- *St. Johns, Clinton County* CHERT: N on U.S. 27 to Kinley av., E 1 mile to Scott road, then N ½ mile to Walling gravel pit.
- *Spalding, Menominee County* GARNET: In mica schist to W and N in Scott and Howe creeks.
- *Tahquamenon Falls State Park, Luce County* AGATE: On Lake Superior beaches from Whitefish Point to Crisp Point.

Minnesota

Southern Minnesota rises from the midwestern prairies into a rolling upland which, in the northwest, is dominated by the flat bed of the ancient extinct Lake Agassiz. In the northeast lies the Mesabi iron range, and in central Minnesota the Cuyuna range. The whole state is covered with lakes left by glaciers, which also left a rich deposit of Lake Superior agates on beaches and in gravel pits. This deposit can be found generally wherever the soil has a reddish hue, which is roughly from Duluth north to the Ontario line and west to Hwy 71, as well as a small area around the Twin Cities.

Areas marked on state map * are locations where there are active gravel pits. Permission can usually be obtained to examine the stock piles of gravel for agates of the Lake Superior type. These are commonly brown or red, have fine stripes of several colors in what is called fortification pattern, and usually are fist size or smaller.

- *Beaver Bay, Lake County* AGATE: Whenever the lake builds a gravel beach agates are likely to be present. These beaches are formed and washed away by the waves.
- *Bloomington, Scott County* AGATE: S on Int. 35 to Exit 42, up ramp and turn left $1\frac{1}{5}$ mile to Chicago avenue, turn right to Crystal Lake road, then left to farm and park. Hunt agates in gravel pit.
- *Bovey, Itasca County* AGATE: In mine dumps.
- *Buhl, St. Louis County* AGATE: Go E on U.S. 169 to Top's Tavern on N side of road, turn N on dirt road to Dormer dumps on left side of road.
- *Cloquet, Carlton County* AGATE: N 6 miles on Hwy 33, collect at Kinto Bros. pit and to S in Carter pit at Carlton.

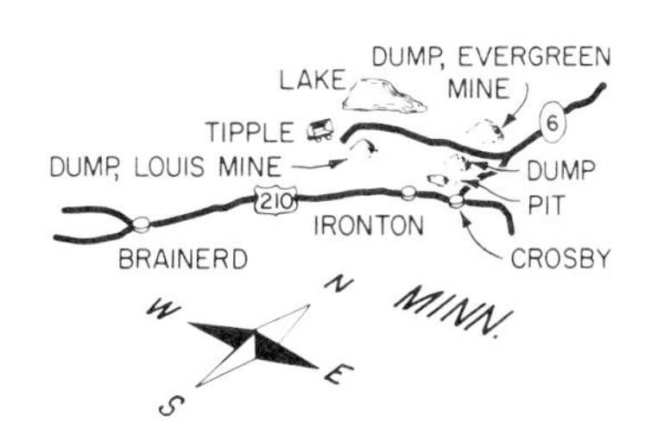

• *Crosby, Crow Wing County* * BINGHAMITE: Silicified iron mineral known as binghamite at Evergreen (Portsmouth) mine dump. The mineral, which resembles red and yellow tigereye, is found in the dump, especially on the E side, and on the W side of the dump S of the road and near the pit.

Farther along a side road W from Hwy 6 and slightly S is the tipple and dump of the Louis Mine, where another form of the same material is obtained. William Perpitch, of the Yankee and Portsmouth Mine, knows the locations of this material in the area.

RHODOCHROSITE: Dump of Hopkins mine at Crosby-Ironton, and also at Pittsburgh-Pacific mine.

• *Duluth, St. Louis County* AGATE: In shoreline gravels (especially at low water) of Island Lake Reservoir 18 miles N.

Also at Coon Bros. gravel pit 8 miles NW at Munger, and Arrowhead pit 20 miles NW at Twig.

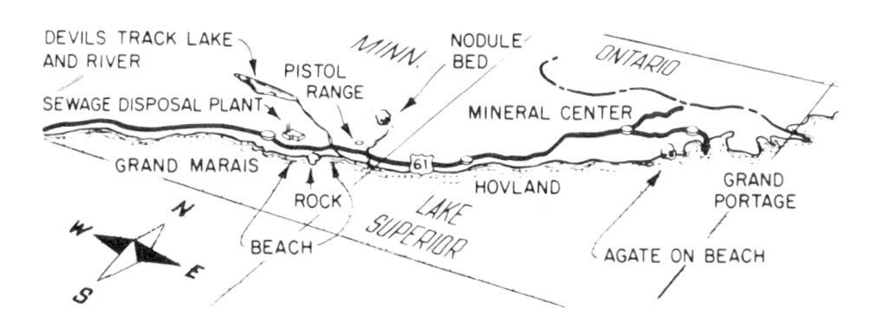

• *Grand Marais, Cook County* * THOMSONITE: 3 miles SW in ledges along road cut where power line crosses Hwy 61, above road in ledges. Also 6 miles S at Thomsonite Beach (fee).

In gravel of lake shore at point. (Permission to collect at shore difficult to obtain.

HOVLANDITE: Just beyond Grand Marais is the town's sewage-disposal plant on the lake shore and just beyond it is a small beach and a rock. An attractive dark-spotted rock known as hovlandite is obtained on the NE side of this rock.

AGATE NODULES: Beyond this spot lies the Devil Track River, and 1½ miles NE of its mouth is a side road to a pistol range. A dim road or trail N 150 to 300 feet from it leads to an area of agate nodules.

AGATE: At Paradise Beach, 13 miles E of Grand Marais, small banded agates can be dug from the basalt.

LINTONITE: Associated with thomsonite at Good Harbor Bay and elsewhere in this area.

• *Lanesburg, Fillmore County* QUARTZ: a mile E in road cut.

• *Little Marais, Lake County* * AGATE: In gravels at County Line Beach.

Five miles SW at the Baptism River's mouth. Park just east of the state's blacktop depot and take trail down to the lake for blue agates. Stay S of the rock in the lake.

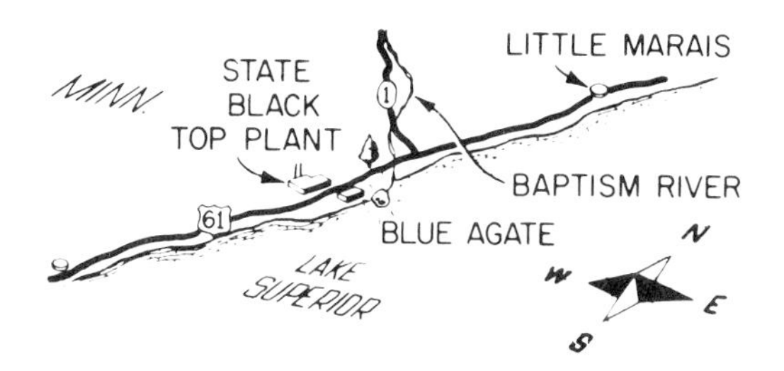

• *Mazeppa, Wabasha County* AGATE: Cold-water type agate in Zumbo River.

• *Mineral Center, Cook County* AGATE: Take side road to Grand Portage until it dips close to the lake. Here a faintly marked road leads through a shale ridge to the collecting spot on the beach.

• *Osseo, Hennepin County* AGATE: At Anderson Aggregate pit. S on Hwy 110, then W, and at two nearby pits.

• *Pipestone, Pipestone County* PIPESTONE (CATLINITE): In a national monument, no collecting.

• *Randall, Morrison County* AGATE: In gravel pits.

• *Red Wing, Goodhue County* QUARTZ CRYSTALS: In cavities in limestone bluffs along Mississippi River.

• *Royalton, Morrison County* STAUROLITE: In schist outcrops at Blanchard Dam; best under railroad bridge. Sieve gravel for staurolites, agate, and garnet.

• *St. Paul, Hennepin County* AGATE: In gravel pit E on Hwy 12.

• *Tofte, Cook County* AGATE: In gravels at Two Islands Beach.

• *Two Harbors, Lake County* AGATE: NE 11 miles in gravels at Gooseberry Falls State Park beach.

• *Virginia, St. Louis County* * AGATE: Up a side road from U.S. 169 about 10 miles W of Virginia are the Atkins and the Wade mines. About 3 miles up this side road is a large spoil bank. On its W face Lake Superior agates can be dug.

Beyond and to the left of this spoil bank is another which contains the same type of agates along its S face.

JASPER: Take Hwy 135 from Virginia toward Biwabik, stop a mile short of Biwabik, take mine road marked "M.E." to Mary Ellen mine; look for jasper with swirl patterns on dump.

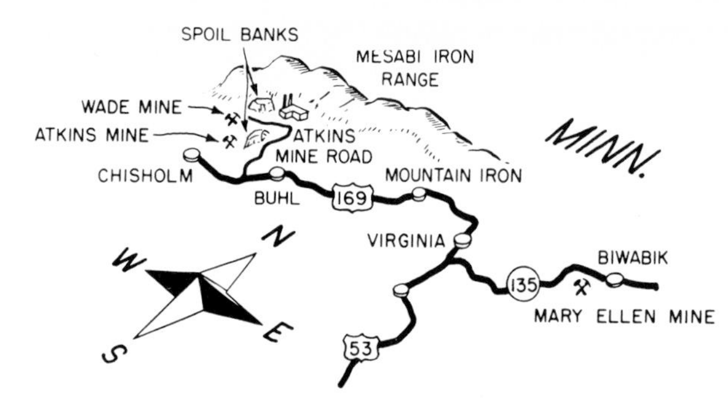

Also on Hwy 135 1 mile W of Biwabik at Corsica mine.

- *Wabasha, Wabasha County* AGATE: In gravel pits.

Mississippi

Much of the state is built up of sand, gravel, and mud brought down by the Mississippi River and which has filled a great bay in the Gulf Coast. The surface rises from the Gulf Coast and the river toward the oldest sedimentary rocks in the state that form a ridge in the northeast counties. Thus, petrified wood and agates in river gravels are the major gem resources.

- *Anding, Yazoo County* AGATE, PETRIFIED WOOD: In Thompson and Perry creeks.
- *Carpenter, Claiborne County* PETRIFIED PALM WOOD, AGATE: S 3½ miles at Traxler Co. gravel washing plant at Bayou Pierre. Also banded chert.
- *Fair River, Lawrence County* AGATE, CHERT: N 3 miles of U.S. 84 and ½ mile W of Hwy 27, at Fair River gravel bars and Green Bros. gravel washing plant.
- *Fearn Springs, Winston County* OPALIZED WOOD: Along Hwy 25 near Webster in Mill Creek.
- *Georgetown, Copiah County* AGATE, PETRIFIED WOOD: W 2 miles to Green Bros. gravel washing plant just S of Hwy 28, collect in Copiah creek. Also collect in creek S of town and W of Hwy 27.
- *Greenville, Washington County* AGATE: In gravel dredged from Mississippi river. Feldspar moonstone is to be found in the Mississippi river gravels here and elsewhere.
- *Gulfport, Stone County* PETRIFIED WOOD, JASPER: In Bell Creek, 18 miles NW and generally in creeks to NW.
- *Meadville, Franklin County* AGATE, CHERT: To W at Middle Fork creek, also petrified wood.
- *Natchez, Adams County* AGATE, JASPER: Lake Superior agates and jaspers at St. Catherine Gravel Washing plant at Carthage Point.
- *North Foxworth, Marion County* AGATE, PETRIFIED WOOD: In gravels at Pearl River Washing plant.
- *Quentin, Franklin County* AGATE, PETRIFIED WOOD: S ½ mile of U.S. 84 in gravel bars in McCall Creek.

  AGATE: NW at gravel pit at Oldenburg and NE of Hamburg.
- *Tylertown, Walthall County* AGATE, PETRIFIED WOOD: At Walthall Gravel Washing plant on Bogue Chitto River just N of Louisiana line. Also chert.
- *Wesson, Copiah County* AGATE: E 6 miles, in Bahala Creek.
  W 4 miles, in gravel pit.
- *Yazoo City, Yazoo County* PETRIFIED WOOD, AGATE: Between Hwy 3 and 49 as far S as Hwy 433. Also in gravel terraces above Yazoo River at its tributaries.

  AGATE, CHERT: S on Hwy 49 to Little Yazoo, then W 4½ miles to Oil City, N for 2 miles and W 1⅓ miles to collect in gravel bars in river.

Missouri

Missouri north of the Missouri River is, like most of Illinois and Iowa, a fertile plain formed by glacial action and underlain by sedimentary rocks. Southern Missouri, however, contains not only an area of rolling plains to the west, as in Arkansas, but also the Ozark Highland which becomes gradually rougher as it sweeps from southern Illinois southwestward into Arkansas and Oklahoma. These peaks and valleys expose not only sedimentary rocks but also granites.

- *Alexandria, Clark County* GEODES: S 8 miles on Hwy 61, in open pit on Scheffler's property (fee).
- *Cadet, Washington County* AGATE, QUARTZ: In barite mines, also at Potosi and Old Mines nearby.
- *Creighton, Cass County* PETRIFIED WOOD: In quarry on Cornett farm 3 miles E.
- *DeSoto, Jefferson County* AGATE: At Washington State Park. Take U.S. 21 to Hwy CC, then W on Hwy E to Tiff, then E across railroad to mine.
- *Farmington, St. Francois County* CHERT (MOZARKITE): W on Hwy W past Hwy 67, then in a block, turn N a block. Go 2⅕ miles W on blacktop road to fork, take right fork for ⅔ mile to road to right with chain across it. Collect to E and N where ground is bulldozed.
- *Gainesville, Ozark County* CHERT: At Timbered Knob.
- *Kahoka, Clark County* GEODES: N on Hwy 81 to nursing home, right 1 block, turn left, cross river, turn right, and then left at next corner to Easterday farm (fee).
- *Lincoln, Benton County* CHERT (MOZARKITE): To E in roadcuts or at Brice Patt farm (fee). (See James Melton at motel in Lincoln).
- *Malden, Madrid County* JASPER, CHERT: Go W on Hwy J for 5⅘ miles to gravel road to right, and N on ridge to pits on Crowley's Ridge.
- *Rolla, Phelps County* AMETHYST: S on Hwy 63 for 8 miles, then W on dirt road 2 miles to fork;

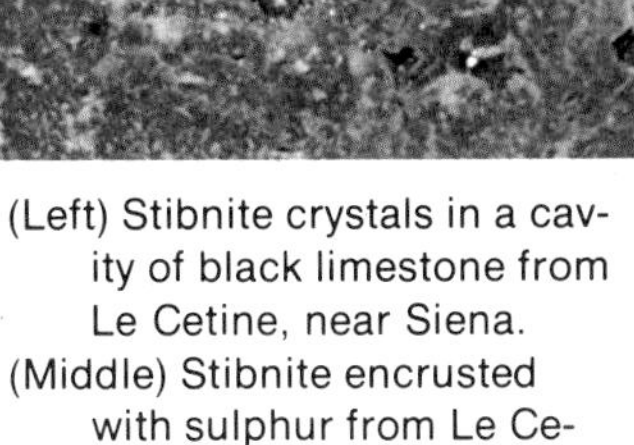

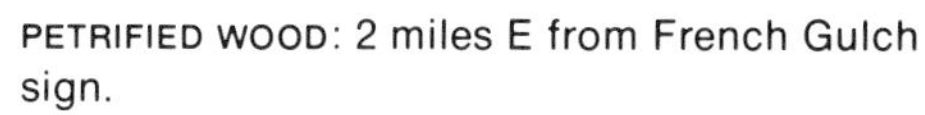

(Left) Stibnite crystals in a cavity of black limestone from Le Cetine, near Siena.
(Middle) Stibnite encrusted with sulphur from Le Cetine.
(Right) Brecciated limestone, a rock found near Florence.

take right fork to Moselle mine No. 10. Also quartz and jasper.

- *St. Francisville, Clark County* GEODES: At Sinotte property (fee).
- *St. Louis, St. Louis County* GEODES, JASPER. N on U.S. 67 to St. Ferdinand creek, search creek gravels.
- *Stanton, Franklin County* RUTILATED QUARTZ: At Cherry Valley iron mine.

Montana

The Rocky Mountains dominate the western part of Montana, crossing the state from northwest to southeast, and exposing a great variety of rocks. From them have come the gold, silver, copper, corundum, and other minerals which have caused Montana to be called the Treasure State. Eastward lie the High Plains, sloping eastward, formed of erosional deposits and broken by bluffs, gullies, and isolated mountains. In these areas are found most agate and like materials.

- *Alder, Madison County* BANDED RHYOLITE (WONDERSTONE): Take road S along Ruby River from Alder 12 miles to righthand fork. Take road 8 miles; collect along road NW toward Dillon.

  ALMANDINE GARNET: In gravels of Ruby River above storage dam to S.
- *Anaconda, Deer Lodge County* AMAZONSTONE: N 3 miles at falls of Lost Creek, in pegmatite.

  PETRIFIED WOOD: 2 miles E from French Gulch sign.
- *Butte, Silver Bow County* AMETHYST: To E in Little Pipestone Creek and in W fork of Rader Creek.
  At old Pohndorf mine reached by taking Hwy 10 E to 19 Mile Inn, then dirt road 1½ miles N.

  SMOKY QUARTZ: In pegmatites of Whisky Gulch N of Pohndorf mine. Also at Timber Butte, to S, and just E of railroad cut at Janney substation.

  SAPPHIRE: In Brown's Gulch to NW.

  RHODONITE: In Alice mine dumps and at Lexington mine.
- *Canyon Ferry Dam, Lewis and Clark County* GREEN SAPPHIRE: At Magpie Gulch, 1 mile above in Missouri River.
- *Columbus, Stillwater County* MOSS JASPER, PETRIFIED WOOD: To SE and E and W of bridge and on island in Yellowstone River.
- *Deer Lodge, Powell County* SAPPHIRE: To SE in Dry Cottonwood Creek.
- *Dillon, Beaverhead County* PETRIFIED WOOD: To NW in Frying Pan Basin.

  STAR CORUNDUM: 18 miles SW in Sweetwater Creek on the Rebish ranch.

  SILLIMANITE: E 13 miles at Christenson ranch.

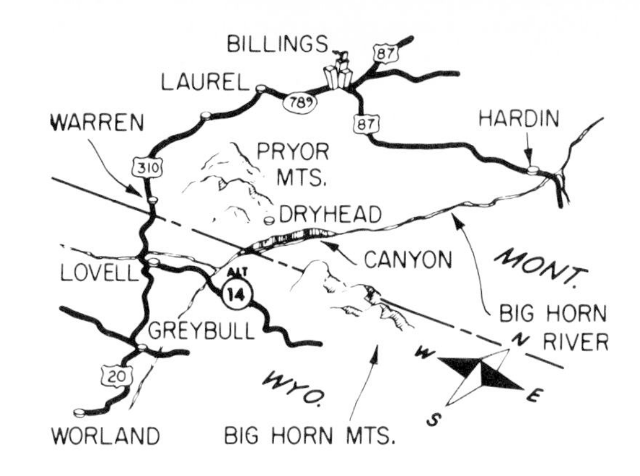

SOAPSTONE: SE ¾ mile on Sweetwater Road at Keystone quarry.

- *Dryhead, Carbon County* * AGATE: Take road N to ranch at foot of Pryor Gap. Agate is found on the rim rocks of the canyon where Dryhead Creek flows into the Big Horn River, and at the mouth of Big Horn Canyon. It is also scattered over much of the surrounding grazing area.
- *Elkhorn Hot Springs, Beaverhead County* AMETHYST: N 4 miles at Crystal Park.
- *Gardiner, Park County* AGATIZED WOOD: The Tom Miner basin collecting area lies 16 miles N on U.S. 89, then left 10 miles into Gallatin National Forest. From the campground hike up trail N and then NW above bluffs toward Ramshorn peak.
- *Helena, Lewis and Clark County* SAPPHIRE, GARNET: These can be found on a number of bars in the Missouri River, such as the American, Eldorado, Emerald, French, Metropolitan, Ruby, and Spokane bars. The Eldorado bar is reached from Helena by taking Last Chance Gulch Road N to N. Montana Street and on it to gravel road E; then N on road along the Missouri River to York bridge, cross it to York, and then N to Eldorado Sapphire Diggings (fee).

  SMOKY QUARTZ: SE 3 miles at Three-Mile Gulch.
- *Lewistown, Fergus County* SAPPHIRE: Near confluence of South and Middle forks of Judith River.
- *Livingston, Park County* PETRIFIED WOOD: In gravel halfway to Big Timber.
- *Manhattan, Gallatin County* ALABASTER (ONYX): 5 miles NW in quarry.
- *Miles City, Custer County* * MOSS AGATES: Montana moss agates are found all the way from the Big Horn River upstream on the Yellowstone River to beyond Sidney near the North Dakota line. They are in old gravel beds, on bluffs, and in ravines below bluffs. West of Miles City, the best collecting seems to be S of the Yellowstone, but farther E it ranges for 50 miles N of the river on ranches.

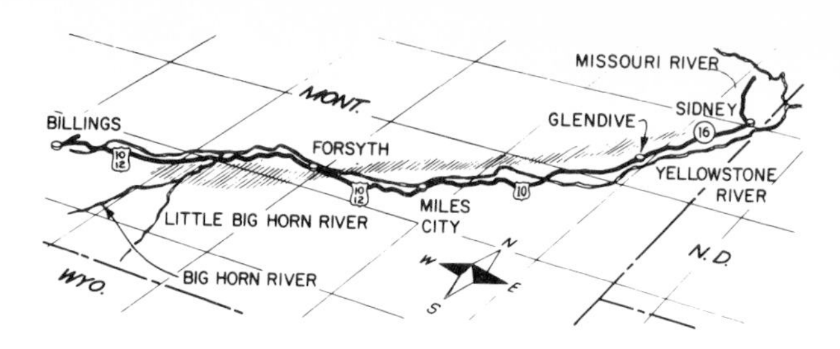

Heavy ice in the winter and spring floods uncover new supplies of agate. The best months to collect are in April and in August when the water is low and the island gravel beds are accessible. Heavy rains also lay bare agates in tributaries of the Yellowstone river and on hillsides far from the major highways. Most of the land is privately owned and permission to collect is needed. (Agate-bearing areas are shaded on the accompanying map.)

One recommended place to collect is S of Pompey's Pillar on Int. 94, where there are gravel banks, and another is farther E on Int. 94 at Hysham, where the collecting spot is S on Sarpy road in the hills.

- *Neihart, Cascade County* GREEN SPHALERITE: In Hartley mine.
- *Philipsburg, Granite County* SAPPHIRE: Take U.S. Alt. 10 S to Porters Corners, W 17 miles on Hwy 38 to bridge over fork of Rock Creek, follow sign to collecting area in Basin, Sapphire, Malay, Anaconda, and Coe gulches, where the gems are found in decomposing rock.

  Also S 6 miles on Hwy 26A to Hwy 28, then right for 17 miles to Chaussee Sapphire mine (fee).
- *Red Lodge, Carbon County* SERPENTINE: In chrome prospect dumps on Hellroaring Plateau.
- *Sula, Ravalli County* BERYL: In pegmatite 2 miles N via dirt road.
- *Twin Bridges, Madison County* QUARTZ CRYSTALS: W at Crystal Butte.
- *Utica, Judith Basin County* SAPPHIRE: 11 miles SW by gravel road to Yogo Gulch at foot of Little Belt Mountains, sapphire-bearing dike runs 5 miles E from Yogo Gulch. (fee).
- *Vaughn, Cascade County* BLACK AGATE, PETRIFIED WOOD: Along U.S. 89 and 91 E and S.
- *Warren, Carbon County* AGATE: N 5 miles, in the Pryor Mountains.
- *Whitehall, Jefferson County* SPHENE, SMOKY QUARTZ: 18 miles NW in Hay Canyon at the Gem Queen claim.

Nebraska

Nebraska is a plain sloping from northwest to southeast, including rich loess farmlands in the east backed by a region of sand hills to the west which lead into the more rugged bluffs, tablelands, and occasional mountains of the High Plains. In the extreme northwestern corner, Nebraska shares an area of badlands with

South Dakota. Agates in stream gravels and petrified wood are the principal gem materials under such geological conditions.

- *Ashland, Saunders County* AGATE, PETRIFIED WOOD: In sand pits along Platte River and downstream to Louisville and LaPlatte.
- *Bayard, Morrill County* AGATE, PETRIFIED WOOD: In gravel beds along the N side of the Platte River all the way to Lake Guernsey, Wyo. Some of the wood is dendritic.
- *Beaver City, Furnas County* CHERT: Red and green material in the Niobrara chalk deposits.
- *Bridgeport, Morrill County* MOSS OPAL: Take Hwy 385 N to Angora Hill. Halfway up, turn E on dim road for 2 miles, then N up hill on another faintly marked road. Park here and walk to deposit on top of hill.
- *Chadron, Dawes County* CHALCEDONY: In northern part of county and as far W as Crawford and Harrison. Some of the chalcedony is blue.
- *Chappell, Deuel County* JASPER: Red and yellow float in South Platte river basin as far E as Hershey in Lincoln County.
- *Crawford, Dawes County* RED JASPER: Take Hwy 2 for 20 miles NW toward Orella railroad station, turn W ½ mile S of station, cross tracks and drive into badlands 2 miles W. Collect in hills.

  AGATE: Go ½ mile beyond Orella and turn E for 2 miles to Bald Butte. Also to NE near state line.
- *Fairbury, Jefferson County* JASPER, AGATE: In gravel pits as well as at Steele City, with petrified wood, and as far NW in Blue river basin as Ayr in Adams County.
- *Fullerton, Nance County* AGATE, PETRIFIED WOOD: In local gravel pits.
- *Gothenburg, Dawson County* PETRIFIED PALM WOOD: In sand pits.
- *Humboldt, Richardson County* AGATE: Along Nemaha River.
- *Kearney, Buffalo County* PETRIFIED WOOD: In sand and gravel pits as far west as Cozad and south to Holdrege.
- *Lincoln, Lancaster County* LAKE SUPERIOR AGATES: In gravel pits in nearby counties, especially near the cities of Winnebago, Norfolk, Fremont, Saunders, Wahoo, and Garland.
- *McCook, Red Willow County* PASTEL JASPER: In Republican river basin as far east as Franklin.
- *Mitchell, Scotts Bluff County* AGATE: In gravel terraces along the North Platte River.
- *Orella, Sioux County* AGATE: N 5 miles in Waldron Hills.
- *Palmyra, Otoe County* MOSS AGATE: In gravel pits here and at Dunbar.
- *Platte Center, Platte County* JASPER, PETRIFIED WOOD: In gravel pits and as float near junction of Loup and Platte rivers.
- *Plattsmouth, Cass County* SILICIFIED CORAL: Cream-colored material in limestone.

  ONYX: At Onyx Ace Hill quarry.

  CHERT (RICE AGATE): At Weeping Water and Lincoln.
- *Valentine, Cherry County* BLACK PETRIFIED WOOD: In hills along Minnechaduza creek and the Niobrara River.
- *Waterloo, Douglas County* AGATE: In Lyman-Ritchie gravel pit to SW.

Nevada

Nevada is part of the Great Basin area of ancient sedimentary rocks that have been deformed and folded by granite intrusions, especially those associated with the Sierra Nevada uplift on the western edge of the state. Mineral occurrences are associated with the granite intrusions and the lavas. Much of the state is made up of arid plains and valleys broken by short mountain chains.

- *Battle Mountain, Lander County* CHALCEDONY, PETRIFIED WOOD: Go N across Southern Pacific railroad tracks, continue 18 miles to windmill, take E fork to bridge over Rock Creek and collect in and along creek.

  CINNABAR: Continue 7 miles farther, take left fork N for cinnabar in chert (myrickite) in washes and at dumps of Silver Cloud mercury mine.

  TURQUOISE: At No. 8 mine, 30 miles NE.
  At Blue Gem mine on Pedro claim, 4 miles SW on Hwy 8A.
  At Blue Matrix mine, 31 miles SE, near Tenabo.

  CINNABAR IN OPAL: At mercury mine to S.
  OBSIDIAN: NW 25 miles.
- *Beatty, Nye County* MARBLE: S 8⅓ miles on U.S. 95 to road E 3 miles to Carrara marble quarry.

  PETRIFIED WOOD: N 44½ miles on Hwy 95 past Stonewall Pass sign, then turn W 5 miles and S 4 miles.
- *Boulder City, Clark County* CHALCEDONY, ROSES, NODULES: S on Hwy 95 to road to Nelson, SE on it 8½ miles, then E and N on it 2 miles.

  AGATE: Cross Hoover Dam S and take Hwy 93 SE 3 miles, then W ¼ mile, park and hike over saddle into ravine to collect in lava on west hillsides.
- *Carlin, Elko County* GREEN TURQUOISE (FAUSTITE): NW 10 miles at Copper King mine in Tuscarora Mountains.
- *Coaldale, Esmeralda County* TURQUOISE, VARISCITE: NE 4 miles at Bonnie Blue mine on W side of canyon.

  JASPER:W 5 miles on Hwy 6, then N to collect on flats.

  OBSIDIAN: Hwy 6 W for 6 miles, turn S on Hwy 3A for ⅓ mile, leave paved road, angle left on bladed road 4½ miles to fork, keep right of Fish Lake, collect along road for 5 miles.

OBSIDIAN, LIMB CASTS: Hwy 6 W for 6 miles, then S on Hwy 3A for 11½ miles and turn E to Sump Hole. Collect on north rim and in hills to W.

AGATE: E on Hwy 6 for 7½ miles, S to Blair Junction and SW on road to Emigrant Pass for 6¾ miles, then S 2 miles to collect icicle agate on side of Silver Peak Mountains.

PETRIFIED WOOD, AGATE: Take Hwy 6 7½ miles E, then N to Esmeralda Lake bed. From highway, take same side road but keep right 7 miles, watch for bluff; sagenitic agate is in debris from bluff face.

- *Cortez, Lander County* TURQUOISE: At Fox and Smith mines.
  At White Horse mine, 2½ miles NW.
- *Currie, Elko County* AGATE, QUARTZ: S on Hwy 93 to U.S. 50A and S to "Victoria Mine" sign, turn left to mine.
- *Denio, Humboldt County* FIRE OPAL: At Rainbow Ridge mine, 30 miles on Hwy 8A, then S 7 miles to trail from Virgin Valley to mine on side of Big Mountain (fee).
  At Bonanza mine farther up Virgin Valley (fee).
  At Green Fire mine on E side of Virgin Valley.

COMMON YELLOW OPAL: At Virgin Valley ranch.

CARNELIAN: On hills above Denio road and Bonanza diggings.

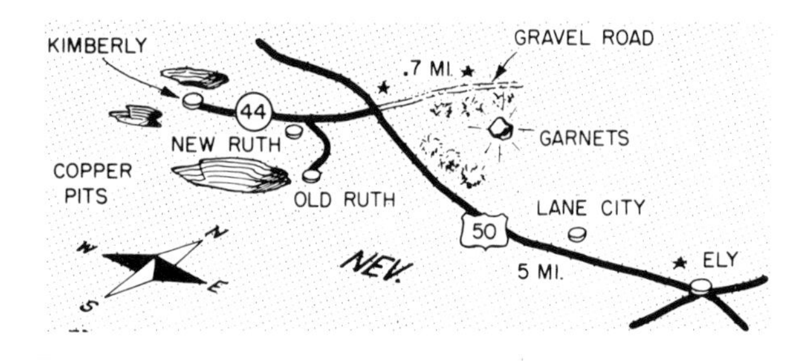

- *Ely, White Pine County* * GARNET: Take Hwy 50 NW from Ely for 5 miles, then right on a gravel road 7/10 of a mile along the power line into canyon. Go to summit on foot. The largest garnets are in rhyolite in area marked on map.
  Canyons N from Lane City for a mile in either direction also contain garnet-bearing rhyolite.

BANDED RHYOLITE (WONDERSTONE): 40 miles W on U.S. 50 at Little Antelope summit.

- *Fallon, Churchill County* * BANDED RHYOLITE (WONDERSTONE): Take U.S. 50 E and then SE for 11½ miles, turn E through dump and 2½ miles into saddle to gravel pit.

GREEN AGATE: Mile south of the above gravel pit.

RED AND YELLOW JASPER: Continue on to turnoff 32 miles S from Fallon on Hwy 50, 7 miles

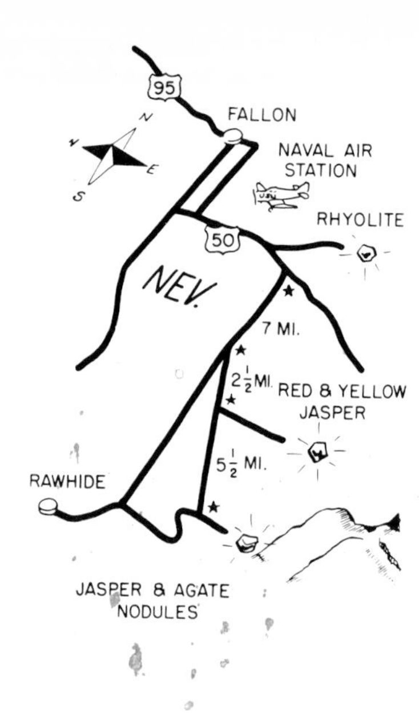

to road angling to E, take a branch road E 2½ miles on and go to end for red and yellow jasper in weathered volcanic rock in canyon.

JASPER, AGATE NODULES: Come back to angling road and go 5½ miles to another branch road E. Take it into hills for jasper and agate nodules on hillsides.

- *Fernley, Lyon County* AGATE: On W side of Lake Lahontan and between lake and Fernley, 7½ miles S in hills E of U.S. 95A.

PETRIFIED WOOD, AGATE NODULES: NE on Hwy 95A for 15½ miles; collect on flats and low hills.

PETRIFIED WOOD, RHYOLITE: Hwy 95A SE 7½ miles to Fernley Park road, then W on farm road to Swartz ranch (fee). Return to Hwy 95A, go N nearly 1 mile to collect rhyolite (wonderstone).

- *Gabbs, Nye County* PETRIFIED WOOD: Take Hwy 23 N to road E to Broken Hills and Quartz Mountain, collect white wood around old LeFevre mine. Go back to Hwy 23, cross it and collect wood to W. Return to Hwy 23, take it a short distance toward Gabbs, then turn W again for green limb fragments.
- *Gerlach, Washoe County* PETRIFIED WOOD: Hwy 34 N for 41 miles past Black Rock desert, turn left to site of Leadville (fee).
  13 miles N on Hwy 34, collect in ravine.

FIRE OPAL: Little Jo mine 40 miles N on Summit Lake road (fee). Get directions from Ray Duffield, 85 Tiger Dr., Carson City, Nev. 89701.

- *Goldfield, Esmeralda County* COLORFUL OPAL, AGATE: N on U.S. 95 2⅓ miles, then dirt road W 3½ miles (fee).

PETRIFIED WOOD: S 18 miles on U.S. 95, at 3½ miles S of junction with Hwy 3 take dirt road

(Left) Botryoidal chalcedony from Le Cetine.
(Right) Celestite from La Pentolina, Siena.

W 6 miles, then W into red hills. Collect in ash beds.

- *Henderson, Clark County* GREEN JASPER: E past manganese plant a scant quarter of a mile, then NE 6 miles, park and walk to hill to N.

  BANDED CHALCEDONY: S 1⅔ miles on Hwy 93 turn W across tracks and go 4 miles, collect in hills.

  CHALCEDONY, NODULES: S on U.S. 95 to Hwy 2, take Hwy 2 8½ miles, turn E on dirt road through waste dump, park and collect chalcedony. Return to Hwy 2, continue SE 1 mile, collect nodules in hills W and S.

  OBSIDIAN, AGATE: S 7 miles on U.S. 95, W 13 miles, ignoring side roads.
- *Jackpot, Elko County* PINK LIMB CASTS: S 5 miles on road across Trout Creek, then W for twig casts. Go 5 miles farther to dig limb casts from Granite range.
  Also 2 mi. S on Hwy 93, 3 mi. E, S across bridge for 10 miles, turn E a mile, then S 6 mi. to Texas Springs for pink limb casts.
- *Jarbidge, Elko County* AGATE: Take road N along Jarbidge River to Jack Creek, then trail into canyon SE to seam agate deposit near fork in creek. (Get permission, Rene Sprague in Jarbridge.)
- *Las Vegas, Clark County* * BLACK AGATE: Take U.S. 91 to turnoff road to Nellis Air Force Base,

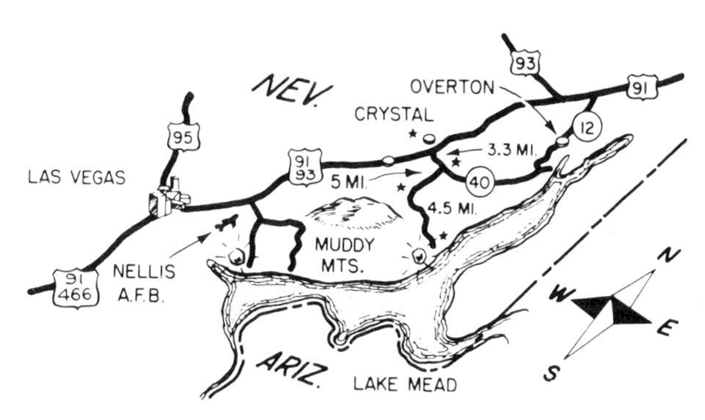

then 2½ miles to entry road to Lake Mead Base. Go SE to Base hobby shop, turn left on unpaved road 4½ miles, then right to a gypsum wash. Walk S through gypsum piles to black agate field.

  RED JASPER, PINK OPAL NODULES: Go back to U.S. 91 and continue N to Crystal, turn E for 3⅔ miles, then take right fork toward Muddy Mountains and go 5 miles to entrance to a canyon. Continue 4½ miles more to area where red jasper and pink opal nodules are found.

  AGATE, JASPER: Collect by boat in gravels of N shore of Lake Mead between Las Vegas and Callville Bays.
- *Lida Junction, Esmeralda County* AGATE: Take road E from U.S. 95 for 1½ miles, collect along road for a mile.

• *Lovelock, Pershing County* AGATE, PETRIFIED WOOD: Take Western Avenue, then NW 10 miles, go W on same road 6½ miles to collect N of campsite in saddle.

AGATE AND OPAL: 2 miles W to fork, take left fork 16 miles, then N. Go back to fork, take right fork 20 miles for opal and plume agate.

JASPER, AGATE: Take road into Trinity Mountains for 15 miles NW and W to Eagle-Picher mine sign. About a mile farther collect on surface in saddles and canyon.

• *Luning, Mineral County* PINK THULITE, OPALIZED WOOD (HOWARDITE): Hwy 23 N almost to bridge, take left fork 34 miles to Rawhide, then 6 miles farther to ravine; collect in ash.

• *McDermitt, Humboldt County* PURPLE SAGENITIC AGATE: 4 miles W on Cordero mine road, collect in grave pit. Also limb casts in nearby areas. Ask at McDermitt Rock Shop.

• *Midas, Elko County* CINNABAR IN OPAL: At Rand mine.

• *Mill City, Pershing County* AGATE GEODES: To S on Hwy 50 and then W to collect on E slope of Star Peak.

• *Millers, Esmeralda County* TURQUOISE: At Myers & Bona mine, 13 miles NW on W slope of Monte Cristo Mountains.
At Petry mine, 11 miles NW in foothills of Monte Cristo Mountains.
At Royal Blue mine, 12 miles NW on E edge of plateau.

OBSIDIAN, CHERT: Take dirt road NW from U.S. 95, keeping NW at forks 9⅓ miles into pass, then follow faint tracks onto mesa.

• *Mina, Mineral County* SATIN SPAR: 3 miles S on Hwy 95, follow power line to mine.

TURQUOISE: At Nevada Turquoise Co. mine.

VARISCITE: Mile S of Candelaria and on E side of hill in Candelaria Mountains.

COPPER MINDERALS: In dumps of Wilson mine near Candelaria.

JASPER, PETRIFIED WOOD: S on U.S. 95 to ruins of Sodaville, turn on road SW for 1 mile, then ½ mile up wash into Excelsior mountains.

• *Oreana, Pershing County* BLUE DUMORTIERITE: In quartz in Bullion Canyon.

• *Paradise Valley, Humboldt County* CHALCEDONY: At Coyote Springs.

FIRE OPAL: 22 miles N at Firestone opal mine.

• *Reno, Washoe County* CINNABAR IN OPAL: S on U.S. 395 to Steamboat, backtrack to macadam road, go W ½ mile and take dirt road left across bridge into canyon to road junction. Collect in hills above road.

• *Rochester, Pershing County* PINK DUMORTIERITE: At Lincoln Hill.

• *Schurz, Mineral County* PETRIFIED WOOD: W on dirt road 19 miles to cattle guard, S on faint road.

• *Silver Peak, Esmeralda County* OBSIDIAN: SE 10 miles.

• *Tonopah, Nye County* TURQUOISE: At Smith Black Matrix mine, 3 miles NE.

GREEN MOSS AGATE: W 26 miles on Hwy 6, N on Gilbert Road into canyon. Park at right-hand wash off canyon. Collect there and in hills to right.

PETRIFIED WOOD: Take road NE past city reservoir, then follow power line over ridge into canyon. Fossil algae cover limbs.

JASPER, AGATE: E 3 miles on U.S. 6, then N less than a mile to collect in hills and washes. Return to U.S. 6, go E 2⅓ mile, then N on Hwy 8A ⅓ mile and ½ mile W to collect petrified wood in wash.

• *Verdi, Storey County* QUARTZ: Go 5 miles NW on Dog Valley road to collect at Crystal Peak. Get permission from Mrs. E. G. Margrave, Reno Silica Company (fee).

• *Warm Springs, Nye County* THULITE, ZOISITE: SE on Hwy 25 for 58½ miles to road to Tempiute. Follow it to building by dry lake for a mile, then S on dirt road into mining camp in mountains.

• *Wendover, Elko County* CHALCEDONY: Take Hwy 50A S 38 miles, turn right at sign to Victoria, go N 12 miles to mine dumps.

• *Winnemucca, Humboldt County* AGATE, GEODES: Take U.S. 95 N to Hwy 8B and go through Paradise Valley to Hinkley Summit along road to N.

JASPER, AGATE: Grass Valley road S 30 miles to hot springs, collect to E.

• *Yerington, Lyon County* OPALIZED LIMB CASTS: E on U.S. 95A to Hwy 3, S to second crossing of Walker River, then hike E into hills.

New Hampshire

The White Mountains of the Appalachians are the dominating geographical feature of New Hampshire. They occupy the north-central part of the state, an area of noteworthy mineral occurrences but of rocky, thin soil. Above the mountains is a region of ridges and valleys and south of them is the plateau characteristic of the New England upland. Glaciers have stripped the rocky granite highlands and created many lakes.

• *Acworth, Sullivan County* BERYL, ROSE QUARTZ: Less than 2 miles S at mine dump on W side of Beryl Mountain.

• *Alexandria, Grafton County* BERYL: In mine dump at 2,000 ft. level on N side of Hutchins Hill.

• *Alstead, Sullivan County* BERYL: In Beauregard mine (fee) and at Blister and Island mines.

• *Berlin, Coos County* JASPER: At cave W of trail and at 1,200 ft. level on S side of Jasper Mountain.

• *Center Strafford, Strafford County* BLUE BERYL, APATITE: At Foss mica mine mile NW. Go 2⅓ miles on Hwy 9, then mine road to right to Parker Mountain mine on Blue Hill.

• *Chatham, Carroll County* BROWN AND BLUE TOPAZ, PHENACITE, AMAZONSTONE: At 2,900 ft. level on E side of South Baldface Mountain, in pockets where pegmatites meet talus slope.

• *Concord, Merrimack County* SMOKY QUARTZ: In Crowley granite quarry.

RUTILATED QUARTZ: In New England Granite Works.

• *Conway, Carroll County* AMETHYST: At Redstone granite quarry, E of Hwy 302 between Conway and North Conway.
At White Mountain granite quarry, at 700 ft. level on W side of Birch Hill.

TOPAZ, SMOKY QUARTZ, AMAZONSTONE: Hwy 16 N ¼ mile, then left on Passaconaway road. Cross bridge, go ⅓ mile, then left to gravel road and N ¼ mile to collect in Lovejoy Pit.

AMETHYST, SMOKY QUARTZ: 2 miles N of North Conway, then E on Hurricane Mountain road 3½ miles. Take trail from top ¼ mile W, follow old road and collect in ledges on Hurricane Mountain.

• *Danbury, Merrimack County* BERYL: At Wild Meadows mine.

• *Eaton Center, Carroll County* SMOKY QUARTZ: NE 2 miles at Randall lead mine.

• *Enfield, Grafton County* QUARTZ CRYSTALS WITH EPIDOTE INCLUSIONS: At Shaker Hill granite quarry.

• *Fitzwilliam, Cheshire County* RUTILATED QUARTZ: At Victoria White and Webb-Fitzwilliam granite quarries.

• *Franconia, Grafton County* JASPER: In Ammonoosuc River.

• *Gilsum, Cheshire County* GOLDEN AND BLUE BERYL: North of Gilsum along W side of road to Mill Hollow is a group of mines where golden and blue beryl has been found on dumps:
At the Blister mine.
At the Davis mine, ¾ mile N of Mica Mine School.
At the Island Mica mine, 2½ miles N of Gilsum, 400 yards E of Hwy 10, and W of school on knoll between swamp and pond.
At the Big mine, N of school.
At the Golding-Keene mine, NW of the Big mine.
S of Gilsum on E side of Hwy 10 at the J. White mine.

APATITE: At Fitzgibbon mine.

• *Grafton, Grafton County* BLUE BERYL: In dumps of mine 3 miles SW on E side of Melvin Hill.

BLUE AND GOLDEN BERYL: At Kilton mine, reached via Ruggles Mine Road, crossing Manfeltree Brook, keeping right and then ¾ mile NE.
At Ruggles mine on Isinglass Hill, reached by taking direct road W from Grafton Center 1½ miles to crossroads, then right across brook and up hill ¾ mile (fee).
At Sargent mine, on N end of Horse Hill, reached by driving to top and taking ridge trail on foot.

BLUE BERYL, ROSE AND SMOKY QUARTZ: At Alger mine, reached by taking road S where Ruggles Mine Road leaves Grafton Road and going mile.

• *Hanover, Grafton County* RUTILATED QUARTZ: At Moose Mountain.

• *Haverhill, Grafton County* QUARTZ CRYSTALS: In limonite at Black Mountain.

• *Hebron, Grafton County* BERYL, LEPIDOLITE: SW 2 miles at mine dump on E side of Hobart Hill.

• *Hinsdale, Cheshire County* PINK RHODONITE: Mile SE near Ashuelot River.

• *Keene, Cheshire County* BERYL: NE 5 miles in pegmatite of Bassett Hill.
4½ miles E at Horse Hill.

BERYL, SMOKY AND ROSE QUARTZ: At Keene granite quarry 3 miles SE.

FLUORITE: At Will Wise mine. Hwy 9 W for 11 miles, pass Sherman Store, turn right at sign saying "1st Methodist Church in New Hampshire," go ½ mile, then right on dirt road 1½ mile, then left 3 miles, and a sharp left onto mine road. Park and walk up Bald Hill.

• *Lincoln, Grafton County* AMETHYST: On upper slopes of Mount Nancy.

• *Littleton, Grafton County* STAUROLITE: On hill ¾ mile W of Garnet Hill.

• *Marlboro, Cheshire County* ALMANDINE GARNET: Mile S at Webb granite quarry.

• *Marlow, Cheshire County* GREEN TOURMALINE: At Turner mine.

ROSE AND SMOKY QUARTZ: In E cut of Windham mine.

• *Milan, Coos County* AMETHYST, TOPAZ: To W and 3 miles S at 1,700 foot level of Green's Ledge.

• *Milford, Hillsboro County* RUTILATED QUARTZ: In Bishop and Carlton granite quarries 2 miles NW.
In Connoli granite quarry 3½ miles SW.
In Kittridge granite quarry 1½ miles SW.

• *Newport, Sullivan County* BERYL, APATITE: At G. F. Smith mine and 3 miles E at Young's Hill (fee).

• *North Conway, Carroll County* TOPAZ, SMOKY QUARTZ, AMAZONSTONE: Take road W to Echo Lake, then jeep road W to Camp Albite, park and walk ¾ mile W to dig in Moat Mt. There is also collecting at South Moat and the hogback E of Middle Moat. (Now under Federal Bureau of Land Management supervision. Fee.)

• *North Groton, Grafton County* * GREEN QUARTZ, APATITE, BERYL: SW 1 mile, then turn N less than a mile to Palermo No. 1 mine. Also at the Rice mine, a mile farther from North Groton.
At the Charles Davis mine. About ¾ mile W of North Groton, the dirt road S from the

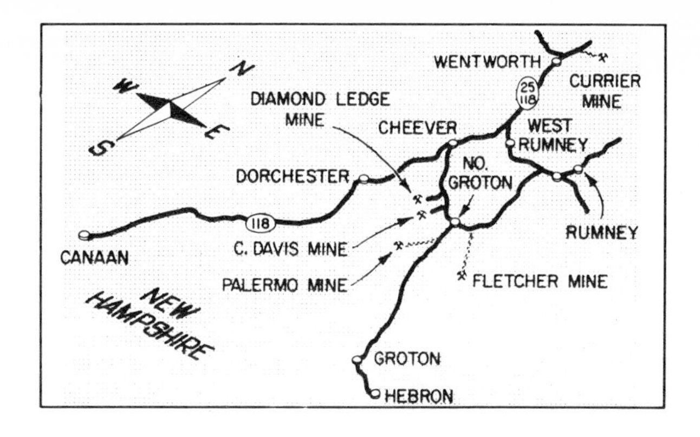

Cheever Road leads to the mine. Lazulite here, too.
At the Diamond Ledge mine, reached by a road a mile W of North Groton leading from the Cheever Road.
At the Mica Products mine located on a hillside a quarter mile W of the Davis mine.
At the Fletcher mine. Take the Rumney Road but turn off on a side road up Fletcher Mountain and go 1¼ miles.

BERYL, APATITE: At the Valencia mine, located on the next hill NW of the Fletcher mine.

- *Orange, Grafton County* BERYL: At Keyes Mines, N 2½ miles on dirt road.
- *Orford, Grafton County* STAUROLITE: On Strawberry and Blackberry Hills.
- *Ossipee, Carroll County* SMOKY QUARTZ: In ledge S of road at Passaconway quarry near Albany.
- *Percy, Coos County* AMETHYST: On W slope of Hutchins Mountain.

TOPAZ: NW 1¾ miles at Victors Head.

- *Raymond, Rockingham County* BERYL, GARNET, ROSE QUARTZ: Take Old Manchester road W, then Lane road a total of 2 miles to Chandler, Smith, Welch, and Blake mines.

QUARTZ CRYSTALS: In boulders on ridge just N of Raymond-Nottingham town line and W of road.

- *Richmond, Cheshire County* CORDIERITE: In Richmond soapstone quarry.
- *Rumney, Grafton County* BERYL: At Belden mine.
- *Springfield, Sullivan County* GOLDEN BERYL, AMETHYST, SMOKY QUARTZ: At Columbia gem mine on N end of Springfield Mountain.

AMETHYST, QUARTZ CRYSTALS: In soil at George Hill.

BERYL, SPESSARTITE GARNET: At S end of Melvin Hill in ledge on Joe Hill farm.

GREEN BERYL: At Playter mine on S end of Pillsbury Ridge.

BLUE BERYL, GARNET, QUARTZ CRYSTALS: At Reynolds mine near top of NE slope of Robinson Hill.
At Davenport mine just below.

AMETHYST, SMOKY QUARTZ CRYSTALS: At Diamond Ledges on Long Mountain.
SE on Hwy 4A for 1½ miles, then ½ mile N to Globe mine, collect on dump.

- *Stratford, Coos County* AMETHYST: Along road near Sugarloaf.
- *Sugar Hill, Grafton County* GREEN QUARTZ: S 1½ miles at Franconia iron mine.

STAUROLITE: In slate near Franconia iron mine, S of summit of Ore Hill.

- *Sunapee, Sullivan County* RUTILATED QUARTZ: At Perry Sunapee quarry.
  At Spectacle Pond quarry.
- *Wakefield, Carroll County* BLUE BERYL: At Weeks mine ½ mile W of Province Lake.
- *Walpole, Cheshire County* ROSE QUARTZ: At Howe Lodge on W side of Derry Hill.
- *Warner, Merrimack County* ROSE QUARTZ: Near top of Mount Kearsarge.
- *Warren, Grafton County* GOLDEN BERYL, QUARTZ CRYSTALS: SW 1½ miles on SW side of Beech Hill.
- *Wentworth, Grafton County* BERYL: At the Currier mine. Take Hwy 25 N past railroad tracks, then first dirt road right ¾ mile. Park. (Ask permission to collect at houses nearby and take road through fields to mine.)
- *West Lebanon, Grafton County* RUTILATED QUARTZ PEBBLES: In Connecticut River.
- *Westmoreland, Cheshire County* AMETHYST, QUARTZ CRYSTALS: At Stoddard mine.

STAUROLITE: At Park Hill.

- *Wilmot Flat, Merrimack County* BERYL: In mine dumps at Stuart Hill.
- *Winchester, Cheshire County* RHODONITE: Near top of Stony Mountain.

New Jersey

The northwest corner of New Jersey contains the famous Delaware Water Gap, where the river has cut through the Kittatinny mountain range of the Appalachians. Southeast of these mountains is a belt of ridgeland know as the Highlands, and paralleling it is a lowland marked by traprock ridges, such as the Watchung Mountains and the Palisades on the Hudson. Southeast New Jersey is coastal plain, much of it marsh. Glacial terminal moraines cross the central part of the state.

- *Andover, Sussex County* ACTINOLITE, SERPENTINE: Take road ½ mile N, turn right at Exxon station to Limecrest sign, go 6 miles crossing Newton-Sparta road, then 1½ miles to Limecrest quarry. It also contains corundum and tourmaline.
- *Bernardsville, Somerset County* AMETHYST: Take Hwy 202 for ¼ mile S to Somerset Crushed Stone Quarry.
- *Bound Brook, Somerset County* AGATE, AMETHYST, JASPER: At the New England quarry.
- *Cape May, Cape May County* QUARTZ (CAPE MAY DIAMONDS): In beach sand, especially just S of

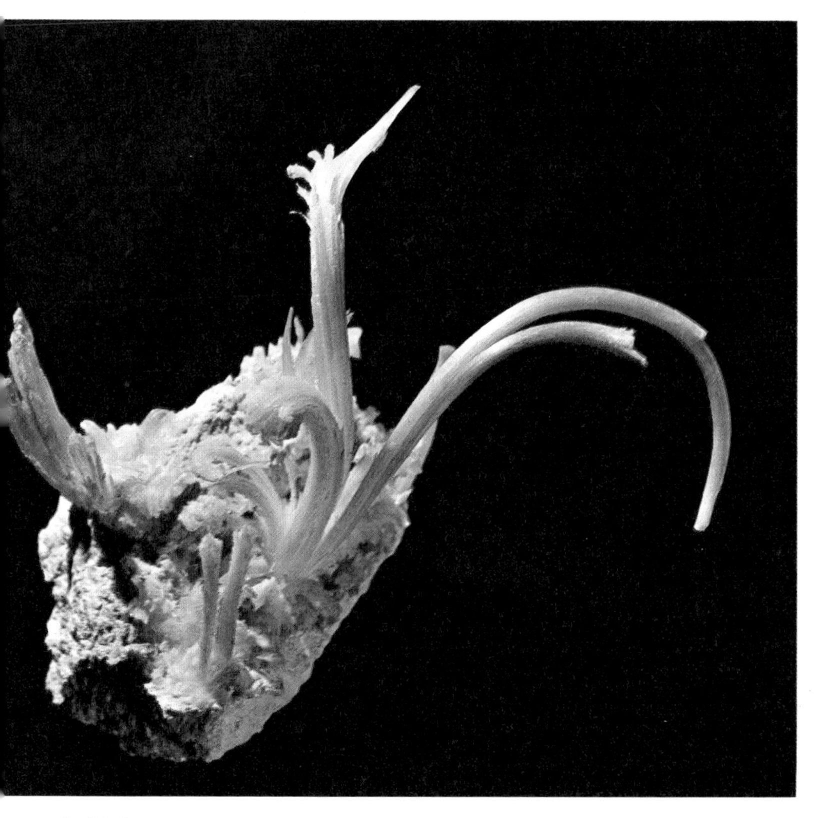

(Left) Ram's horn selenite from Rosia, Siena.
(Right) Selenite on pyrite and quartz from Niccioleta, southwest of Siena.

sunken concrete ship at Cape May Point, and at Point Lookout, in water at waterline.

- *Clifton, Passaic County* AMETHYST, AGATE: 3 miles W and S of U.S. 64 at Houdaille Industries quarry.
- *Dover, Morris County* SUNSTONE: In Alan Wood iron mine dumps on Mine Hill.
- *Franklin, Sussex County* RHODONITE (FOWLERITE), VESUVIANITE (CYPRINE): In dumps of New Jersey Zinc Company mines. Best are Buckwheat dump outside Franklin and the Trotter dump.

  BLUE APATITE: In Atlas quarry.
- *Hawthorne, Passaic County* AGATE: In Braen's quarry.
- *Lambertville, Hunterdon County* PREHNITE, DATOLITE: In quarry to S on River Road.
- *Montville, Morris County* * SERPENTINE: Take U.S. 202 W to sign for Valhalla Lake. Turn up hill to a left turn between stone gate posts marked Valhalla Lake. Continue on hardtop road N and around lake for a mile to a brook. Park here and walk up a wagon road parallel to brook to a fork. Take left-hand trail for 130 paces. Here, a faint trail leads to the left ¼ mile to the top of the mountain and to a large white boulder. The dump is a few feet beyond. Yellow to green translucent serpentine in dump.

- *Neptune City, Monmouth County* AMBER: In marl along Shark River.
- *Paramus, Bergen County* GARNET: At Green farm.
- *Phillipsburg, Warren County* GREEN SERPENTINE: At Royal Green marble quarry. Go NE to Harmony, take road to right marked Harmony Station, go 2 miles to quarry dumps.
- *Rudetown, Sussex County* DIOPSIDE, SERPENTINE: Take Quarry road to narrow bridge, cross and turn right to Edison quarry. Permission needed.
- *Sewell, Gloucester County* AMBER: In tributary of Mantua creek.
- *Sparta, Sussex County* UNAKITE: In dump S along Hwy 15.
- *Summit, Essex County* AGATE, PREHNITE, AMETHYST: In Houdaille Construction Materials Quarry.
- *Trenton, Mercer County* BLACK JASPER: N 9 miles on Hwy 29 in Delaware River at Washington Crossing State Park.

  AMBER: 4 miles S in lignite at Crosswicks Creek.

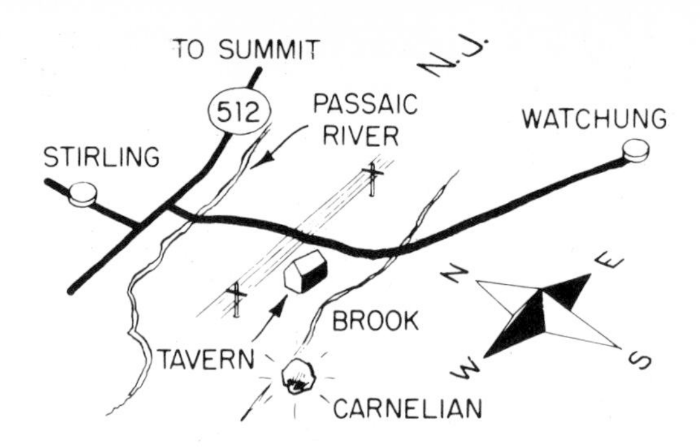

• *Watchung, Somerset County* * CARNELIAN, QUARTZ: Route 512 from Summit intersects the road S to Watchung just E of the road N to Stirling. Turn S on the Watchung Road. Cross the Passaic River, and go almost 2 miles toward Watchung to a power line over the road and past a tavern beside a brook. Park here and follow the brook S ¼ mile. Dig in the green sand about 18 inches down for carnelian and quartz crystal. It is convenient to dam off a bit of the bank, dig, and wash the sand in a screen.

New Mexico

New Mexico lies at the southern end of the Rocky Mountains, the Sangre de Cristo range extending down into the state from Colorado. Through the central part of the state, short chains of mountains run to the Mexican border, while another group parallels the Rio Grande River to the west. Plateaus cut by canyons form the borders with Texas and Arizona, and long plateaus lie between the central mountains. New Mexico owes its great variety of mineral and gem wealth to these exposures of many kinds of rock.

• *Abiquiu, Rio Arriba County* AGATE, PETRIFIED WOOD: Along Chama River and in hills ¼ mile N.

• *Albuquerque, Bernalillo County* PETRIFIED WOOD: Take road N across mesa toward old craters to the rim of the Rio Puerco valley. Collect on rim.

JASPER NODULES: W on Int. 40 15 miles to Rio Puerco bridge, turn N 16 miles in Rio Puerco valley, then left into low hills.

RED MOSS AGATE: W on Int. 40 to Rio Puerco bridge, go on further to white sign, turn N ½ mile to windmill, take side road to a white bluff.

RED AGATE, JASPER: NE on Int. 25 for 25 miles, then S up Tonque Arroya to old clay pit. Collect to S of pit.

UNAKITE: Through area traversed by Int. 40 on S slopes of Sandia mountains as far as Tijeras.

• *Aleman, Sierra County* PETRIFIED WOOD, AGATE: S to within mile of Dona Ana county line, then E toward Point of Rocks.

• *Ancho, Lincoln County* JASPER: N 2 miles.

• *Artesia, Eddy County* * QUARTZ (PECOS DIAMONDS): See Roswell entry.

• *Bernardo, Socorro County* OPALIZED WOOD: E on U.S. 60 3 miles, search banks of Rio Grande for gray wood.

• *Buell Park, McKinley County* * PYROPE GARNET, PERIDOT: The garnet area extends into three states.
Garnet Ridge lies close to the Utah border, and a few miles W of Mexican Water, Apache County, Arizona.

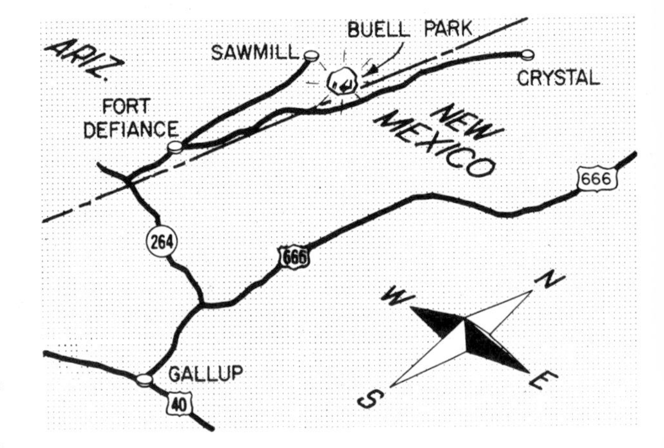

Ten miles N of Mexican Water, in San Juan County, Utah, is the Moses Rock field.
Best known of the areas, however, is Buell Park, a basin almost on the Arizona–New Mexico line and 10 miles N of Ft. Defiance. The garnets and peridot are found in the soil, and, to a lesser degree, W and N of Red Lake, and E and S of the lake to the edge of the Nacimiento desert. (Permission to collect in Indian reservation should be obtained at Chinle or Window Rock.)

• *Caballo, Sierra County* RHODONITE: Take Hwy 90 W to Hillsboro and collect at Comstock mine 10 miles W.

• *Cebolla, Rio Arriba County* AGATE NODULES: In canyon to E, take dirt road 2 miles S of Cebolla.

• *Cerrillos, Santa Fe County* PETRIFIED WOOD: At Sweet's ranch 3 miles E, and Keith ranch, which is E from Hwy 10 at ranch sign (fee).

TURQUOISE: Take Hwy 10 S for 12 miles, turn on to dirt road to dumps W at Mt. Chalchihuitl and to N at Castilian and Tiffany mines. (May be off limits.)

• *Chaco Canyon, McKinley County* JASPER: Just to N.

• *Columbus, Luna County* HONEY ONYX: At mine 4 miles W on N side of Hwy 9 (fee).

PURPLE AGATE: W on Hwy 9 20 miles and collect just E of railroad station in Hermanas.

DUMORTIERITE: In quartz, 13 miles NW in Tres Hermanas Mountains.

• *Cuba, Sandoval County* PETRIFIED WOOD: Along Hwy 44 to W and from Hwy 44 S in Rio Puerco.

• *Deming, Luna County* AGATE NODULES: Generally to S between Florida and Little Florida mountains. Specific locations, most of which charge fees for collecting, follow:
On Spanish Stirrup ranch 5 miles E on Int. 10
On Spaulding property to SE.
At Baker ranch on Hwy 11.
At the Lindberg claims on Hilborn and Gore ranches. Take Hwy 11 for 8 miles S to Hermanas road, then E and S 30 miles to nodule beds.
Free collecting at the Rockhound State Park. Go S on Hwy 11, take road E to park for agate, carnelian, and amethyst in geodes.

CARNELIAN: Hwy 26 NE for 5 miles and then N on Cooks Peak road for 5 miles. Hunt in hills E of road and S of Cooks Peak.

• *Domingo, Sandoval County* JASPER, OPALIZED WOOD: Hwy 22 N 1½ miles, take right fork, pass Cochita Pueblo and take gravel road N and then W past Tent Rocks to Peralta Lookout. From there go 4 miles to Peralta Canyon and up canyon ¼ mile. Walk ½ mile N to tributary. Collect in it and along E side of canyon. Return to road, continue ½ mile, collect seam agate in ravine, and just beyond road is opalized wood in another ravine.

• *Eagle Nest, Colfax County* AGATE, APATITE: Take U.S. 64 to Mexican Gulch, which is first side canyon from Palisades and on right side of Cimarron Canyon.

• *Engle, Sierra County* TUBE AGATE: W 8 miles N on side of railroad tracks.

PETRIFIED WOOD: In hills ½ mile W near road and to S as far as Cutter.

• *Ft. Sumner, DeBaca County* RED AGATE: N on U.S. 84 to Hwy 203, cross dam, turn N to fork, take W fork a mile to shallow valley.

• *Galisteo, Santa Fe County* JASPER: Along Galisteo River near Kennedy.

• *Glorieta, Santa Fe County* PETRIFIED WOOD: Along Glorieta River.

• *Grants, Valencia County* OBSIDIAN: Hwy 547 NE for 7½ miles past U.S. Gypsum mine sign, then less than a mile to dirt road W. Take it a mile and then S to fence. Collect to W outside fence on public land.

• *Hachita, Grant County* TURQUOISE: At Turquoise Montain 6 miles W on Hwy 9.

• *Hatch, Dona Ana County* MOSS OPAL: Drive S, then hike to diversion dam and dig opal from seams in side of arroyo.

OPALIZED WOOD: To W of Hatch over wide area N and W.

GREEN ALABASTER (ONYX): S 1½ miles on Mammoth Creek.

RHYOLITE (WONDERSTONE): At S end of Caballo Mountains.

• *Laguna, Valencia County* AGATE: Along Rio San Jose.

• *La Madera, Rio Arriba County* NODULES: Turn right at general store across bridge and take Petaca road (Hwy 519) N for 1¾ miles to collect in mica mine.

• *La Union, Dona Ana County* PERIDOT: Take road W across Hwy 273 and continue about 7 miles W across railroad tracks, then follow road along tracks NW for 4 miles to a siding called Lanark. Turn W here for 8 miles to Kilbourne Hole.

• *Las Cruces, Dona Ana County* PETRIFIED WOOD: Along Hwy 478 S.

FELDSPAR, PSILOMELANE, JASPER: Hwy 25 up Rio Grande valley for 31 miles to rail crossing; ½ mile farther is dirt dam. Collect to N of it in hills.

• *Lordsburg, Hidalgo County* AGATE NODULES: NW on U.S. 70 10 miles, turn W at ranch sign, go 20 miles to ranch house for permission to collect N about 3 miles.

FIRE AGATE, CARNELIAN: U.S. 70 NW for 25 miles, then take road SW for 18 miles, keeping to left at all forks, then turn right to Harry Day ranch. Collect at Round mountain (in Arizona).

• *Los Lunas, Valencia County* RED AGATE, JASPER: W on Hwy 6 16 miles. Collect in gravel along E side of river and to N of road.

AGATE, OBSIDIAN: Hwy 6 W for 9 miles to sign ¼ mile E of railroad overpass, turn S to Dalies and continue S, keeping right at all forks for 6 miles to Rio Puerco rim.

• *Luna, Catron County* AGATE: In San Francisco river N of Alpine and N, NE, and NW of Luna. One location is N of Luna 2 miles to road fork, take left fork 9 miles to road to left. Look here and along the road.

• *Magdalena, Socorro County* BLUE SMITHSONITE: On dumps of Kelly Mine 3 miles SE and also in the Graphic mine nearby (both fee).

PETRIFIED PALM WOOD: Take road N for 16 miles, then left on ranch road through ranch yard and 6 miles farther to collect in Bear Mountains area.

MOSS AGATE: Go 20 miles W on U.S. 60, then S 9 miles and turn right and go 27 miles to Farr ranch.

• *Mule Creek, Grant County* OBSIDIAN: W on Hwy 78 at Arizona line for silver sheen obsidian.

• *Orogrande, Otero County* TURQUOISE: To N in mines near Turquois.

• *Petaca, Rio Arriba County* BLUE BERYL: At Sunnyside Mine 3 miles S.

AMAZONITE, GARNET, QUARTZ: Take road to La Madera S for 3½ miles and W for 1½ miles; collect in dump of Cribbenville mine and nearby old pegmatite mines.
Also take Sawmill road W to old mines and prospects and N into La Jerita Canyon to other diggings.

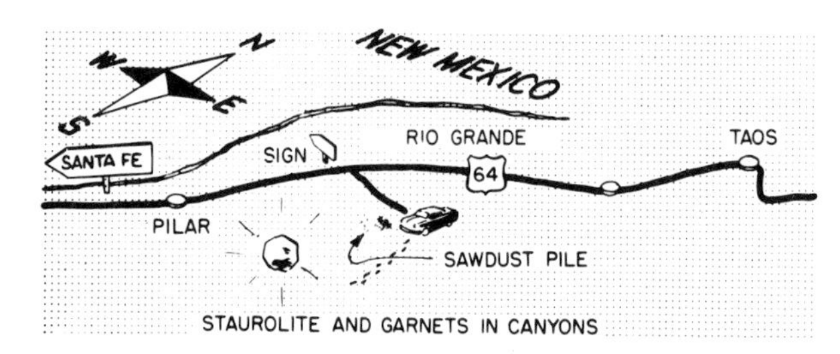

• *Pilar, Taos County* * STAUROLITE, GARNET: Just N of the hamlet of Pilar on the left side of Hwy 64 is a sign pointing out the Rio Grande Gorge. Continue 2 miles past this sign, then turn right into a dirt road and go 3 miles to a big sawdust heap. Park and take right-hand trail into Hondo Canyon. In this canyon and those to the S (Piedras Lumbres, Tierra Amarila and Agua Caliente Canyons) staurolites are plentiful in the schist, along with small garnets.

THULITE: In pegmatite, just S of Pilar on E bank of Rio Grande.

BERYL, LEPIDOLITE: S on U.S. 64, E on Hwy 75 7½ miles, then ½ mile S to Harding mine. (Permission is needed.)

• *Playas, Hidalgo County* CHALCEDONY, AGATE: W at dry lake and S of road.

• *Portales, Roosevelt County* PETRIFIED WOOD: SW 68 miles on Hwy 70 to Bob Crosby Draw, go back 2½ miles and take dirt road S into Bitterlake wildlife refuge. Collect in hills.

• *Quemado, Catron County* CHALCEDONY ROSES, PETRIFIED WOOD: N 40 miles at Zuni Salt Lake.

• *Radium Springs, Dona Ana County*
OPAL NODULES, SEAM OPAL: To N in Broad Canyon W of Hwy 85.

• *Ramon, Lincoln County* AGATE, JASPER: E 8 miles.

• *Redrock, Grant County* SERPENTINE (RICOLITE): Take road N across Gila River to first road E, follow it for 3 miles to Ash Creek canyon. A half mile W of main vein of green serpentine is one of yellow serpentine.

• *Raton, Colfax County* AMBER: In coal at Sugarite mine.

• *Red Hill, Catron County* AGATE, JASPER: Go N about 12 miles to windmill and red hill and collect on hillsides to NE.

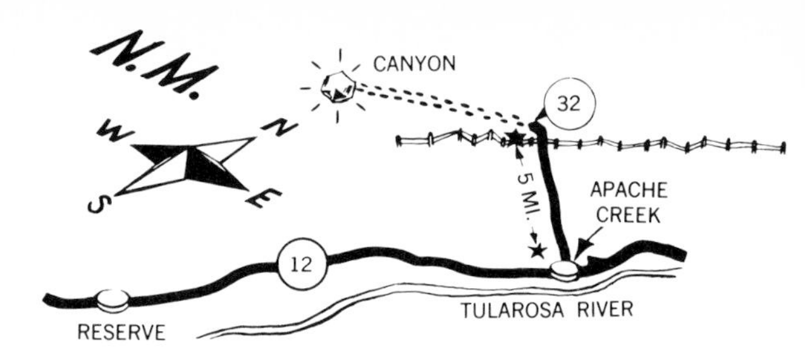

• *Reserve, Catron County* * BANDED AGATE: Take Hwy 12 for 11 miles NE to Apache Creek; then take Hwy 32 NW for 5 miles to national forest fence. Park above fence, take trail to left to Lee Russell Canyon until it widens out into a flat, which is the best collecting area.
Also in hills N of highway and W of Apache Creek.

FELDSPAR (BYTOWNITE): W on Hwy 12 to U.S. 180, then S 6 miles to road toward Blue, Ariz. Search on mesa S of Pueblo Forest Campground for yellow faceting feldspar.

• *Rincon, Dona Ana County* GEM FELDSPAR, JASPER: Drive N on W side of railroad tracks and 2 miles into hills toward television tower. Collect between dam and new highway.

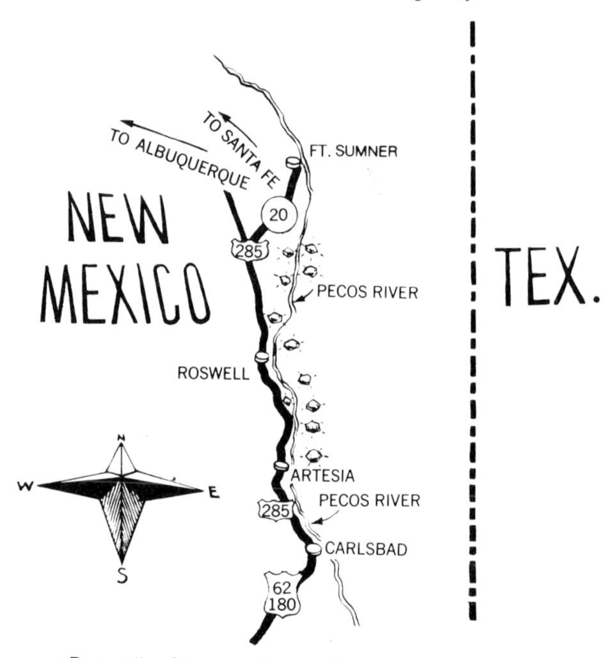

• *Roswell, Chaves County* * QUARTZ (PECOS DIAMONDS): In soil along Pecos River and in its gravels generally from Carlsbad to Ft. Sumner. Specifically in hills W of river from Carlsbad to Artesia and on both sides of river to Roswell and Hwy 70, then over a cone-shaped area from Hwy 285 NE to Ft. Sumner. One good place is at Lake State Park SE of Roswell.

- *Santa Fe, Santa Fe County* RED JASPER, NODULES: Hwy 85 S for 30 miles, then E 7 miles up Tonque wash.

  AGATE, OPALITE: 12 Miles SW at La Cienega as float in hills 2 miles to S.
- *Sheep Springs, San Juan County* NODULES: In Washington Pass to W.
- *Silver City, Grant County* MOONSTONE (SANADINE): Hwy 80 E to Noonday Canyon sign in Gila National Forest. Take canyon road, make hard left downgrade and park to continue in jeep beyond stream crossing and park. Take trail into Rabb Canyon to N to where stream splits and follow W side of N branch to a corral to dig. Another site ½ mile NW up small stream from left.

  AGATE, NODULES, CHALCEDONY: 8 miles N of Sapillo creek W of Hwy 15 and S of Gila Cliff Dwellings National Monument.
- *Socorro, Socorro County* DENDRITIC AGATE: Take Int. 25 N for 13 miles to San Acacia. Take frontage road 1½ mile W, then road W into arroya for 3 miles into canyon.

  AMETHYST: Take Int. 25 across Rio Salado, follow ranch roads W, and collect on SW slopes of Ladrones Peak.

  OPALIZED WOOD: Continue N past the Rio Salado, and turn W before crossing Rio Puerco. Bear left around Ladron Peak after crossing cattle guard, passing broken windmill and cow skull nailed to tree, and go 1½ miles farther. Collect on both sides of road.
- *Tres Piedras, Taos County* OBSIDIAN: Hwy 285 for 7 miles N, then E to collect obsidian nodules (Apache tears) in perlite beds.
- *Truth and Consequences, Sierra County*

  OPALIZED WOOD: Along Rio Grande to N at Nogal Canyon.

  AGATE: Take U.S. 85 S to Hwy 90, turn W through Hillsboro and just past Perchas Creek to collect N of road on side and top of mountain.

  RHYOLITE (WONDERSTONE): To NW at Ellis claims and on E side of Cabollo Lake, reached by taking road N 1¼ mile after crossing dam.
  Also at Eagle Peak 20 miles SW on Chavez road.

  YELLOW AND BROWN PETRIFIED WOOD: In swamp at S end of Elephant Butte reservoir.
- *Tyrone, Grant County* TURQUOISE: In creeks and dumps all the way S to Leopold.
- *Valle Grande, Sandoval County* OBSIDIAN: In headwaters of Jemez River.
- *Wagon Mound, Mora County* AGATE, JASPER: Few miles E.
- *Winston, Sierra County* AMETHYSTINE QUARTZ: In Montezuma mine dumps at Chloride.
- *Youngsville, Rio Arriba County* VARICOLORED AGATE: From Hwy 96 turn SE on road to Canones, look for spotted agate along road and to W of Abiquiu Dam.

New York

More than half of New York State is a plateau sweeping down from the Adirondacks in the northeast and underlain by very old sedimentary rocks. The Adirondacks, however, are formed of crystalline rocks like the Laurentians in Canada. The central plateau rises from Lake Erie and Lake Ontario, becoming mountainous in the south and east, where the Appalachians enter the state, and where the plateau has been carved into the Catskill Mountains. The topography of lower New York is like that of New Jersey, except that Long Island is a part of the coastal plain.

- *Balmat, St. Lawrence County* APATITE: At Gouverneur Talc mine.
- *Bedford, Westchester County* ASTERIATED ROSE QUARTZ: Take Hwy 22 S, turn off on road to Greenwich, Conn., take first dirt road N and follow around old quarry to dump at mill ruins.
- *Blooming Grove, Orange County* BLOODSTONE: To S on Hwy 94 at Craigsville.
- *Canadice, Ontario County* LABRADORITE: On E side of Canadice Lake and 2 miles W of Honeoye Lake.
- *Clintonville, Clinton County* JASPER: Take Harkness road across first railroad tracks, just before reaching second tracks turn left up steep hill to Arnold mine. Collect jasper with martite in dumps.
- *DeKalb, St. Lawrence County* MOONSTONE, DIOPSIDE, BROWN TOURMALINE: In old marble quarries and to S at Richville. Also 5 miles SE at former Mitchell farm in talc.
- *Edwards, St. Lawrence County* HAUYNITE: In pockets in St. Joe Minerals Corp. mine.
- *Fonda, Montgomery County* * QUARTZ (HERKIMER DIAMONDS): Fonda and Middleville are the two areas where rocks are found containing the glittering quartz crystals known as Herkimer diamonds. There are several collecting sites near Fonda. Take Exit 28 from the New York State Freeway at Fultonville, cross bridge to Fonda, continue to creek and beyond it, take the first road right, Hickory Hill road, go right to Martin road to Stone Arabia road at left, cross England road and the Diamond Acres mine is at left (fee).
  S of Fonda at Exit 28, take Hwy 55 SW to Sprakers. This is a fee area, as most of the others, but there is a free area 1 mile E of Sprakers on the S side of Hwy 55 on the crest of a hill known as Little Nose.
- *Geneseo, Livingston County* CORAL: Silicified material is to be found 3 miles N in banks and bed gravels of a creek.

- *Gouverneur, St. Lawrence County* TOURMALINE, APATITE: Brown tourmaline and red and brown apatite in old quarries.
- *Johnsburg, Warren County* SERPENTINE: In asbestos mine to SW at Garnet Lake.
- *Keeseville, Clinton County* SERPENTINE: At Buttermilk Falls.
- *Malone, Franklin County* SUNSTONE: Take road SE to Owl's Head Village and make inquiry there for trail up mountain to iron mine. Collect in dumps.
- *Middleville, Herkimer County* * QUARTZ (HERKIMER DIAMONDS): Middleville is one of the two major areas for collecting the brilliant quartz crystals known as Herkimer diamonds. There are several collecting areas, mostly open for a fee.
  The Ace of Diamonds collecting area is within the village limits on Hwy 28, and a mile S on Hwy 28 is the Atty area known as the Herkimer Diamond Grounds. Several other collecting areas have at one time or another been open N and NW of Middleville.

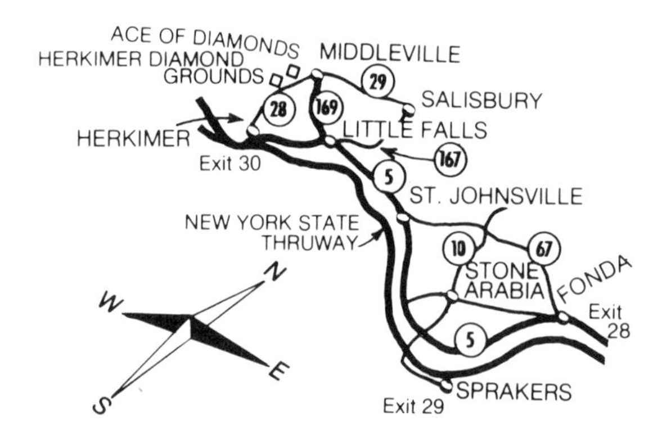

- *Mineville, Essex County* SUNSTONE: At Fisher Hill Mine.
- *Newcomb, Essex County* MOONSTONE, BROWN TOURMALINE: On S shore of Lake Harris.
- *North Creek, Warren County* ALMANDINE GARNET: Take Hwy 28 N for 4 miles, turn at Barton Mines sign, go 5 miles up Gore Mountain to shop.
- *Olmstedville, Essex County* MOONSTONE: 1 mile W on road to Minerva; pit is in outcrop on S side of road.
- *Pierrepont, St. Lawrence County* BLACK TOURMALINE: At Powers Tourmaline Diggings ½ mile W on Hwy 68 (fee).
  Also at West Pierrepont.
- *Plattsburgh, Clinton County* MARBLE: Take Grand Island ferry S to Hwy 2 and SE to quarry for scenic "zebra" marble.
- *Port Henry, Essex County* ROSE QUARTZ: NW 6 miles.
- *Port Kent, Essex County* LABRADORITE: Along shore to S.
- *Rochester, Monroe County* AGATE: In limestone along E bank of Genesee River near Norton Street and past Avenue E.
- *St. Johnsville, Montgomery County* * QUARTZ (HERKIMER DIAMONDS): At Crystal Grove campsite. Take Division Street, go 4½ miles to Crystal Grove, take right fork to Lassallsville and to picnic grove (fee).
- *Saranac Lake, Franklin County* MOONSTONE: Take Hwy 3 N for 4 miles to Leib's rock shop. Drive up hill and park and take trail to moonstone mine (fee).

  LABRADORITE: Along Indian Pass road off Kiwassa road.
- *Saratoga Springs, Saratoga County* CHRYSOBERYL: In pegmatite dike, 12 miles W of road intersection on Hwy 9 N of Saratoga Springs.

  QUARTZ CRYSTALS: In Maple Avenue (Gailor) quarry on W side of Hwy 9 on N edge of city.
- *Star Lake, St. Lawrence County* SILLIMANITE: In Benson mines to E.
- *Wading River, Long Island, Suffolk County* AGATE, JASPER: In beach pebbles at Wildwood State Park.
- *Wells, Hamilton County* LABRADORITE: In anorthosite boulders to N along Hwy 8 in E branch of Sacandaga River.
- *West Chazy, Clinton County* FOSSIL LIMESTONE: In old quarry.
- *Wolcott, Wayne County* LARVIKITE (FOSSIL LIMESTONE): Take new Hwy 104 to Hwy 414, then left on old Hwy 104, go N toward Lake Ontario, then right on Lummisville road to East Bay road and left on it to Chimney Bluff road to lake. Park and collect along shore. Epidote is also present there.

North Carolina

The eastern half of North Carolina is the low-lying coastal plain extending to the fall line, which divides it from the Piedmont plateau, a somewhat elevated level region containing the principal cities of the state. In the western part of the state the Blue Ridge escarpment rises abruptly to define the Appalachian Mountains, which in North Carolina form the greatest mountain mass in the eastern United States. In the varied rocks of these mountains are found most of the gem minerals in the state.

- *Alexis, Gaston County* RUTILE: At Lowe farm on Chubb Mountain on Hwy 27 between Lincolnton and Charlotte.

  KYANITE, LAZULITE, RUTILE: As float in fields 1½ miles E.
- *Bakersville, Mitchell County* GREEN FELDSPAR, THULITE, MOONSTONE: At Hawk Mine 1 mile N by road in Cave Creek valley. Also 12 miles NW on Hwy 261 at Roan Mountain Flower Garden and 12 miles NE on road to right at fork N of Bakersville.

  UNAKITE: N 10 miles at Roan Mountain.

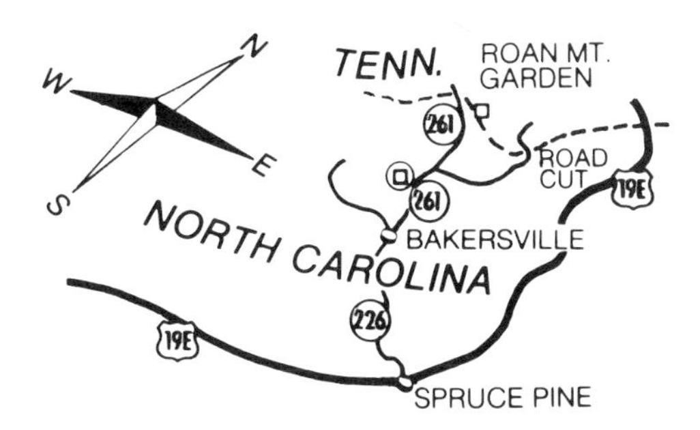

SUNSTONE: A mile N at Medlock Mountain.

KYANITE: SE 4 miles on Hwy 226 in quartz near top of Yellow Mountain.

- *Balsam Gap, Buncombe County* KYANITE: S on Hwy 276 to Balsam Gap, then 1½ mile SE. Also on Lookout Mountain.
- *Bayleaf, Wake County* SOAPSTONE (STEATITE): W to Hwy 50, then 2 miles to Barton Creek crossing.
- *Beaver Creek, Ashe County* GOLDEN BERYL: At South Hardin Mica mine, 1½ miles SW on hill. Beryl is in the footwall of a pegmatite.
- *Bluff, Madison County* UNAKITE: On Roaring Fork Creek, ½ mile W of its junction with Meadow Fork, 2 miles SW of Bluff; also ⅓ mile N of Bluff.
- *Brasstown, Clay County* * STAUROLITE (FAIRY CROSSES): In bank along gravel road and nearby pastures and in matrix on mountainside. Get permission from Robert Trout to collect except along the road.

- *Bryson City, Swain County* KYANITE, STAUROLITE: 1½ mile N of Deep Creek campground, in schist.
- *Burch Station, Surry County* BLUE JASPER: On C. Greenwood farm 1½ miles off Hwy 268 to E, also along Yadkin River.
- *Burnsville, Yancey County* * AQUAMARINE, GOLDEN AND GREEN BERYL, AMAZONSTONE: Some of the best aquamarine in North Carolina comes from the Ray Mine. From Burnsville go E on Hwy 19E to traffic light opposite a funeral home. Turn S toward Pensacola for 1½ miles to a fork. Take left fork and go 1½ miles to a church on right-hand side of road. Opposite this church, a jeep road leads one mile to the mine.

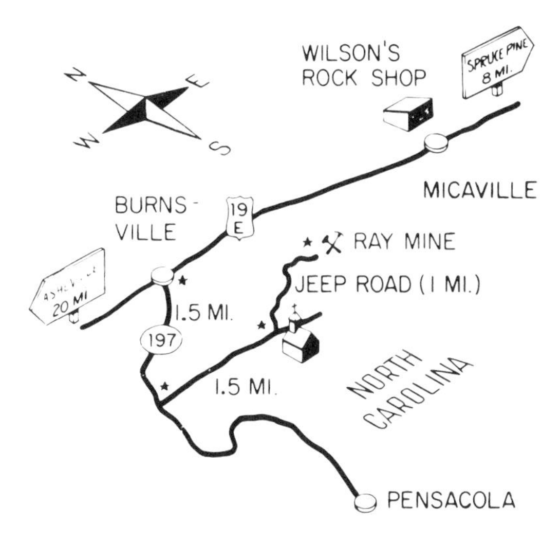

- *Canton, Buncombe County* CORUNDUM: At Pressley Corundum mine. Take Main street to Newfound street, turn left across Int 40, left again at first road past church, and left again on first gravel road. Pay fee at second house on left, mine is at end of next road left.
- *Casar, Cleveland County* RUTILATED QUARTZ: As float on ground 2 miles W and S.

  BERYL: At Elliott mine 3½ miles SW.
- *Cashiers, Jackson County* SAPPHIRE: 7 miles SE in Whitewater mine on Whitewater River.

  RUBY: E 7 miles on south shore of Sapphire Lake at Bad Creek mine.

  AQUAMARINE: At Rice mine.
- *Centerville, Franklin County* AMETHYST: SW on Hwy 561 to Taylor farm.
- *Cranberry, Avery County* EPIDOTE, GARNET, KYANITE: At Cranberry Iron mine 1 mile S.
- *Danbury, Stokes County* CARNELIAN: In gravels of the Dan River.
- *Dysartsville, McDowell County* CORUNDUM: 1 1/5 mile SE in stream on Mills farm on N side of Hwy 26.
- *Ellenboro, Rutherford County* ROSE QUARTZ, BERYL: Turn right on paved road off U.S. 74 W of Ellenboro, go a mile and then right to Dycus mine.
- *Franklin, Macon County* *

  The Franklin area is the most popular collecting area in North Carolina. Besides the diggings that charge a fee to allow collectors to wash gravel for ruby and sapphires, there are many other mines which offer a wide variety of gem materials.

  RUBY, SAPPHIRE: Take Hwy 28 N for 7 miles to the Cowee Creek road E at West's Mill. Follow road 2½ miles and then follow signs along gravel road to mines.

  Take Hwy 28 N 4 miles to Burningtown road, turn W 8 miles to Burningtown. From there take trail to Roy Mason's mine (fee).

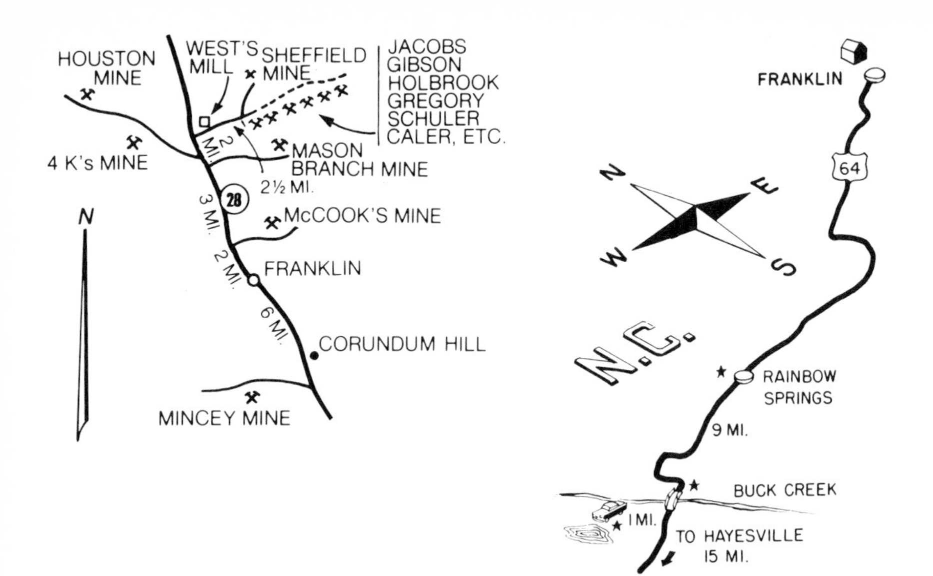

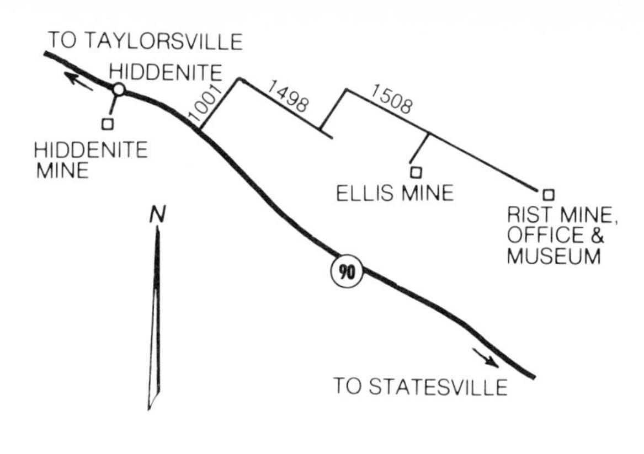

CORUNDUM, ENSTATITE, PERIDOT: 6 miles SE on Hwy 28 to the Cullasaja mine at Corundum Hill (fee).

PYROPE, GARNET, RUBY IN SMARAGDITE: SW on Hwy 64 to Rainbow Springs, then 9 miles to bridge where Buck creek crosses highway. Turn right at bridge and go mile to another bridge. Park and hike up mountain to outcrops.

MOONSTONE: N 5 miles on Hwy 28, right to head of valley to Mason Mountain.

AMETHYST, AQUAMARINE: S 9 miles on Hwy 441 to Otto, E 3/5 mile to Long and Connally Mines at Tessentee Creek.

AQUAMARINE: 10 miles E at Sheep Knob Mountain.

GARNET, SAPPHIRE: One of the most reliable locations for rhodolite garnet, one of the distinctive North Carolina minerals, is at the Mason Branch Mine formerly known as the Ried mine.
Take Hwy 28 NW from Franklin 5 miles to Mason Branch sign pointing to mine. Take road ¼ mile to mine.
Rhodolite garnet is also found at McCook's mine to E of Hwy 28 2 miles N of Franklin, and star garnet at the 4K's mine to W of Hwy 28 on the Rose Creek road. Sapphire is also found at Houston's mine beyond the 4K's mine.

STAR CORUNDUM: 3 miles SE to Ellijay road; take it 3½ miles along Ellijay creek to Ellijay, turn right in town and right again to the Mincey mine. Gems have bronzy luster.

• *Gibsonville, Guilford County* GREEN QUARTZ: With inclusions of asbestos.

• *Hiddenite, Alexander County* * EMERALD, QUARTZ: Take Hwy 1001 N from Hwy 90, then right on Hwy 1498 and left on Hwy 1508 and follow signs to Rist mine on American Gems, Inc., diggings. Pay fee at office. On the way Hwy 1508 passes the Ellis mine, also owned by American Gems.

RUTILATED QUARTZ: Just S of the old Hiddenite mine and with beryl in dump of old Payne mine 1 mile S.

• *Highlands, Macon County* CORUNDUM: Hwy 106 SW 5½ miles to Scaly Mountain, search in mine dumps.

ALMANDINE GARNET: Hwy 64 E 3 miles, then take trail to Whiteside Mountain.

• *Hillsboro, Orange County* ANDALUSITE, LAZULITE, TOPAZ: At Piedmont Minerals mine.

• *Iron Station, Lincoln County* AMETHYST: N on Hwy 1314 to Hwy 73, turn right, then right on Hwy 1509, and right again on Hwy 1417. Pay fee at trailer and walk to digging area on Reel farm. Also nearby at Goodsen and Lynch farms.

• *Lexington, Davidson County* ORBICULAR GRANITE: W 10 miles and 1 mile W of Oaks Ferry on Yadkin River on Hairston farm.

• *Little Switzerland, Mitchell County* * EMERALD: Leave Blue Ridge Parkway at Little Switzerland exit, N on Hwy 1100 to Crabtree church, then 1 mile NE on Hwy 1104 to end of road, walk to Crabtree mine, dig in dumps. (Fee).

BERYL, THULITE, AMAZONSTONE: Return to Hwy 1104 and back to Hwy 1100–1104 to intersection, go W on Hwy 1100 to McKinney mine.

THULITE: Go W to Crabtree Road and N to sharp right curve on steep downward slope, take road left here ¾ mile to No. 20 mine.

• *Marble, Cherokee County* MARBLE: 1⅓ mile N in Hyatt creek, and 1 mile S in Valley River and on Bettis farm.

• *Marshall, Madison County* ALMANDINE GARNET: N 6 miles on Redmon Dam Road. Cross dam, turn right, go to forks, take left fork to Lone Pine Mine.

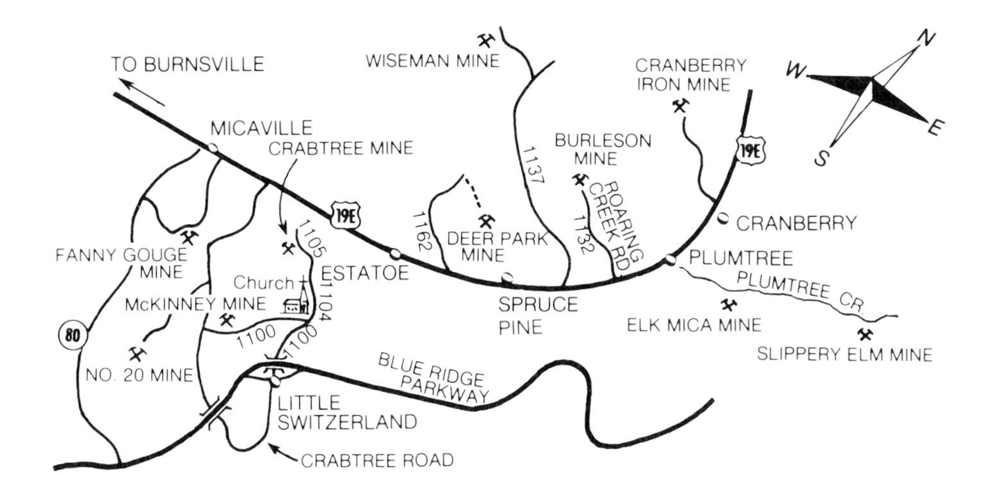

SMOKY QUARTZ, RUTILE: Hwy 74 W to second stoplight, take Hwy 1313 past fiber plant to next road, turn left, cross creek, drive to mill with waterwheel and collect behind it on hillside below mine.

GARNET, MOONSTONE: Hwy 74 past town to second stoplight, turn S to stop sign, continue straight ahead to old school, go W around construction to site.

• *Sparta, Alleghany County* RHODONITE: Hwy 18 NE for 3 miles, then W for ½ mile to fork, take W fork ⅓ mile, collect in dumps.

• *Spruce Pine, Mitchell County* * AQUAMARINE: The Grassy Creek Mine near Spruce Pine has been a producer of fine aquamarine. Go S from Spruce Pine on Hwy 226 for 3 miles, turn left at church on dirt road and go ½ mile to mine.

• *Micaville, Yancey County* * AQUAMARINE, GARNET: U.S. 19 E for 2 miles across South Toe River, take Blue Rock Road, the first graded road, S a mile to Fanny Gouge and Spec mines.

CORUNDUM: Hwy 80 S to Celo, collect in gravels of Toe river.

• *Morgantown, Burke County* GARNET: Go 5 miles S on Hwy 18 to Tweedy house on E side of road, pay fee and collect.

AQUAMARINE, GOLDEN BERYL: 8 miles S and ½ mile E of Walker to the Walker Prospect.

• *Murphy, Cherokee County* SMOKY QUARTZ: At Voiles Cabins off Route 290 on Hiawasee Dam road.

• *Plumtree, Avery County* * GARNET: 2 miles E at dumps of Elk Mica mine and Slippery Elm mine on Plumtree Creek.

MOONSTONE: 2 miles N of Roaring Creek road, at Burleson mine (fee).

• *Price, Rockingham County* QUARTZ, GARNET: U.S. 220 to road left that goes to Va. 692 at Virginia line, take it to Va. 691 to first dirt road, go left mile to Long Tom Smith mine. Also at Rosa Evans mine reached from Va. 691 by continuing a mile farther before turn-off.
Also at Clifton mine mile W at state line.

• *Raleigh, Wake County* AMETHYST: U.S. 64 E to Wilder's Grove, continue ½ mile, turn N a mile, and collect near the Neuse River.

• *Redmon, Madison County* ALMANDINE GARNET: 2 miles SW at mine on Little Pine creek.

• *Shelby, Cleveland County* EMERALD, RUTILATED QUARTZ: SW 5 miles on Hwy 18 to Stice Dam on the Broad River, then E 1½ miles to Turner mine on Allen property. Also at Old Plantation mine 1 mi NE of dam at bend in river.

QUARTZ: Hwy 18 S to Hwy 150, then W nearly 2 miles and S ½ mile. Also 1 mile S of Sharon Church.

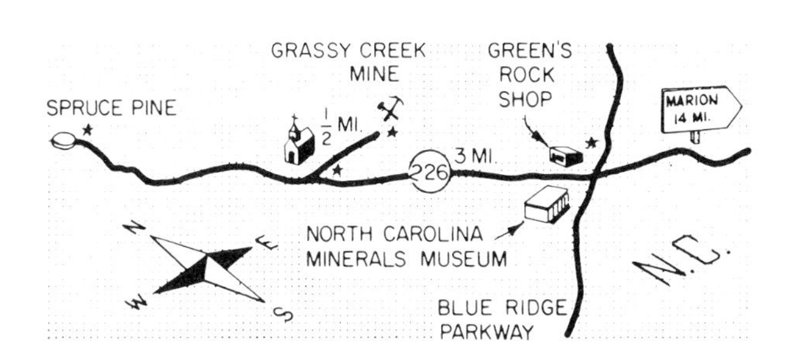

MOONSTONE: Go 13 miles E on Hwy 19E, then left on Rt. 1132 ½ mile.

KYANITE: On surface loose in soil of Young farm.

• *Statesville, Iredell County* AMETHYST: S 11 miles on Hwy 21. Collect in fields in vicinity of Sheperd's School and north to Oswalt and east to Smith Hill.

• *Valdese, Burke County* GARNET: At Tweedy's mine along Laurel creek.

• *Waynesville, Haywood County* * ROSE QUARTZ: An outstanding locality for rose quartz is Shining Rock ledge. E on Hwy 276 for 7 miles to Bethel. S through Sunburst to U.S. Forest Ranger station. Get permit and key to gate and drive 10 miles to Shining Rock.

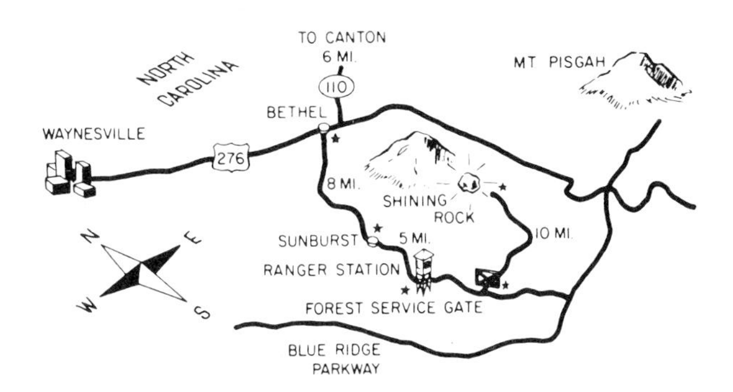

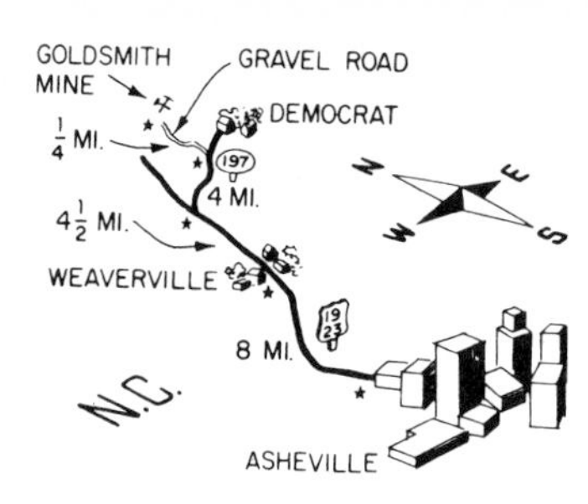

- *Weaverville, Buncombe County* * MOONSTONE: From traffic light go N on Hwy 19–23 for 4½ miles to junction with Hwy 197, then E on Hwy 197 4 miles and turn N on gravel road ¼ mile to Goldsmith mine.

  SERPENTINE: N 1⅔ miles to Pleasant Gap church, take next road E for ½ mile to mine on creek.

North Dakota

Eastern North Dakota lies in the level bed of the ancient Lake Agassiz, an area of rich farm land. To the west is a hilly plain, ridged with glacial moraines and dotted with lakes. An abruptly rising ridge separates this area from western North Dakota, which is part of the Missouri plateau, an almost unglaciated region of buttes and coulees culminating in the picturesque badlands. Petrified wood is found in the sandstones of the plateau, often associated with other quartz minerals.

- *Cartwright, McKenzie County* AGATE, PETRIFIED WOOD: Lime-coated agates in Little Missouri river gravels along with agatized wood.
- *Mandan, Morton County* PETRIFIED WOOD, AGATE: Worm-bored petrified wood and agate in gravel pits.
- *Medora, Billings County* PETRIFIED WOOD: In canyons S.
- *Minot, Ward County* JASPER: In gravel pits to S.
- *Mott, Hettinger County* PETRIFIED WOOD: In hills 11 miles NW along river.
- *Richardton, Stark County* CHALCEDONY: S 25 miles along Hwy. 8.
- *Tappan, Kidder County* AGATE: In gravel pits to E.
- *Watford City, McKenzie County* MOSS AGATE: In gravel pit ¾ mile E.
- *Williston, Williams County* MOSS AGATE, CHALCEDONY: On river bank near Hwy 85.

Ohio

Limestones and other sedimentary rocks underlie the state. They arch upward toward the west so that progressively younger rocks are exposed from west to east across the state. Most of the upper part of the state shows the typical appearance of midwestern glaciation. Fossils are abundant but, with one exception, gem materials are few.

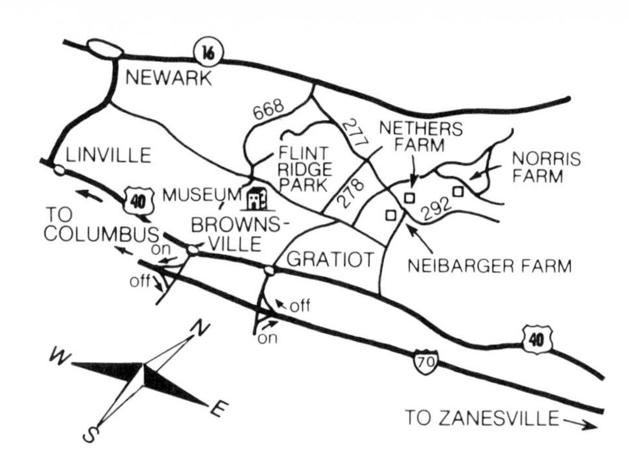

- *Flint Ridge* *FLINT: Flint Ridge is an area about 8 miles long and ¾ mile wide in Licking and Muskingum Counties of central Ohio. It was the site of ancient Indian diggings for flint for artifacts and of the workshops where the artifacts were chipped out. Near the center of the area and on Ohio 668 is the Flint Ridge Memorial Park. The best collecting is on the corn fields S and E of this park, but it is also worthwhile to explore all along the E-W road E of Hwy 668.

  Three favorite places to collect are on the John Nethers farm, the Neibarger farm, and the Norris farm, all E of Hwy 278 and near the intersection of Hwys 292 and 277. Explicit directions can be obtained at the small museum in the Flint Ridge park, which will introduce the collector to the nature of the flint deposit as well as the variety of the material itself. Collectors say that much well-colored flint has been picked up from the cornfields in the fall, when they are bare. There is a fee for admission to the park and for collecting at the several farms.

Oklahoma

Much of Oklahoma is rough and even mountainous. The Ozarks cross into the east central part of the state and die out in hills in the south central region occupied by a plateau known as the Arbuckle Mountains. Northwest of this area rise the steep Wichita Mountains and the Chautauqua Mountains. Northwest Oklahoma is part of the High Plains, and northeastern Oklahoma is a region of buttes and valleys carved from shales and sandstones. Despite this diversity of geological features, Oklahoma affords only a limited variety of gem minerals, mostly agate and petrified wood.

- *Ada, Pontotoc County* BLACK PETRIFIED WOOD: To S in Jack Fork and Canyon Creek.
- *Alva, Woods County* PETRIFIED WOOD, MOSS AGATE: To S and W.
- *Boise City, Cimarron County* AGATE: Take highway W toward Kenton to the Roberts ranch.

• *Buffalo, Harper County* AGATE: Go 3 miles S on Hwy 183 and then collect along highway for several miles.

AGATE, PETRIFIED WOOD: W on Hwy 64 for 3½ miles to Ed Price place; collect on hill ½ mile W of ranch house. Aragonite crystals are found in Buffalo creek here. Go on 4 miles, then N 3 miles for agate in road cut.

• *Camargo, Dewey County* AGATE, JASPER: At Ames gravel pit.

• *Dougherty, Murray County* PETRIFIED WOOD, AGATE: At Makins gravel pit.

• *Hobart, Kiowa County* QUARTZ CRYSTALS: In quarries near Altus Reservoir.

• *Hollis, Harmon County* AGATE, JASPER: N 10 miles at Wilkerson pit.

• *Idabel, McCurtain County* PETRIFIED WOOD, JASPER: NE 9 miles at Mountain Fork River.

• *Jet, Alfalfa County* AGATE: S ½ mile at Cherokee Creek pit.

• *Kenton, Cimarron County* JASPER: Red dotted material with milky agate 5 miles S.

• *Lugert, Kiowa County* PETRIFIED WOOD: Generally in area.

• *Newcastle, Cleveland County* AGATE, PETRIFIED WOOD: In Dolese gravel pit.

• *Oakwood, Dewey County* PETRIFIED WOOD: S 6 miles at Gooch gravel pit.

• *Okemah, Okfuskee County* AGATE, PETRIFIED WOOD: NE 13 miles at Coffman gravel pit.

• *Orion, Major County* AGATE: In canyons cutting old shore line in hills N of Hwy 60.

• *Rosston, Harper County* ARAGONITE: So-called dollars. On twin buttes 1 mile E of Hwy 283 and 7 miles N of junction of Hwy 283 with Hwy 64.

• *Seiling, Dewey County* PETRIFIED WOOD: SE 7 miles at Carney gravel pit.

• *Talihina, Le Flore County* CHERT: To S along highway.

• *Taloga, Dewey County* AGATE: S 4 miles at Lovett gravel pit.

• *Welch, Craig County* JASPER: In Bill Patch strip coal mine 8 miles W.

Oregon

The Cascade Mountains, many of them extinct volcanoes, divide Oregon north and south into two diverse regions. West of the mountains, the land is well watered and contains the fertile Willamette Valley lying east of the Coast range, which merges in the south with California's Klamath Mountains. The eastern part of the state is a high plateau, generally arid, rugged, and made up of lava and rock debris, a region of salt lakes and even desert. Most of southeastern Oregon falls into the Great Basin. Oregon is celebrated for the agate formed in its lavas and the petrified wood and obsidian also associated with volcanic rocks.

• *Adrian, Malheur County* (Also see Homedale and Marsing, Ida.) AGATE: Nodules are found in area to S along the irrigation canal with red petrified wood to W at Alkalin Lake. Canyon Road along Succor Creek passes diggings in the walls of the canyon S of Rockville.

• *Antelope, Wasco County,* AMETHYST, GREEN MOSS AGATE: Hwy 218 E toward Clarno, cross bridge, turn S at Antelope Agate Bed sign (fee).

RED JASPER: Mile E on Hwy 218, and ¼ mile S to old quarry.

• *Ashland, Jackson County* GREEN AGATE NODULES: E 7½ miles from Klamath Falls Junction on hills near road cut in Hwy 66.

AGATE: Along Jenny Creek near U.S. 66 in Goodsprings Mountain area.

• *Ashwood, Jefferson County* AGATE: A number of fee ranch diggings are nearby, including Norton ranch, 9 miles S, McDonald and Bedortha ranches just S, Swanson and Friend ranches to the north, Palmer's Eagle Ranch and Forman's Indian Creek ranch with Brown's ranch nearby, and the Keegan ranch to the E.

• *Austin, Grant County* AGATIZED FERN: NW 17 miles in creek beds from Susanville to Bates.

• *Baker, Baker County* OPALIZED WOOD, ALMANDINE GARNET: Near Pleasant Valley.

• *Bandon, Coos County* AGATE, PETRIFIED WOOD: To N at Bullards Beach State Park beach. Take Hwy 101 N to Seven Devils Road to sign to Whiskey Run beach. Here and to S is brown petrified wood. Seven Devils Wayside Park is 2 miles farther N, for agates in creek and on beach.

• *Bend, Deschutes County* OBSIDIAN: At Glass Buttes, from milepost 72 to Milepost 82 on U.S. 20. At milepost 79 take old road S into area, also at milepost 82. Another place to collect is reached by taking U.S. 97 S for 30 miles, then E and collect along road between Paulina Lake and East Lake.

• *Biggs, Sherman County* AGATE: At Fields farm 5 miles S on Hwy 97 (fee).

JASPER: Along E side of U.S. 97 2 miles S (private claim).

• *Brothers, Deschutes County* QUARTZ CRYSTAL: At Sugarloaf Mountain.

• *Brownsboro, Jackson County* * PETRIFIED WOOD, AGATE: Found W of the road NE from Brownsboro to Butte Falls and in the area E of the road and S of Butte Falls.

DENDRITIC AND CLEAR AGATE: In the desert 5 miles N of Medford and E of Hwy 62 in Antelope Creek and Little Butte Creek area.

MOSS AGATE, JASPER, QUARTZ CRYSTAL GEODES: In the area S and W of Crow Foot, both in the creeks and washes and on the hills.

PETRIFIED WOOD: At Table Rocks on the side of Table Rock Mountain.

• *Burns, Harney County* AGATE NODULES: E for 23

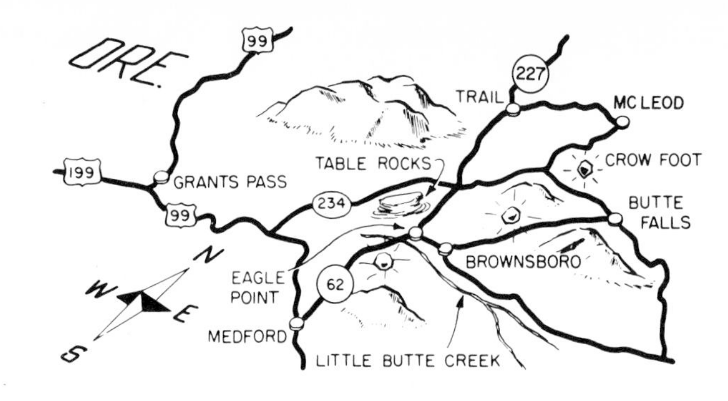

miles on Hwy 20, then 4 miles S of Buchanan, at Robbins thundereggs diggings (fee).

PETRIFIED WOOD: Take Hwy 20 E for 28 miles to Stinking Water Summit, then S for 4 miles on BLM road, and jeep trail left to diggings.

PLUME AGATE: Hwy 20 to milepost 167, at foot of hill on N side of road (fee).

PETRIFIED WOOD: Hwy 20 to milepost 168, cross creek on bridge, take road S 7 miles, turn W on jeep trail to top of hill above Clear Creek. Hike to next ridge beyond Clear Creek, back up and take first trail right to diggings.

PLUME AGATE: Take Hwy 20 E for 40 miles, then S 26 miles on county road toward Warms Springs reservoir, turn W and go through two washes to collect on top of hill.

AGATE: Take Hwy 78 E for 1½ miles, S on Hwy 205 past milepost 16, then W 2 miles and N 2 miles to Wright ranch for snakeskin agate. Continue to milepost 24 on Hwy 205, take road E to Malheur Wildlife Refuge and collect in pumice on both sides of road. Just N of the Refuge, turn W, go 1½ miles around Eagle's Nest cliff and uphill on back of it to collect oolite and petrified wood, especially to S.

PETRIFIED WOOD: Take Hwy 205 to milepost 32, collect around Saddle Butte E of road.

OPALIZED WOOD: 18 miles N on Hwy 395 and W 7 miles at Silvies Canyon.

- *Canyon City, Grant County* SERPENTINE (VERD ANTIQUE): to S along Canyon Creek.
- *Chenoweth, Wasco County* PETRIFIED WOOD: NW at Johnson ranch.
- *Corvallis, Benton County* CARNELIAN, JASPER: Take Hwy 99W, watch for Keiger Island sign, cross bridge and keep right for access to river and bars, collect in gravel bars in middle channel of Willamette River between Keiger and Smith Islands. Also generally on bars in river from N of Salem to S of Corvallis.
- *Crabtree, Linn County* PETRIFIED WOOD, JASPER: E 4 miles to Brewster Station, N 5 miles to schoolhouse, then left a mile and N a mile to farmhouse (fee).
- *Durkee, Baker County* CHALCEDONY: In Shirttail Creek.

  FIRE OPAL: To E where stream cuts through volcanic rocks.
- *Enterprise, Wallowa County* MARBLE: Black marble on Alder slope of Wallowa Mountains.
- *Estacada, Clackamas County* PETRIFIED WOOD, GREEN JASPER: In Clackamas River.
- *Gold Beach, Curry County* PETRIFIED WOOD: Follow road on S side of Rouge River 7 miles to Huntley Park to collect on river bar.

  AGATE: S on Hwy 101 to Lone Ranch State Park, collect at Rainbow Cove around point at S end of beach.
- *Hampton, Deschutes County* GREEN MOSS AGATE, JASPER, PETRIFIED WOOD: Take U.S. 20 NW, then N 10 miles to Hampton Butte. Collect at next butte W.
- *Harper, Malheur County* AGATE GEODES, OPALIZED WOOD: S 32 miles at Skull Springs.

  AGATE NODULES: S for 25 miles to Dryck, then W ½ mile to diggings.
- *Heppner, Morrow County* OPAL: At Opal Butte.
- *Holland, Josephine County* JASPER, MASSIVE GROSSULARITE GARNET: S 1½ miles in Althouse Creek.
- *Jamieson, Malheur County* PETRIFIED WOOD: Take road NE to Huntington sign, then 6 miles N to dig bogwood agate.
- *Lakeview, Lake County* BLUE AGATE: Take Hwy 395 S 4 miles and hike mile into hills.

  AGATE NODULES: S 5 miles in Crane Creek Canyon to E of Hwy 395.

  AGATE, PETRIFIED WOOD: W 36 miles on Hwy 140 at Quartz Mountain Pass.

  JASPER AND QUARTZ CRYSTALS: Take Hwy 395 S to New Pine Creek, then Fort Bidwell Road to summit. Collect in old mine tunnels.

  AGATE, ORBICULAR JASPER: In Bullard and Deadman canyons on outskirts.

  AGATE: In Dry Creek area to W.
- *Lebanon, Linn County* CARNELIAN: Take Hwy 20 S to Central Ave., then W on Sodaville Road to Tyler ranch (fee). Also at Moore diggings nearby.

  AGATE: Hwy 20 3 miles S, to Enco station, go on to stop sign, turn left on to Tin road, left again and next right to first gate on Tye road at Drummond Agate Beds (fee).
- *Madras, Jefferson County* AGATE NODULES: NE 17 miles on Hwy 97 almost to Willowdale, take road E to Priday ranch. [Diggings closed temporarily but agate for sale.]

  Just S of Priday ranch is the Kennedy ranch for petrified wood and nodules (fee). Just N is the Richardson ranch, where new thunderegg diggings are open.

(Left) Pyrite.
(Middle) Native copper on calcite.
(Right) Siderite from Seravezza, Lucca, Italy.

JASPER, NODULES: In Hay Creek area 11 miles E.

• *Maupin, Wasco County* AGATE: Take Hwy 216 16 miles W and then S to Sunflower Flats.

BLACK AGATE: In Deschutes River to N.

• *Medford, Jackson County* * GREEN JASPER: N on Hwy 62 to Hwy 234, then 1 mile farther and E on Butte Falls road 16 miles and S on Gunderson road to railroad tracks. Hike W to ravine to collect.
• *Newport, Lincoln County* BEACH AGATE AND JASPER: Dig at Beverly Beach just to N. Also generally N and S on other beaches.

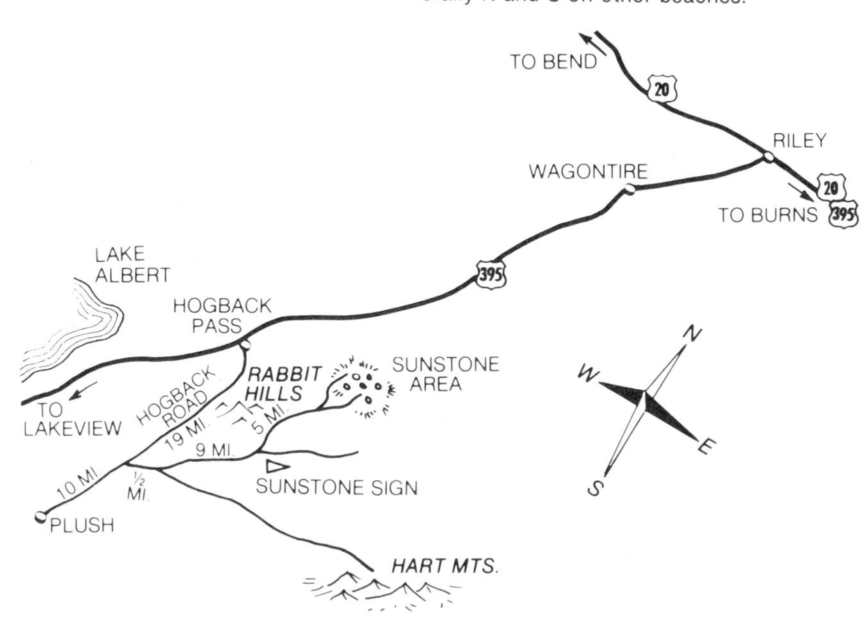

• *Oceanside, Tillamook County* SAGENITIC AGATE: N of Maxwell Point and elsewhere on nearby beaches with petrified wood and jasper.
• *Oregon City, Clackamas County* GREEN AND RED JASPER: In gravel bars of Clackamas River.
• *Plush, Lake County* * AVENTURINE LABRADORITE: Take road N 10 miles, go right ½ mile, take left fork NE 9 miles to fork, take left fork, go 5 miles, passing Rabbit Creek dam, hike ½ mile up dry wash to collect sunstone fragments in soil and decomposed basalt. The collecting area is in the Rabbit basin in Warner Valley.

CHALCEDONY NODULES: Go 9 miles N, take the right fork 18 miles to refuge headquarters and S to Hart Mountain area. Hike to top and collect nodules in slopes of five canyons facing W.

FIRE OPAL: Collect in basalt on W rim of canyons.

• *Prineville, Crook County* * Prineville has organized its numerous collecting spots into a tourist attraction with camping facilities and town-owned collecting areas. Some of them are:

DENDRITIC AND ANGEL WING AGATE: At Eagle Rock. Take Post (Combs Flat) Road 18 miles to Eagle Rock, turn right past rocks, and follow a sharp incline left 1¼ miles.

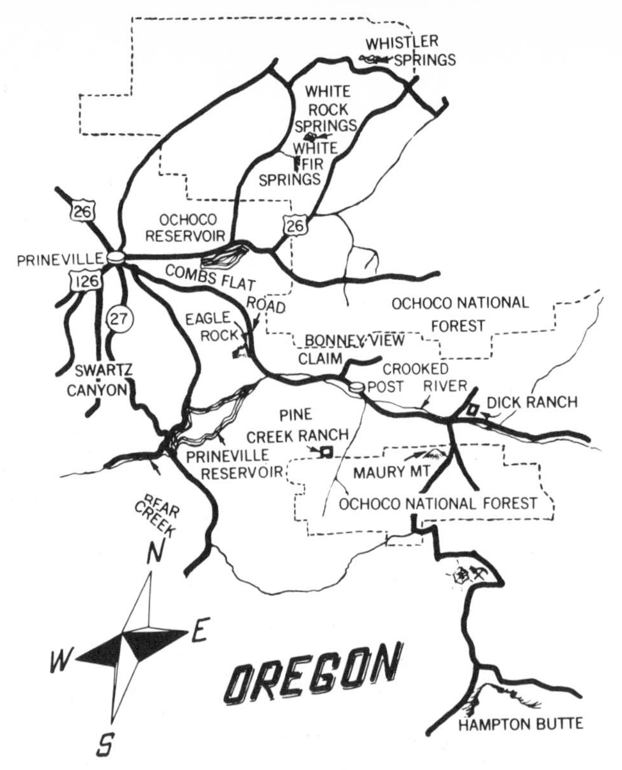

PETRIFIED WOOD: At Bonnieview ranch, 6 miles short of Post. (Fee, get directions at Recreation Unlimited in Prineville.)
Likewise for Dick ranch claim 14 miles past Post.

AGATE, PETRIFIED WOOD: E on Post Road mile past Post, right across bridge and left on Shotgun Road to Booton ranch (fee).

RED, GREEN AND MOSS AGATE: At Maury Mountain. E on Post Road 8 miles past Post to Milepost 33, turn right over wooden bridge, continue over 5 cattle guards to first road right past national forest sign, go a mile and then right a mile to diggings.

LIMB CASTS: At Milepost 43 on Crooked River Hwy, take Camp Creek Road S and then W to plateau. Dendritic and colored limb casts found in area between creeks both sides of S Fork of Crooked River.

MOSS AGATE: At Reservoir Heights. Take Juniper Canyon road SE to road just N of reservoir; follow it to end to collect.

PETRIFIED WOOD: Take road S along Crooked River to dam, then N and go S and E to Bear Creek road past Little Bear Creek and on to point shortly after road leaves creek. Go left on rough road to collect at its end.

LIMB CASTS: Continue E on main road to McCormack ranch, take road along Soldier Creek E to turnoff S along Middle Fork of Camp Creek to collect at Smoky Mountain. Return N to turnoff, go 1½ mile, then S 2 miles to collect at South Pole Creek.

AGATE NODULES: At White Fir Spring. Take U.S. 26 E 9 miles, turn left at store onto Mill

(Left) Hematite from Rio Marina, Elba.
(Middle) Ilvaite on quartz from Rio Marina.
(Right) Pyrite on hematite from Rio Marina.

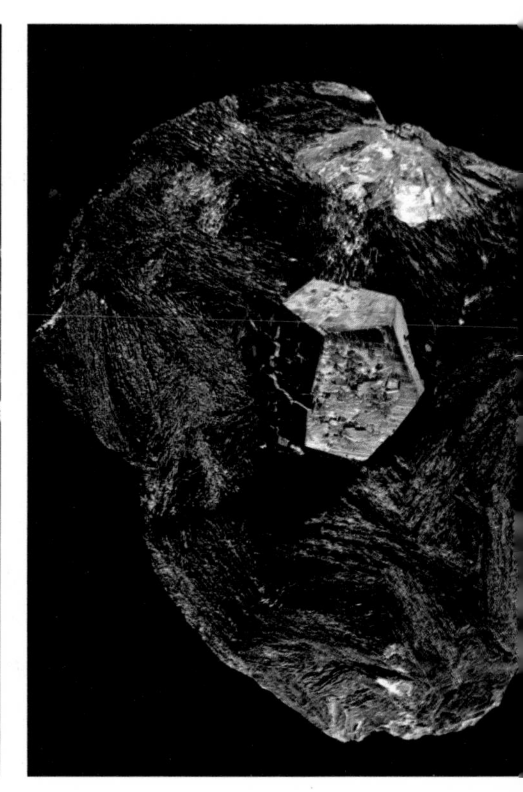

Quarry of leucite basalt near Casal Rotondo, Rome.

Creek Road 10 miles, then right across bridge 4½ miles to road junction and collect a few hundred yards ahead.

MOSS AGATE: U.S. 26 E 31 miles to Marks Creek Guard Station, turn left and follow Viewpoint signs on Road 127 to Whistler Spring dig. Road 125 leads to Road 123 (at sign) to the Valley View and Lucky Strike fee claims for thundereggs.

MOSS AGATE: U.S. 26 NE 31 miles to Marks Creek Guard Station, then Road 127 1 mile, NW on Road 123 to Road 1203 and N to Road 1256 and E to campground. Dig in Ochoco Mountains 2 miles W.

BLUE AGATE AND NODULES: At White Rock Spring. Turn left at White Fir Spring junction 2 miles to campsite, then rough road mile to diggings.

WHITE AGATE: At Sheep Creek. U.S. 26 16½ miles E, angle right on gravel road 3 miles, turn right on Wolf Creek Road to Sheep Creek sign and take Cadle Road to Arvid Nelson Road and left to 21 mile sign.

JASPER: At Coyle Spring. Take Hwy 26 E to fork at Marks Creek road; do not take it but take right fork on Ochoco Creek road. Continue to Road 13026 and go left on it to collect.

MOSS AGATE: At Shotgun Creek. Take Post road past Booton ranch to Road 1728, go S to road W, continue on it to fork and then go right ¾ mile.

NODULES: At Dry Creek: Take Hwy 26 to Road 133 N just past Ochoco Reservoir, go 5 miles, and left to Road 13015 and continue to creek. Return to Road 133 and take it N and then NW along Harvey Creek to Harvey Gap, then NE on Road 1307 to collect. Backtrack on Road 133 about a mile and collect in Harvey Creek. Also from the turn NW off Road 133 is a rough road E. Take it to end and then hike a mile E to Forked Horn Butte for nodules.

MOSS AND WHITE PLUME AGATE: At Bear Creek. S down Main Street 20 miles over Prineville Dam and continue on new road until it joins old road. Turn left on old road several miles to Bear Creek and collect in diggings on W side of bank.

PETRIFIED WOOD: At Swartz Canyon petrified forest. W to Redmond Hwy to road sign indicating turnoff to left.

- *Rockaway, Tillamook County* AGATE, JASPER: Pebbles on beach.
- *Rogue River, Jackson County* RHODONITE: Take road along Evans Creek N for 15 miles to mine, collect in road cut and creek.

(Left) Gismondite from Fossa dell'Osa, Rome.
(Middle) Leucite on volcanic tuff from Capo Bove, near Rome.
(Right) White hexagonal prisms of nephelite from Capo Bove.

- *Rome, Malheur County* AGATE (SNAKESKIN): Hwy 95 SW to a mile E of rest area and just E of Crooked creek. Go S 1 mile and then take right fork a mile, turn left to end of road. Rake agate from soil.
- *Roseburg, Douglas County* PETRIFIED WOOD, AGATE: In North Umpqua River to Glide.
- *Rufus, Sherman County* AGATE: In gullies mile S of Hwy 30.
- *Salem, Polk County* PETRIFIED WOOD, JASPER: At River Bend Sand and Gravel company works.
- *Scio, Linn County* PETRIFIED WOOD: E on Hwy 226 for 3 miles to Richardson Gap road, turn right, then left on next paved road, go 1½ miles to first gravel road. Take it left to end and dig at Rogers Mountain.

  PETRIFIED WOOD, AGATE: Go 9 miles SE to hunt at Prospect Mountain Mine, which is 2 miles NW of Roaring River hatchery (fee).
- *Seaside, Clatsop County* AGATE, JASPER: Pebbles on beach.
- *Sweet Home, Linn County* BLUE AGATE: Take Hwy 228 for 4 miles SW to Holley school, then right a bit more than 2 miles, and again right 2 miles to farmhouse. Hike logging road for 1 mile to site. Another location is at end of a gravel road from Holley to river. Cross the river and dig.

  PETRIFIED WOOD: At Belveal farm 5 miles SW on Hwy 228 and 1⅓ miles E of Holley church (fee). Another location is just N of Hwy 228 bridge over Calapooya River and then E 1⅓ miles.
- *Tillamook, Tillamook County* ORANGE AGATE, JASPER: Take Third Street to Bay-Ocean Road to its end and collect at Tillamook bar.
- *Trent, Lane County* AGATE WITH REALGAR: S on Hwy 58, then ½ mile to road E to Snyder ranch to dig agate (fee).
- *Unity, Baker County* AGATE: Take Hwy 26 NW to Hwy 7, then NE 6 miles to road N through Whitney toward Sumpter, collect in dredge dumps and river gravels.

  BLUE AGATE: In rhyolite in area SE to Ironside.
- *Vale, Malheur County* PETRIFIED WOOD: Take road S 25 miles to sign reading "Owyhee Dam 8 Miles," go W 2 miles and S in creek bed to collecting area.

  OPALIZED WOOD: NW 12 miles at Willow Creek.
- *Vernonia, Columbia County* AGATE: S on Hwy 47 to bridge, turn right on logging road nearly a mile to farm gate. Ask permission to cross farm, collect in Clear Creek gravels and banks.

  CARNELIAN: In Nehalem River to N.
- *Wasco, Sherman County* JASPER (SCENIC): 1 mile outside town in new road cut; jasper is like Owyhee jasper.

- *Wedderburn, Curry County* MASSIVE GROSSULARITE GARNET, JASPER, PETRIFIED WOOD: In gravels at mouth of Rogue River, at Gold Beach, and on beaches and in coves for 6 miles N.
- *Willowdale, Jefferson County* MOSS AGATE: S 1 mile on U.S. 97, then S 5 miles and E 2 miles to Palmer ranch (fee).

  PETRIFIED WOOD: At Folmsbee place. N on Hwy 97 for a mile, then E on Antelope road 7 miles.
- *Yachats, Lincoln County* SAGENITIC AGATE, JASPER: On Cummings Creek Beach.

  MOSS AGATE, MASSIVE GROSSULARITE GARNET, PETRIFIED WOOD: At Big Creek 10-Mile Creek, China Creek, and Squaw Creek beaches to S.

Pennsylvania

Eastern Pennsylvania falls within the coastal plain made up of marine deposits, and lying west of it is the Piedmont plateau, resting on crystalline metamorphic rocks and sedimentary rocks. The highlands are formed of crystalline and volcanic rocks and culminate in the Allegheny plateau, largely sedimentary rocks, which forms nearly half the state and is its most rugged region. The belts or regions cross the state from northeast to southwest.

- *Avondale, Delaware County** AQUAMARINE, GOLDEN BERYL, GARNET: In dumps of old Leiper (now Faccenda) quarry on E side of Crum Creek.

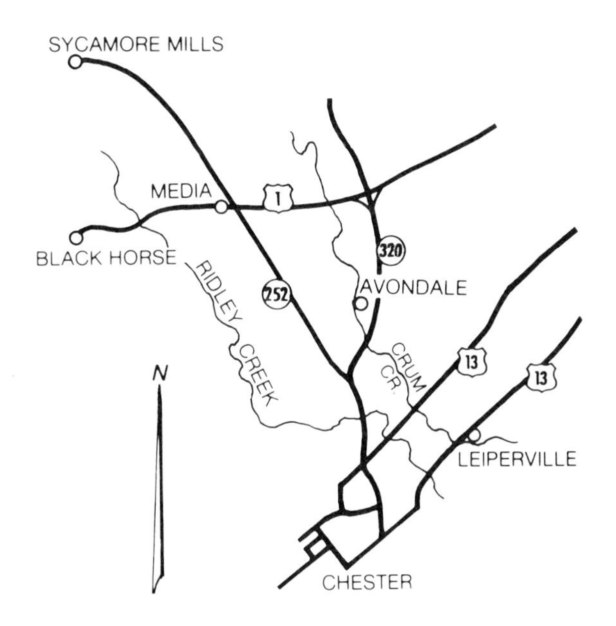

  QUARTZ CRYSTALS: In quarry to SE on W side of Crum Creek.

  AMETHYST: 1 mile W in quarry on George Sharpless farm.
- *Bart, Lancaster County* SMOKY QUARTZ: E of ruins of smelter ¾ mile N of Gap Nickel Mines.
- *Black Horse, Delaware County* AMAZONITE, GARNET: In exposures on Mineral Hill along road from Media.

  SUNSTONE: S ¼ mile at old corundum pits, and ½ mile E on J. Smith farm.

  GREEN QUARTZ: At quarry ½ mile NE of Black Horse.
- *Boothwyn, Delaware County* AMETHYST: At J. B. Okie's farm 2 miles N.
  At Armstrong farm ½ mile N.

  RUTILATED QUARTZ: Loose in soil at McCay's farm.

  QUARTZ CRYSTALS, GARNET: In pits on W side of E branch of Naaman's Creek.
- *Bridgeport, Montgomery County* JASPER, QUARTZ: SE ½ mile on Hwy 202 in Dolomite quarry of the Bethlehem Steel company.
- *Carlisle, Cumberland County* BANDED AGATE: On S side of Hwy 11, a mile E of the Carlisle interchange on Pennsylvania Turnpike.
- *Chester, Delaware County* AMETHYST, BERYL, SMOKY QUARTZ: At Shaw & Esrey's Quarry ¼ mile S.

  ALMANDINE GARNET: In soil above Peter's Mill Dam in Green Creek and in creek mile S of Chester Heights Station.
- *Coatesville, Chester County* BERYL, AMETHYST, SMOKY QUARTZ: In quarry 1½ mile NW and just S of U.S. 30 bypass.
- *Cornog, Chester County* BLUE QUARTZ, SMOKY QUARTZ: With epidote as stringers in gneiss at Keystone Trap Rock quarry just SE.
- *Darlington Corners, Chester County* SERPENTINE, BERYL: In Brinton quarry to SW.
- *Darby, Delaware County* BERYL: Near White Horse 3 miles S.
- *Easton, Northampton County* TOPAZ, SERPENTINE: To N at Chestnut Hill in Verdolite and other quarries.
- *Eureka, Bucks County* SMOKY QUARTZ: At Eureka quarry to NE.
- *Gladhill, Adams County* COPPER IN RHYOLITE: At Bingham mine ½ mile NE of Piney Mountain on W side of road to Maria Furnace.
- *Glendale, Delaware County* BERYL: In quarry on Glendale road just N of place where road parallels Darby creek and mile S of where Hwy 3 meets the creek.
- *Harrisburg, Dauphin County* AGATE, GARNET: Take Int. 83 S across Pennsylvania Turnpike to overpass, then 1 mile farther to Fairview church, collect from weathered material.
- *Jenkins Corner, Lancaster County* SERPENTINE (WILLIAMSITE): At Cedar Hill quarry, reached from Hwy 222 by going E on road along Pennsylvania-Maryland line and following signs to mine. Get permission D. M. Stoltzfus & Son, Talmadge, Pa.
- *Kennett Square, Chester County* SUNSTONE: At Pierce's paper mill ½ mile SE.
  At Cloud's farm 2 miles SE.

TOURMALINE: At Bailey's farm SW of Willowdale.

- *King of Prussia, Montgomery County* QUARTZ: With malachite in McCoy quarry.
- *Knavertown, Chester County* ACTINOLITE, QUARTZ: N past St. Peter's to dumps of French Creek mine.
- *Kunkletown, Monroe County* QUARTZ: Just to S in clay pit E of sand pits, and along stream banks. Permission at Sheesley's Minerals.
- *Leiperville, Delaware County* BLUE AND GOLDEN BERYL, THULITE, QUARTZ CRYSTALS: At Deshong's quarry ½ mile W on E side of Ridley Creek.
- *Lemont, Centre County* QUARTZ: In Neidgh quarry and loose in soil.

  OOLITIC CHERT: To W in fields of university farms.
- *Lenni, Delaware County* SUNSTONE, AMAZONSTONE, MOONSTONE: In cut on railroad ⅜ mile E of station.

  AMETHYST: W ½ mile of Crozierville on S side of Chester Creek.
- *Ligonier, Westmoreland County* QUARTZ CRYSTALS: W 3 miles at quarry on Hwy 30.
- *Media, Delaware County* AMETHYST: NE 1½ miles on Crum Creek road on James Worral, Morgan Hunter and Randolph farms.

  AMAZONSTONE, MOONSTONE: A mile W at Mineral Hill W of Ridley Creek, in quarry N of Crump's Quarry on grounds of School for the Feeble Minded.

  BERYL: At Blue Hill 2½ miles NW and in boulders along Crum Creek. Take Paper Mill road to end, park near bridge over creek and take trail to S bank.
- *Morgan Station, Delaware County* AMETHYST: In quarries to W and near Crozierville and Chad's Ford.
- *Morgantown, Berks County* GARNET, EPIDOTE, QUARTZ: E 1¼ miles at Grace mine of Bethlehem Steel Company.
- *Mt. Holly Springs, Cumberland County* AGATE, NODULES: Take Hwy 34 W at bank, go ½ mile, take right fork about a mile to farmhouse, get permission and collect in fields S of house.
- *Neshaminy Falls, Bucks County* MOONSTONE: N 2 miles at Vanartsdalen's Quarry.
- *New Ringgold, Schuylkill County* QUARTZ: In hill nearby.
- *Oxford, Lancaster County* SERPENTINE (WILLIAMSITE): In dumps at Wood's Chrome mine 9 miles SW, and in nearby mines. The mine is ½ mile N of the state line in a meander of Octorara Creek. (See Maryland for other serpentine localities.)
- *Pocopson, Chester County* AMETHYST: E of station ¼ mile in field NW of Minshall Painter's house.

  At Darlington's farm ¼ mile W.
- *Quarryville, Lancaster County* SERPENTINE (WILLIAMSITE): Take Hwy 472 SE through Kirkwood to Union, then W to fork, take left fork ½ mile. Stillwell quarry is just over bridge on Gables Run.
- *Redington, Northampton County* CAT'S-EYE QUARTZ: On South Mountain.
- *Rock Springs Run, Lancaster County* MOSS AGATE, CARNELIAN: In small branch of run 1¼ miles N of Rock Springs, Md.
- *Stromville, Monroe County* QUARTZ: At Crystal Hill.
- *Stroudsburg, Northampton County* * QUARTZ CRYSTALS: Steep, wooded area located on the Christian Armitage farm S of Stroudsburg. Crystal Hill is reached by taking Rt 611 E from Stroudsburg to a blinker light and turning S

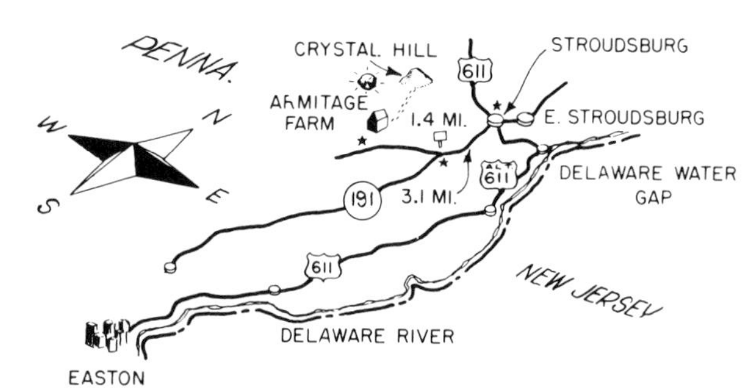

on Hwy 191 for 3.1 miles, then keeping right 1.4 miles to Armitage house. Walk up steep hill to site where quartz crystals are loose in fine-grained quartz conglomerate (fee).

- *Sycamore Mills, Delaware County* SMOKY QUARTZ: W ½ mile on Walker Yarnell's farm for smoky quartz.

  AMETHYST: S ½ mile on Marshall farm near Dismal Run.

  GREEN QUARTZ: S ¾ mile at J. Tyler's farm.
- *Trainer Station, Delaware County* SMOKY QUARTZ, QUARTZ CRYSTALS, GREEN BERYL: At William Trainer's farm ½ mile N.
- *Unionville, Chester County* CORUNDUM, SERPENTINE: NE 2 miles on Northbrook Road at Corundum Hill.

  Upper Darby, Delaware County SMOKY QUARTZ: Along West Chester Pike ½ mile W.
- *Valley Forge, Chester County* AMETHYST: W 1½ miles at abandoned Jug Hollow Mine.
- *Vera Cruz, Lehigh County* JASPER: At quarry to N, along creek and in fields E of road and N of creek. Generally in area from Durham to Kutztown.

Rhode Island

Once a plain not much above sea level, Rhode Island has been uplifted and its surface carved by stream action into low hills and valleys; some of the latter have

The sulphur mine at Pozzuoli, Naples. In the center, the area of boiling mud.

become ocean bays. Glaciation has completed the work of forming the surface.

- *Cumberland Hill, Providence County* QUARTZ, AGATE: Take Hwy 120 to Hwy 114, then N through Diamond Hill and left into state park to collect in dumps of quarries across road.

  SAGENITIC QUARTZ: At Diamond Hill Granite quarry in dumps.

  SERPENTINE: At Iron Mine Hill quarry. With diopside at Sneech Pond. Take Copper Hill road W to West Wrentham road, N ½ mile and W ¼ mile to Ballou Meeting House.

  AMETHYST: At Iron Hill mine dumps.

  SMOKY QUARTZ: At McLaughlin's Ledge.
- *Jamestown, Newport County* STAUROLITE: Near Jamestown bridge abutments on Conanicut island.
- *Johnston, Providence County* BERYL: In Hwy 6 road cuts.
- *Limerock, Providence County* SERPENTINE, QUARTZ, AGATE: In Conklin Lime Company quarry.
- *Narragansett, Washington County* BERYL, QUARTZ: In outcropping pegmatites along eastern shore, at Bonnet Point, Bonnet Shore Beach, Ft. Varnum and Watson Pier.
- *Providence, Providence County* QUARTZ: At Wanskirch Granite quarry.
- *Spragueville, Providence County* BERYL: At junction of Mann School and Wanskuck Hill roads in road cut.
- *Tiverton, Newport County* RUTILATED QUARTZ: In quarry of Fish road.
- *Westerly, Washington County* BERYL: At Westerly Granite quarry.
- *West Greenwich, Kent County* AMAZONSTONE: At Nooseneck, Weaver Hill road and Int. 95.

South Carolina

Near the ocean, South Carolina is a region of islands and marshes in the coastal plain. Behind this is the upcountry, the rolling Piedmont plateau, while the northwest corner of the state rises abruptly into the Blue Ridge Mountains of the Appalachian system, adjoining noted gem areas in Georgia and North Carolina. Most of the gem locations lie in the more mountainous northwestern part of the state.

- *Allendale, Allendale County* CHERT: Take Hwy 301 SW across the Savannah River, turn NW for 8 miles to where road makes sharp turn S, continue ahead on dirt road 12 miles and collect along road. Other favored collecting spots include King's Creek Landing on the Savannah River.

- *Anderson, Anderson County* EMERALD: At J. M. McConnell place 3½ miles NE in schist.

  BERYL: At Ferguson mine 5⅔ miles N on Hwy 187, and ½ mile SW of McConnell place in pegmatite.

  GARNET, QUARTZ: N 9 miles near dam on 26-Mile Creek.

  AMETHYST, GARNET: S 15 miles on Hwy 28 where road cuts dike near lake.
- *Antreville, Abbeville County* AMETHYST, SMOKY QUARTZ: Go 3 miles W on Hwy 284, then a mile N on S-1-72, and ¾ mile farther and right to house, pay fee, return to next road S and go E and N a mile to mine.
- *Blacksburg, Cherokee County* SAPPHIRE: In pegmatite 2½ miles NW on Hwy 83 at Andrew Moon place.
- *Blenheim, Marlboro County* PETRIFIED CYCAD: In sand pits 4 miles S.
- *Buffalo Church, Cherokee County* AMETHYST: At W. T. Gibbons place just to W and in stream gravels.
- *Columbia, Richland County* AMETHYST: At Lake Murray.
- *Cross Hill, Laurens County* AMETHYST: N on Hwy 39 to crossroads with large white house, turn right 3 miles until road takes sharp turn. Stop at farmhouse just before turn, get permission to collect, make turn, go ½ mile to road right into pines. Dig in field to right of road.
- *Due West, Abbeville County* AMETHYST: At Ellis-Jones Amethyst mine, by permission of the Williams family.
- *Easley, Pickens County* SOAPSTONE: In schist.
- *Edgefield, Edgefield County* SERPENTINE: In Turkey Creek within sight of Hwy 25.
- *Gaffney, Cherokee County* SAPPHIRE: At Porter's Hill, on Bowen river.

  GARNET: At Troy Blanton mine 8 miles SW.
- *Greenville, Greenville County* QUARTZ, GARNET: N 5 miles at E end of Paris Mountain State Park in pegmatite at junction of two creeks.
- *Greenwood, Greenwood County* AMETHYST: At Wrenn's place.

  CHALCEDONY: At Harper's place at powerhouse.

  GARNET: At Stockman's Quarry.

  QUARTZ CRYSTALS, SMOKY QUARTZ: At Milford place.
- *Iva, Anderson County* BERYL: Go 3 miles to country store on bank of Lake Secession, get permission and directions to collect nearby.

  BERYL: NW 1¾ miles on Wilson's Creek, and on Hwy 413 at Frank Pruitt place, and at J. B. Anderson farm 3 miles SW.

  AMETHYST: SW 8 miles at Sherard place.
- *Jefferson, Chesterfield County* YELLOW AND BLUE TOPAZ: 3 miles W at Brewer Mine for topaz.
- *Laurens, Laurens County* CORUNDUM: At New Cemetery and inside city at Dead Man's Cut in railroad.

  PYROPE GARNET: At Dead Man's Cut.
- *Liberty Hill, Lancaster County* SMOKY QUARTZ: Near Wateree reservoir in pegmatite near creek. Also take Hwy 21 S to Hwy 97, go 8¼ miles, then right on dirt road for 2¼ miles and right on dirt road 1½ miles, walk to mine.
- *Lowndesville, Abbeville County* AMETHYST: To E at McCalla place and 1⁴⁄₅ miles N at Barnes place.
- *Pelzer, Anderson County* AQUAMARINE, GREEN TOURMALINE: S 1 mile.
- *Piedmont, Greenville County* BERYL: At the D. D. McNeely place.
- *Princeton, Laurens County* AMETHYST: At spring 1½ miles SW.
- *Saluca, Greenwood County* UNAKITE: On W shore of Lake Greenwood.
- *Seneca, Oconee County* SILLIMANITE: N 2 miles on LeRoy property. Collect in soil and dike. Material will cut cat's-eyes. Get permission King's Rock shop, Franklin, N.C.
- *Shoals Junction, Greenwood County* AMETHYST: SE 1½ miles on road to Donalds at the Hadden place, and 1 mile SW at the Dunn place.

South Dakota

East of the Missouri River, South Dakota is a fairly level, glaciated plain; to the west of the Missouri lies rolling prairie broken along the White River and north of it by the Badlands, and in the far south and central west by granite mountains known as the Black Hills. One of them, Harney Peak, is the highest point in the United States east of the Rockies. The agates of the prairies and the pegmatite minerals of the Black Hills are the principal gem resources of the state.

- *Ardmore, Fall River County* * AGATE, JASPER: Generally in area to S along state line and down into Nebraska. Take dirt road E for 7 miles toward the best known collecting spot, known as Sugarloaf Butte.
- *Custer, Custer County* * AGATE: Take U.S. 16 E to State Park, turn off toward State Farm, go beyond cattle gate, search in hills to right.

  PYRITE, BARBOSALITE: Showy black and golden materials in Bull Moose mine dumps 5 miles SE.

  ROSE QUARTZ: At White Elephant Mine. S on Hwy 385 7½ miles to fork, take right fork to mine on ridge. Collect on dumps.

  AGATE: For Tepee Canyon agate, go 14 miles

W on U.S. 16 to campground on left. Continue 1 mile to road on right up canyon. Collect at top of hill left, or go up canyon to small gully and collect on hill left. Also go back to U.S. 16, drive W to logging road on right. Agates are in limestone.

GARNET, TOURMALINE: Go 7 miles W on U.S. 16, turn N at Deer Camp sign, go ¼ mile, and search in stream, or take trail up steep hill and look in mica schists.

• *Fairburn, Custer County* * AGATE: The brightly colored Fairburn agates were never plentiful and they are now difficult to find. Experts advise that the best place to look is where the agates have been found before, and that the fall of the year, after the grass has died back, is the best time. Fairburn-type agates have been found over a three-state area (shown by dotted line on map) extending down into Nebraska and Wyoming. Well-patterned jaspers and agatized fossils are also found in the agate beds.

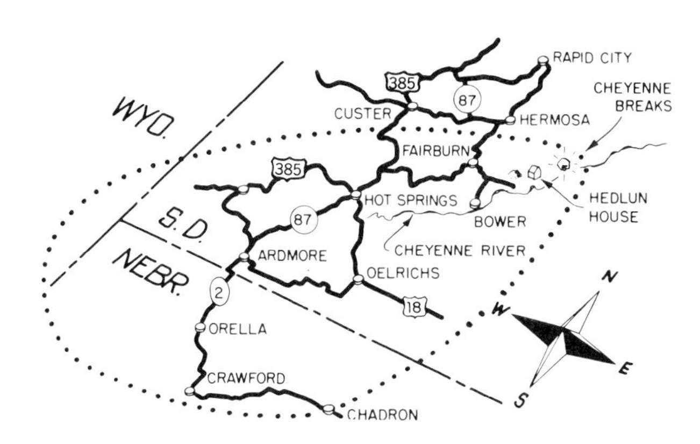

To reach the original collecting location, leave Fairburn on Hwy 79, go E 3½ miles to left fork and follow French Creek 5½ miles to McDermand ranch. Continue to picnic grounds, enter and drive across creek nearly a mile, and collect in the gravelly knolls.

• *Hot Springs, Fall River County* * PETRIFIED WOOD: At Fall River Canyon.

• *Interior, Jackson County* AGATE: Take Hwy 40 W, go ¾ mile farther after it becomes gravel. Along road pick up agates which look like wads of gum.

• *Keystone, Pennington County* * ROSE QUARTZ: In pegmatite dikes along gravel road connecting Alt. 16 and Hwy 87 near Mount Rushmore National Monument.

LEPIDOLITE, TOURMALINE: At Robert Ingersoll Mine.

GARNET: In dumps near tunnel on Alt. 16 between Hwy 16 and Keystone and generally in streams in Black Hills.

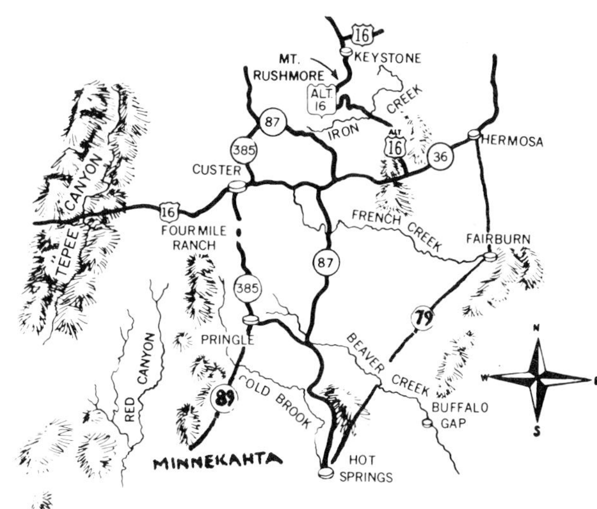

• *Little Eagle, Corson County* PETRIFIED WOOD: Along Grand River.

• *Minnekahta, Fall River County* FOSSIL CYCAD: Take Forest Service trail to left to top of tableland, then keep left on main trail through three gates to collecting site.

• *Murdo, Jones County* CHALCEDONY: On sand bars in White River near highway bridge to S.

• *Mission, Todd County* BLACK PETRIFIED WOOD: W 12 miles along Little White River.

• *Oelrichs, Fall River County* * AGATE: Go S in main street to road E, take it 1 mile, then S 2 miles to a farm, turn E on winding road to a sharp turn, take a dim trail left and N a mile then W to buttes to collect. A similar place is Lone Butte, reached by going 4 miles E to a ranch gate, then ½ mile S to collect on N and E sides of butte.

• *Pringle, Custer County* * AGATE: Along Hwy 89 between Pringle and Minnekahta, and to NW and W of Pringle and near Custer State Park to NE.

• *Rapid City, Pennington County* RUTILATED QUARTZ: To E in Box Elder Creek.

PETRIFIED WOOD: To W and N along Hwy 14.

• *Scenic, Pennington County* * BLACK AGATE: West of Scenic 2 miles and N of the railroad is a formation known as Hart Table, where black agate is found in the gullies and eroded bluffs.

AGATE, PETRIFIED WOOD, ROSE QUARTZ: Loose on ground 3 miles S, mile off road in either direction.

GEODES: On Hwy 40 E from Scenic, the road reaches a pass. Turn S from here and past a railroad trestle for geodes.

BLACK, WHITE AGATE: Farther E past Imlay, a road turns S toward White River for black and white agate along banks.

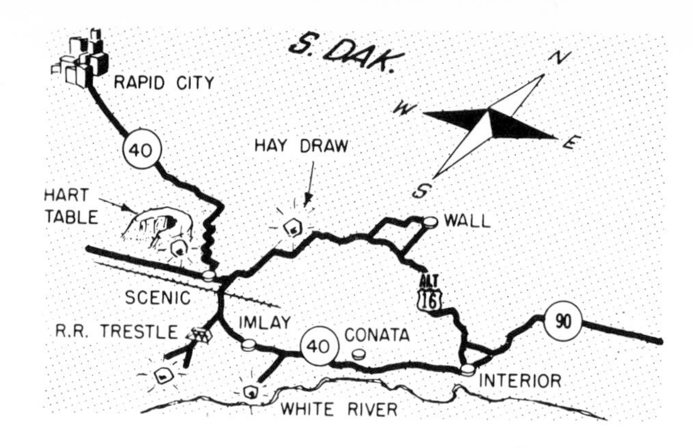

NODULES: Northeast of Scenic on the road to Wall, the road passes a formation known as Hay Draw. Here nodules are found in a clay ironstone matrix, both in the stream and in its banks.

JASPER, AGATE: Hwy 40 W 1 mile to place where red hills are seen to right. Park, walk to them and collect along the way.

AGATE: To W in the breaks of the Cheyenne River is the Hedlun log cabin. Ask permission to collect to N for Fairburn agates.

- *Sioux Falls, Minnehaha County* JASPER, AGATE: In gravels of Big Sioux River.
- *Spearfish, Lawrence County* ONYX: To W on Crow Peak.
- *Whitewood, Lawrence County* AMETHYST: Nodules in Whitewood creek.

Tennessee

East Tennessee rises in the mountains along the North Carolina border, an area of folded crystalline rocks, and extends across the valley of the Tennessee, cut in sedimentary rocks, to the Cumberland plateau. This plateau, bordered by steep escarpments, encloses a central basin running from northeast to southwest, in which Nashville lies. The basin rises to highlands on the west, cut by the lower Tennessee River, and then falls to a bluff along the Mississippi in a plateau which is part of the Gulf coastal plain. Except for the narrow belt of Appalachian Mountains in the east, Tennessee is formed mostly of sedimentary rocks.

- *Beechgrove, Coffee County* CHALCEDONY NODULES AND FRAGMENTS: S and W of U.S. 41.
- *Bluffton, Cocke County* UNAKITE: In nearby streams and granite outcrops.
- *Bristol, Sullivan County* ONYX: At bypass road cut in Hwy 421.
- *Cookeville, Putnam County* JASPER, AGATE: In nodules in streams from Cumberland Plateau.
- *Copper Hill, Polk County* STAUROLITE: Take road to Ducktown for 1 mile, look on right side for a rough place in bank.
- *Erwin, Washington County* JASPER: Go 5 miles N on Hwy 81, cross river and turn left at Embreeville to Bumpas Cove for dark variegated material with blue areas.
- *Friendsville, Blount County* MARBLE: In waste piles of many quarries close to village.
- *Frog Pond, Unicoi County* UNAKITE: N on U.S. 23 1 mile, collect in road cut and creek fill to left. Also at Chandler mine 2¾ miles NW.
- *Jamestown, Fentress County* ONYX: Take U.S. 127 to road W at S edge of town to Herbert Tipton farm in Buffalo Cave area (fee).
- *Jellico, Campbell County* AGATE: In road cut between bridge and tavern outside town on LaFollit road.
- *Kingsport, Sullivan County* JASPER: Take Hwy 11W past U.S. 23 intersection, then 1⅔ miles to road N to Lambert quarry.
- *Memphis, Shelby County* AGATE: Material of Lake Superior type in Mississippi river gravels at Richardson's Landing.
- *Murfreesboro, Rutherford County* AGATE NODULES: In chert in road cuts and ditches.
- *Oakley, Cumberland County* GEODES: Go 13 miles N to Dale Hollow lake, dig on south central shore.
- *Roan Mountain, Carter County* UNAKITE: Take Hwy 143 going N to second roadside table on Tennessee side of Roan Mountain. Also collect in Rock Creek and along U.S. 19S.
- *Shelbyville, Bedford County* IRIS AGATE, CARNELIAN: To E and N between Fairfield Turnpike and Hwy 64. Best in valleys off Pannell Ridge, such as those crossed by Horse Mountain road from the mountain to Wartrace. Also on road from Horse Mountain road around Philippi church on way to Wartrace and SW of Wartrace in Stokes Branch section, agate is found in streams and fields, such as along Duck River and its tributaries.
One specific place to collect is at the Velmer Curvow farm, on Rt. 2 (fee.)

FOSSIL CORAL: To W at bridge over Sugar Creek on Hwy 64.

- *Sparta, White County* JASPER: Take U.S. 70 S 1 mile to White Company limestone quarry.
- *Townsend, Blount County* EPIDOTE: In road cuts and stream gravels.
- *Woodbury, Cannon County* GEODES: On farms 5 miles E on U.S. 70S, and in Stone river tributaries.

Texas

Sandy sediments typical of the coastal plain make up southeastern Texas. Behind this lies the Llano uplift, a region of crystalline rocks. The Grand Prairie and Edwards plateaus, primarily sedimentary rocks, link the Llano uplift to the north central plains and, toward the Panhandle, the High Plains themselves. In far western Texas is the Trans Pecos, formed of rugged mountains, both igneous and sedimentary in their structure. The great variety of sedimentary areas affords a wealth of agate and petrified wood, while in the Llano area occur

(Left) Biotite from Vesuvius quarry.
(Right) Leucite from Roccamonfina, Caserta.

Realgar from Pozzuoli, Naples.

topaz and garnet and other minerals characteristic of crystalline rocks.

- *Alpine, Brewster County* AGATE: At Woodward ranch 14 miles S on Hwy 118 and turn at sign. Also at Anderson ranch 21 miles S and to left at sign.
  At Henderson ranch 32 miles S and to left at sign.
  At Cocoanut ranch 33 miles S on Hwy 118.

  PETRIFIED WOOD: At Aqua Fria ranch 58 miles S on Hwy 118, then right 10 miles.
  At Tooter Hill ranch 66 miles S on Hwy 118, then turn at sign 8 miles to ranch.

  AGATE: E on Hwy 90 for 8 miles, then N on Hwy 67 26 miles and W to Hovey ranch.
  All these collecting spots charge a fee.

  POMPOM AGATE: At Needle Peak, 115 miles S of Woodward ranch between end of Hwy 118 and Rio Grande River. This is just W of Big Bend National Park. (By arrangement with Woodwards.)

  YELLOW LABRADORITE: S 20 miles and loose in soil.

  OPAL: In seams in rhyolite 16 miles S.
- *Amarillo, Potter County* AGATIZED WOOD: SE 50 miles near Palo Duro Canyon.
- *Austin, Travis County* SERPENTINE: Just S of Beecaves, reached by taking Hwy 290 to Oak Hill, then NW on Hwy 71.

  LIMESTONE: Fossiliferous material is found on hill 1½ miles upstream from Barton Springs in Barton creek.
- *Balmorhea, Reeves County* BLUE AGATE: Take access road SW to Toyahvale, then E to collect between Lake Balmorhea and Hwy 290. Agate is also found SE of the lake loose in the soil.
- *Bedias, Grimes County* TEKTITES: Found in a large irregular area as far SW as Gonzales County.

  BEDIASITE: The variety found here takes its name from this town.
- *Borger, Carson County* FLINT: Varicolored Alibates flint is found in Plum Creek canyon reached by taking Hwy 1913 to sign to Plum Creek Recreation park, then S to bottom of Plum Creek Canyon and right 4 miles to campground. Hunt in creek and in soil.
- *Brackettsville, Kinney County* JASPER: Near town and in Rio Grande gravels.
- *Caldwell, Burleson County* PETRIFIED WOOD: To S between Hwys 21 and 36.
- *Calliham, McMullen County* PETRIFIED WOOD: W along Hwy 72 as far as Tilden and NE and SW of Falls City.
- *Carmine, Fayette County* PETRIFIED WOOD: Take road N ½ mile, then left ¼ mile and right ¼ mile to dirt road, follow it ½ mile to gate on left; go to creek and hunt in creek and along banks.
- *Columbus, Colorado County* PETRIFIED WOOD: In gravels 10 miles W.
- *Cross, Grimes County* PETRIFIED WOOD: To N along Hwy 39 all the way to Normangee and to NE along Hwy 90 to Madisonville.
- *Eagle Flat, Hudspeth County* AUGITE: Gem grade with black spinel.
- *Eagle Pass, Maverick County* AGATE, JASPER: In gravel pit on Rio Grande and at Hill ranch (fee) 9 miles NW on Hwy 277 to collect south of buildings.

  BROWN AMBER: In Cretaceous coal deposits.
- *El Sauz, Starr County* PETRIFIED PALM WOOD, AGATE: To S along Hwy 649.
- *Fredericksburg, Gillespie County* AMETHYST, CITRINE: To NE at Amethyst Hill.

  ALMANDINE GARNET: In stream gravels.
- *Freer, Duval County* PETRIFIED WOOD: At Stevenson Ranch.

  FIRE OPAL: Seams in rhyolite.
- *Giddings, Burleson County* PETRIFIED WOOD: Take U.S. 290 E to Ledbetter and Rd 2145 S to Matejonsky farm to hunt palm wood (fee).
- *Hemphill, Sabine County* PETRIFIED WOOD: To S along E edge of Rayburn reservoir and W edge of Toledo Bend reservoir.
- *Johnson City, Blanco County* FOSSIL MARBLE: Black material near Cypress Mill and 5 miles S at Honeycut Bend.
- *Karnes City, Karnes County* PETRIFIED WOOD: In fields and in streams to N and E toward Falls City and Helena. Tessman ranch (fee) is 10 miles E of Falls City on Hwy 792, the Pavelick farm is S of Falls City (fee), and the Erdman's Rock Haven in Falls City offers guide collecting service.
- *LaGrange, Fayette County* * PETRIFIED PALM WOOD: LaGrange is near the center of a belt of gravels 100 or more miles inland from the Gulf of Mexico and extending from Huntsville, 50 miles N of Houston, through LaGrange, Gonzales, Whitsett and Freer. In this area, called the Catahoula formation, fossil wood, including palm, is found on the surface and in creeks. Near LaGrange it is found to N along Rabs Creek and to SW toward Muldoon.
- *Laredo, Jeff Davis County* AGATE, PETRIFIED WOOD, JASPER: One of the prime collecting areas in the United States lies along the Rio Grande from Mission and Sullivan City in the south to Laredo in the north. Gem materials are found in fields, along side roads, and railroad cuts, and in the gravel pits along the river. Often they are coated with a white limy layer. Some specific localities:
  W 3 miles of Sullivan City take first road left to Garcia ranch (fee). Also at Fordyce gravel pits.

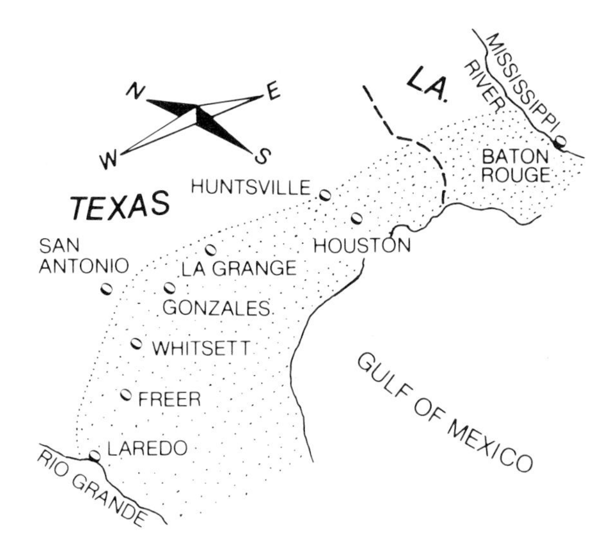

W 4 miles of Rio Grande City and N along road to El Sauz. Collect along road.
E 12 miles on Hwy 83 to road S to Grulla. Just before reaching railroad track take road E and N to collect in gravel.
NW on Hwy 83 to river gravels at Roma.
At Falcon, where gravel from the dam was dumped.
At Lajitas behind store and in wash to W.
At Laredo, 10½ miles from turnoff from Hwy 83 to Rd. 1492, then left over cattle guard to Diaz ranch (fee).
N 9 miles from Laredo on Delores road, then left to river to collect. Farther along Delores road is Singing Hills ranch (fee).
(Also see Zapata entries.)

- *Llano, Llano County* GRANITE (LLANITE): In dikes, fields, and streams N near Hwy 16, such as 10 miles N in quarry just W. Also 15 miles S at Enchanted Rock (fee).
- *Marathon, Brewster County* AGATE: S on U.S. 385 to Hwy 2627 then SE 6½ miles to Stilwell ranch (fee). Nearby is a similar collecting place, the Brushy Creek ranch.
- *Marfa, Presidio County* AGATE: Take U.S. 67 to Hwy 169, then left 18 miles to Bishop ranch (fee).

  AGATE: Along Hwy 67 S of intersection with Hwy 169.
- *Mason, Mason County* * TOPAZ: White to blue topaz is found on several ranches in Mason County, near Mason, Grit, Katemcy, and Streeter. Specific directions are: Take Hwy 87 NW to Grit, then SE on Hwy 377. The first ranch on N side of road is the Seaquist (Honey) place, 1 mile from Grit to gate. Get key and pay fee at 400 Broad St., Mason, and collect in streams or dig in granite hills W of parking lot, or in Hickory branch of Honey Creek and the Gulch.
  Go W from Seaquist gate 3½ miles to dirt road on left into Ernest Lange (Bolt) place.

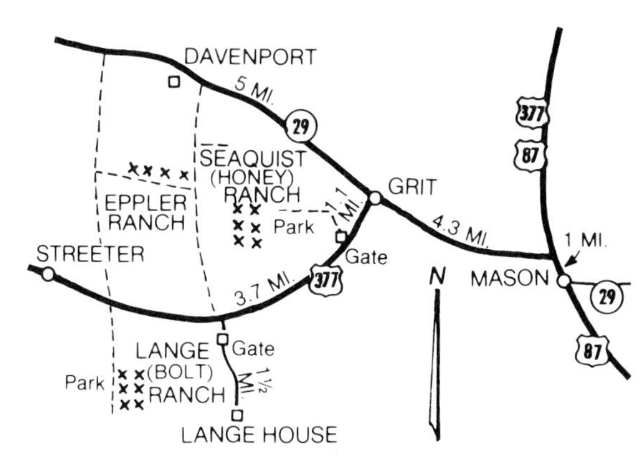

  Take it 1½ miles to Lange house, pay fee. Hunt in ravine behind house and ¾ mile back on dirt road.
  Across from the Lange ranch is the Eppler place.
  For directions to Schwanke place, see Robert Raspberry in Mason. The place lies N of Grit.
  The Davenport ranch lies N of the Eppler place. It is on Hwy 29. Take Hwy 29 out of Grit 5 miles, turn left and collect in dry gravel and in creek in S end of the ranch. Get key from Mrs. Loeffler in Grit.
  Another collecting place is the Giersch ranch S of Hwy 377 at Streeter.
  Nearby at Katemcy is topaz at the McWilliams ranch on Hwy 1222.
- *Oxford, Llano County* AMETHYST: In quartz veins near old town site.

  SERPENTINE: To N in quarry near Hwy 16.
- *Pecos, Reeves County* PLUME AGATE: Along roads N and S of Toyah, 19 miles W of Pecos.
- *Pumpville, Val Verde County* AGATE, JASPER, PETRIFIED WOOD: On Sidney Smith ranch N of Hwy 90.
- *San Saba, San Saba County* LIMESTONE: Limestone containing crinoid fossils is found on the C. B. Lambert ranch. Take Hwy 190 W 2 miles, then 7 miles S on Rt. 1030, and then E to ranch (fee). SE of San Saba are several quarries containing similar material.
- *Sierra Blanca, Hudspeth County* TURQUOISE: NW 8 miles in Sierra Blanca Mountains.
- *Smithville, Bastrop County* PETRIFIED WOOD: in creeks and gravels near town.
- *Terlingua, Brewster County* YELLOW AMBER: In Terlingua Creek.

  RUIN AGATE: Along Hwy 170 E on way to Big Bend National Park.
- *Tilden, McMullen County* PETRIFIED PALM WOOD: To E along course of Frio and Nueces Rivers.
- *Voca, Mason County* QUARTZ: Near the town and in Katemcy creek. Often asteriated.
- *Whitsett, Live Oak County* PETRIFIED PALM WOOD: To N and along Hwy 99.
  To E in creeks and gullies for petrified palm wood.

- *Trinity, Trinity County* PETRIFIED PALM WOOD: Along Hwy 405 toward Huntsville, and to N in road cuts toward Groveton and Lovelady.
- *Zapata, Zapata County* AGATE, JASPER, PETRIFIED WOOD: Collect in two hills between Hwy 83 and the Rio Grande 15 miles to S.
  Take Hwy 83 E for 13 miles to signs for Bob's Knob, follow signs for 9 miles (fee).
  Cross Rio Grande and go 8 miles to Guerrero, Mexico, and collect along road.
  At Hines Ranch 23 miles NW on Hwy 83, then S at gate (fee). (Also see Laredo entries.)

Utah

Utah falls into two grand divisions, the plateau, east of a line from the middle of the northern border running to the southwestern corner and for a long way following the Wasatch Mountains, and the Great Basin region to the west of this line. The Great Basin, formerly the bed of a lake of which Great Salt Lake is a remnant, is level except for isolated mountains. To the north the plateau is bounded by the wild Uinta Mountains, which descend into the sandstone buttes and cliffs that in southern Utah form the fantastic regions of erosion seen in Zion and Bryce Canyon National Parks and in the Grand Canyon of the Colorado. These sandstone areas are rich in fossils and petrified wood.

- *Beaver, Beaver County* AGATE: Take left-hand road past city dump and then next right-hand road for 2 miles.
- *Blanding, San Juan County* BLACK PETRIFIED WOOD: Hwy 95 W through Natural Bridges National Monument, then 18 miles farther past monument entry road into White Canyon.
- *Boulder, Garfield County* AGATE, PETRIFIED WOOD: In canyons to E and S.
- *Cainesville, Wayne County* AGATE, CONGLOMERATE: Hwy 24 6 miles E to small canyon, collect just W of canyon and to S of road. Best material is S of small creek.
- *Cedar City, Iron County* AGATE: Take rim road in Cedar Breaks National Monument to gate and cattle crossing. Turn outside monument into field and take first turn right toward Brian Head. Collect in washes below peak. Also found on W side of road leading from S gate of monument.

  BLUE AGATE: N on access road to Int. 15, through gates and E into Fiddler's Canyon. Farther N and just E of access road are several gates on way to summit that mark roads E to red agate collecting areas in hills.
- *Central, Washington County* AGATE NODULES: Take Hwy 18 to Dixie National Forest sign, turn left through gate before reaching sign, and take left fork N into canyon. Go ½ mile and search on hill to left. Go on, take left hand road to camp at end of road to collect S and W of camp. Go back to fork, take right fork into canyon, and then into a second canyon and follow ditch to diggings.

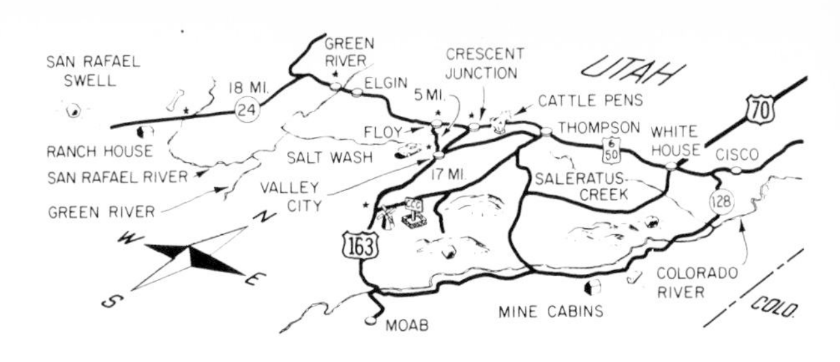

- *Cisco, Grand County* * JASPER: Take Hwy 128 S for 7 miles, then take left fork to river and drive into canyon. Jasper is in ledges on sides of canyon.

  RED AGATE PSEUDOMORPHS: Farther west in the hills are red agate pseudomorphs after barite concretions.

  AGATE, PETRIFIED WOOD, AND DINOSAUR BONE: Some 17 miles S of Thompson is a windmill and former CCC camp. In the hills E and SE of the windmill, agate, petrified wood, and petrified dinosaur bone weather out of the Morrison formation.

  LACE AND GRAPE AGATE: Farther W and about five miles S of a deep wash across the road S from Floy, park and go into the wash and hills to S for agate.

  RED AGATE, SEPTARIAN NODULES: Take Hwy 163 S 13 miles from Crescent Junction to Seep Spring sign, then E 4 miles and right to collect in creek.

  AGATE: Farther S, a dim road cuts S from the road that swings from Thompson to Hwy 163 N of Moab. After crossing a wet wash on this dim road, look in the hills to S for agate.
  Below Green River, take Hwy 24 S until it crosses the San Rafael River (about 18 miles). In the hills just N of the reef is agate; to the W, dinosaur bone.

  JASPER-AGATE: Farther S on Hwy 24 the road passes several ranches and then plunges into the San Rafael Swell. In this area jasper-agate is loose on the desert floor.
- *Delta, Millard County* * TOPAZ: To reach the Thomas Mountain collecting area, go NE on Hwy 6 for 10 miles, turn left and go NW for 40 miles to a gravel road, turn right 2 miles to a track N, follow it a mile to fork, take left fork a mile, then N in dry wash. In the valley or amphitheater of the mountain is a white knoll W of the campsite. Sherry-colored topaz can be dug out of the rhyolite there, and on slopes ½ mile W and ½ mile E are complex crystals. A mile NE of the knoll is a saddle where yellow etched crystals are found. Garnet is found with the topaz midway between the knoll and the V of Topaz Mountain, and on the W side of the mountain above the fluorite mine. The

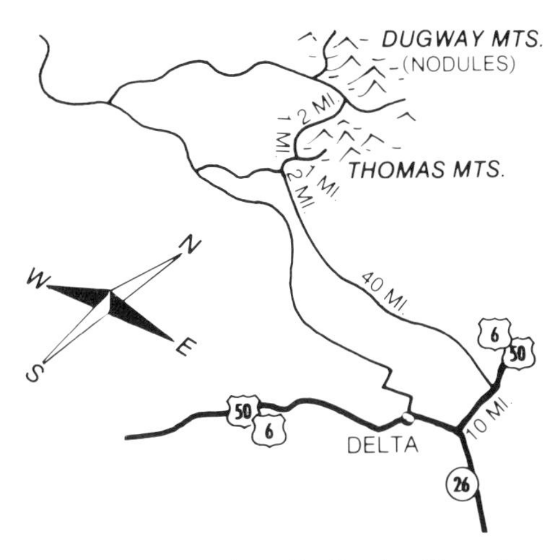

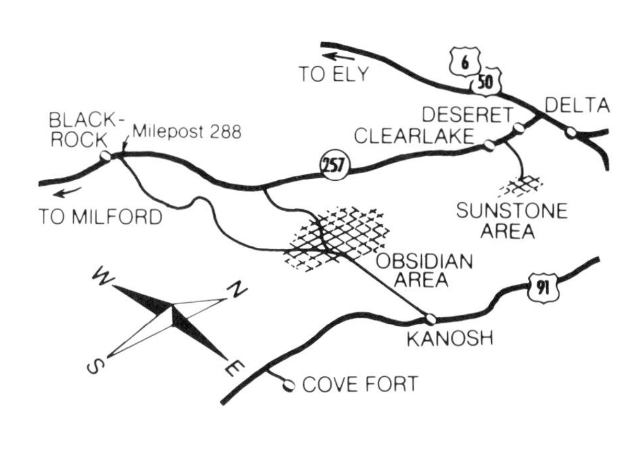

crystals are found in the rhyolite and loose in the sand, but those exposed to sunlight are bleached white.

NODULES: The Dugway nodule location is reached by going from Topaz Mountain E 2 miles on the Jericho road, then N 15 miles to a road W. Follow it 8 miles to a sign to the nodule bed.

- *Deseret, Millard County* * YELLOW LABRADORITE: S on Hwy 257 to cinder mounds 1 mile N of Clearlake Station, cross tracks to E and search flats for transparent gems.
- *Escalante, Garfield County* AGATE, JASPER: N 2 miles, collect along fence. Go on toward campground for jasper in hills, then SE to collect near ranch road. The road circles back to Escalante.
- *Eureka, Juab County* RHYOLITE (WONDERSTONE): Take Hwy 36 N 17 miles, cross railroad tracks, go right 2 miles to dig in ridges.

  AGATE: Go 4 miles NE to a gravel road NW, cross railroad tracks and drive into Pinyon Canyon. Collect on surface.
- *Fairfield, Utah County* VARISCITE: Take Hwy 73 N 4 miles, then left on dirt road up Manning Canyon past old gold mine and continue 1 mile to trail into Clay Canyon. Take trail 1/10 mile to mine.
- *Grantsville, Tooele County* VARISCITE: S 9 miles at Amatrice Hill in Stansbury Mountains.
- *Green River, Grand County* AGATE, JASPER: W on Int. 70, then S on Hwy 24 to road W into Goblin Valley.

  AGATE: W on U.S. 70 for 11 miles to overpass, turn S on road and hunt W of it. Go on 4 miles farther to road SE and N of the San Rafael River to hunt in hills.

  PETRIFIED WOOD, FOSSIL BONE: Take U.S. 70 3½ miles W, then N 17 miles on Hwy 6-50 to road W under railroad tracks, follow it 6½ miles and collect in hills to S.

  AGATE: Hwy 70 E for 12 miles, then S under power line for 6 miles, and E ½ mile to dig pink agate. Go back to road and continue 7 miles S, then mile E to collect red-spotted agate.
- *Hanksville, Wayne County* AGATE: W on Hwy 24 for 3 miles, then N 4 miles to collect red agate in Muddy Creek area. Return to Hanksville, go 26½ miles S to sign for Star Springs Park, then W to fork, take S fork a mile to collect near dam and in cliffs W of dam.

  JET: S 10 miles in Coaly Basin.

Autunite from Camigliatello Silano, near Cosenza.

- *Heber City, Wasatch County* RED HORN CORAL: N on Hwy 40 to Hwy 35, then E 7 miles to Francis and 3 miles more to Woodland. Go 2 miles to gate, park and walk 2 miles to site in Riley's Canyon, which is W of Camp Kildare in the Kamas district of the Wasatch National Forest. The coral is in limestone scarps or loose on the ground.
- *Hurricane, Washington County* FLOWER AGATE: Go 5 miles W, then S 1½ miles through 2 gates and S 2 miles through another gate and collect to right of road in red dunes. Fawcett Hobby Shop in Hurricane advertises it will give directions and guide service.
- *Jericho, Juab County* CHALCEDONY ROSES: Take road W for 35 miles and collect on S side of Keg Mountain. On the N side obsidian and nodules are found.

  AGATE: To E just off Hwy 6.
- *Kanab, Kane County* AGATE, PETRIFIED WOOD: Take U.S. 89 E for less than 16 miles, then N through gate 6½ miles to collect red agate, jasper, and wood along Vermilion Cliffs. Continue on U.S. 89 13 miles to rest area, go through gate and NE 7 miles to hills for petrified wood.
- *Leeds, Washington County* PETRIFIED WOOD: Take U.S. 91 NE a mile to a road S, cross two pole lines in first ½ mile, turn right through gate into canyon.
- *Levan, Juab County* BLACK AGATE: Take Hwy 28 S 13 miles, then mile E on dirt road into valley. Collect to the right beyond buildings in ravines and on ridges.
- *Lucin, Box Elder County* VARISCITE: NW 5 miles at Utahlite Hill (private claim).
- *Milford, Beaver County* * OPAL: Take Hwy 257 N to McDonald ranch (fee).

  QUARTZ CRYSTALS: E 12 miles at Mineral Mountain in Miner's Basin.

  OBSIDIAN: Take Hwy 257 N for 23 miles, E across railroad tracks, then nearly 2 miles farther to poor road S to collect snowflake obsidian in hills. Go back to Hwy 257, continue N 11 miles, then E 2½ miles to a big sink for more obsidian.
- *Mt. Carmel Junction, Kane County* SEPTARIAN NODULES: Go NE 1⅔ miles on U.S. 89, then N 3 miles to gate and 2½ miles farther, park, and collect nodules in steep canyon to right and canyons opening into it.
- *Moab, Grand County* AGATE, FOSSIL BONE: Take U.S. 163 to road E a mile below airport, and continue into Burro Seeps, and S in valley to collect.
- *Nephi, Juab County* FOSSIL PALM WOOD: Take Hwy 132 W for 12 miles toward Delta, turn S at gravel pit, go 8 miles to a gate, then a mile farther to a fork. Take left fork a mile and dig for wood. Return to fork, take right one and walk E into hills for agate.

  RED ONYX: Go E on Hwy 132 for 6 miles, then N on Mt. Nebo road 3½ miles to a cattle guard. Park, climb to shelf, and then go left to diggings.
- *Panguitch, Garfield County* JASPER, AGATE: Take road to Panguitch Lake to end of pavement; then go ½ mile to camp grounds and collect S of camp.
- *Parowan, Iron County* AGATE: Take road E up Parowan canyon to second fork, then left to top of ridge. Also farther along road on way to Cedar Breaks National Monument.
- *Pelican Point, Utah County* BLACK CALCITE ONYX: Along Utah Lake.
- *St. George, Washington County* AGATE: Go E on Hwy 17 for 17½ miles to dirt road S, continue 4 miles to red dunes.

  BANDED RHYOLITE (WONDERSTONE): At quarries.

  MALACHITE: In Dixie Apex Mine.
- *Salina, Sevier County* RHYOLITE (WONDERSTONE): Go 3 miles SE, then take right turn S for 3 miles and take right fork to ranch. Collect to E.
- *Thompson, Grand County* PETRIFIED WOOD, BARITE PSEUDOMORPHS: Take Int. 70 E 6 miles, then dirt road SE 8½ miles to collect. Another area, the Yellow Cat area, is reached from Int. 70 by going S 10 miles and then E a mile.
- *Washington, Washington County* SANDSTONE: Scenic sandstone is mined on the W side of Virgin oil dome and SE of Hurricane on Little Creek mountain.
- *Wendover, Tooele County* PLUME AGATE: Take U.S. 40 N for 8 miles and search hillsides in Nevada. Also take Int. 80 E ½ mile and turn 2 miles N to collect.
- *Woodside, Emery County* JASPER, PETRIFIED BONE AND WOOD: S 5 miles on Hwy 50, then NW 5 miles on dirt road to Castle Dale; hunt on slopes.

Vermont

Much of the area of Vermont is broken up by the Green Mountains and, parallel with them in the west, the Taconic Mountains. As a result of its rugged topography and glaciation, Vermont has a number of lakes, of which Lake Champlain is the largest. Its soil is thin, so that underlying rock is often exposed.

- *Barre, Washington County* GRANITE, RUTILATED QUARTZ: At Wheaton Granite quarry in Cobble Hill quarry group.
- *Burlington, Chittenden County* JASPER: N 9 miles at Eugene Parrot farm.
- *Chester, Windsor County* KYANITE, STAUROLITE: In quarries.
- *Eden, Lamoille County* VESUVIANITE, SERPENTINE: At Belvidere Mine of Vermont Asbestos Company, on Belvidere Mountain.
- *Grafton, Windham County* SERPENTINE, KYANITE: In quarries.

- *Lowell, Orleans County* GARNET, DIOPSIDE: In dump at gate of Ruberoid Asbestos mine.
- *Milton, Chittenden County* JASPER: At Parrott quarry 6 miles SW on U.S. 2.
- *Proctor, Rutland County* MARBLE: In local quarries.
- *Rutland Station, Rutland County* AVENTURINE QUARTZ: In saddle on N side of Round Hill 3¾ miles SE.
- *South Alburg, Franklin County* QUARTZ: On shore of Lake Champlain.
- *Williamsville, Windham County* AGATE: In road cut E of bridge over Adams Brook on way to East Dover. Also mile N of bridge just above where Bemis Brook empties into Adams Brook.

Virginia

Drowned valleys along the coastal plain of Virginia form long bays and, in the southeast, swamps such as the Great Dismal Swamp. Behind the coastal, sandy plain lies the Piedmont plateau, its rolling surface broken by ridges of crystalline rocks. This passes into the Blue Ridge Mountains, running from northeast to southwest, and the Allegheny Mountains, with a great valley between them. Gem minerals in the crystalline rocks and caves in the sedimentary regions are notable occurrences.

- *Altavista, Pittsylvania County* BERYL: SW 6 miles in a pegmatite along Hwy 29.

STAUROLITE: In cliffs 8 miles upstream in Roanoke river near its junction with Old Woman Creek.

- *Amelia, Amelia County* * AMAZONSTONE, MOONSTONE, SPESSARTITE, BERYL: The Rutherford mine NE of Amelia is famous for its brilliant green amazonstone, moonstone, apatite, and gem-quality spessartite garnet. To the SE is the Morefield mine where excellent amazonstone can be found.

  The Rutherford mine is 1½ miles NE on Hwy 360 and then N on Hwy 609 (fee). The Morefield mine is 3½ miles NE on Hwy 360 and then S on Hwy 628 (fee).

  Nearby are many other mines, such as the Ligon mine 9 miles NE, notable for star quartz, the Champion mine, the Anderson Mica Prospect, and the Winfree Prospect, which is reached by Hwy 360 to Hwy 627 to

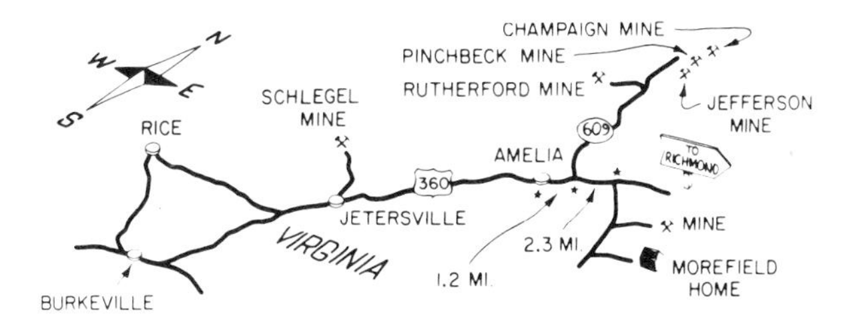

(Left) Celestite crystals on sulphur from the Floristella Mine, Enna.
(Middle) Selenite crystal on aragonite and sulphur.
(Right) Herschelite from Rupe di Aci Castello, Catania, Sicily.

Smack's Creek, then right, and the Vaughan Beryl Prospect, which is 2¾ miles due E on the W side of Hwy 627. Nearby are the Flippen Mica-Beryl Prospect ⅓ mile W of Hwy 628 and 3½ miles NE, and the Dobbin prospect near it. N of the Rutherford mine is a group shown on map.

AMETHYST: Via Hwy 638 to SE on Duncan farm.

- *Amherst, Amherst County* AMETHYST: E for 3 miles to Hwy 604, take it S to Hwy 659, then Hwy 659 to a cross road and sign to Schaar farm (fee).
- *Arrington, Nelson County* AMETHYST: At Saunders farm 8½ miles NW.
- *Bedford, Bedford County* APATITE: At Mitchell mine 6½ miles SE.

QUARTZ: In Peaksville mine 5 miles NW.

MOONSTONE: SE 6½ miles via Hwy 714, together with thulite.

GARNET: At quarry on W bank of Falling Creek 4 miles SE and ½ mile N of Hwy 714.

- *Bent Creek, Appomattox County* CRYPTOMELANE: At Enterprise mine to S.
- *Bland, Bland County* AGATE: Near Point Pleasant N side of Walker Mountain.
- *Brokenburg, Spotsylvania County* BERYL: In dumps of Edenton Mica mine ½ mile E of Brokenburg and Hwy 208.
- *Brookneal, Campbell County* AMETHYST: On Lacey Rush farm ⅓ mile NE and Clay farm 10 miles NE.
- *Browntown, Warren County*UNAKITE: As float in fields and pebbles in streams.
- *Central Plains, Fluvanna County* RHODONITE: Take Hwy 6 W 1 mile to Kids Store, then right-hand fork to Hwy 620 for ½ mile and trail to right (fee).
- *Centreville, Fairfax County* PREHNITE: At Fairfield quarry 4 miles W via Hwy 29 and 211.
- *Charlotte Court House, Charlotte County* AMETHYST: W on Hwy 40 for 2½ miles to Vassar house, take trail S to collect. Also 2½ miles NW at Donald plantation.

KYANITE: NW 12 miles.

- *Charlottesville, Albemarle County* QUARTZ: Behind 7-11 Store on Hydraulic road W of U.S. 29. Also in construction zone NW of the intersection of Ivy road and Hwy 29, and in greenstone in road cut W of Hwy 20 and U.S. 64 intersection.
- *Coatsville, Hanover County* KYANITE, GARNET: At Saunders No. 2 mine on S shore of Little River 2½ miles NE.
- *Collinsville, Henry County* STAUROLITE: Take Hwy 57 W to Fairy Stone park, collect in area outside park.
- *Cullen, Charlotte County* BERYL, GARNET, QUARTZ: In mica mines to S, as well as the Crews No. 1 a mile N.

(Left) Globular mesolite from Rupe di Aci Castello, Catania.
(Middle) Interpenetrating cubes of rock salt.
(Right) Sulphur and celestite.

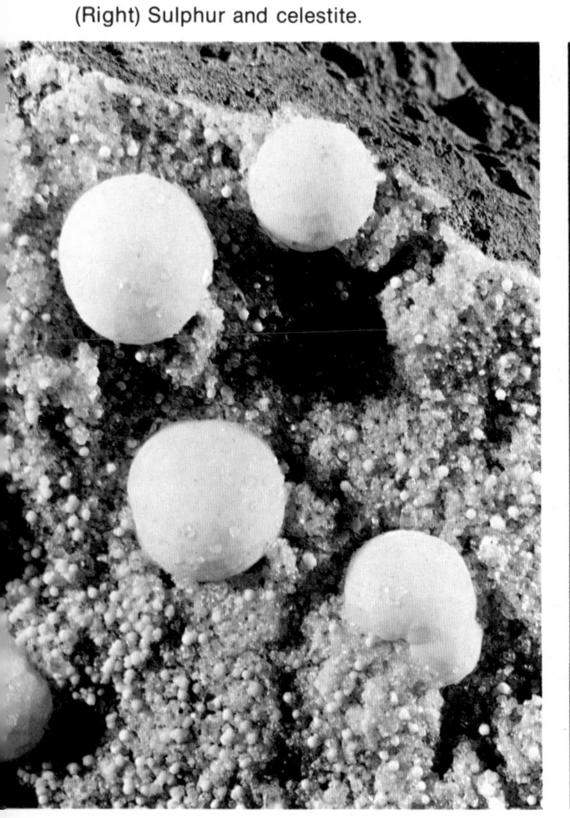

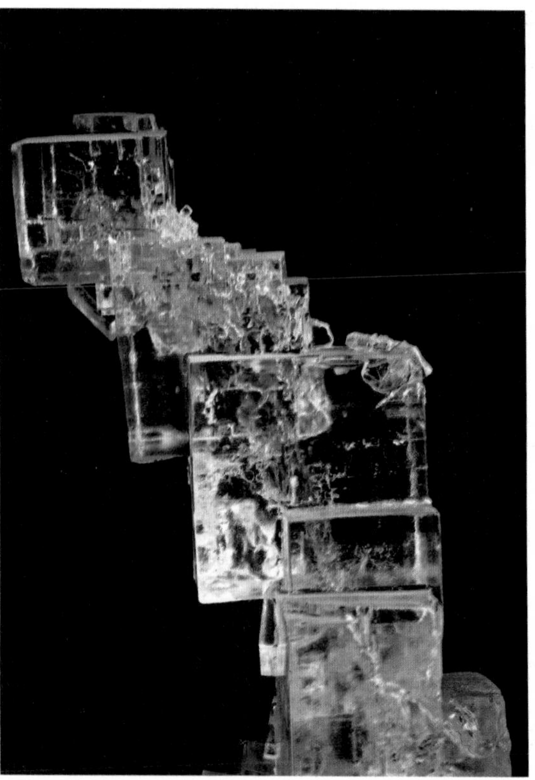

(Left) Aragonite from San Giovanni, Cagliari, Sardinia.
(Right) Copper-bearing aragonite from San Giovanni, Cagliari.

- *Deerfield, Bath County* QUARTZ: Take Hwy 629 S to Hwy 640, then left to the third farm, collect on Chestnut Ridge.
- *Farmville, Prince Edward County* KYANITE: At Willis Mountain.
- *Flat Rock, Powhatan County* BERYL, QUARTZ: Take Hwy 613 NE 3½ miles to Herbb No. 3 mine and Herbb No. 1 nearby.

  STAR QUARTZ: To NE at White Peaks mine.

  TOPAZ, AMAZONSTONE: In Herbb No. 2 mine.
- *Front Royal, Warren County* UNAKITE: As veins in exposed granite and as gravel in streams.
- *Galax, Grayson County* KYANITE, GARNET, CORUNDUM: At J. C. Pierce Prospect ⅓ mile N of West Galax and at Nuchols place 1 mile SW.

  GARNET: In veins on Higgins and Phipps farms to SW.
- *Glade Hill, Franklin County* APATITE: Yellow crystals in schist 1⅓ miles S of Glade Hill school.
- *Goose Creek, Loudoun County* SERPENTINE: In Virginia Lime and Marble quarry to S.
- *Grant, Grayson County* UNAKITE: NW 1½ miles along Hwy 16.
- *Hillsboro, Albemarle County* STAR QUARTZ: Blue material in quarry S of Yancey's Mill.
- *Horse Pasture, Henry County* GARNET: At Wilson quarries to N.
- *Ida, Page County* JASPER: NW 1 mile along road and near Hoak Hill.
- *Ladysmith, Caroline County* BERYL: In Last Chance mine on Lawrence Beazeley farm 6 miles SW by Hwy 229 for 4½ miles to Hwy 603 a mile and then a mile on dirt road.

  UNAKITE: At quarry to S.
- *Laurel Fork, Carroll County* QUARTZ: On A. G. Vaughn farm 6⅔ miles N and a mile E, and at Guy Barnard place 3¾ miles E and a mile S, as well as the Marvin Marshall farm 1 mile NW and the Henry Hall farm ⅗ mile NE of the Marshall farm.
- *Leesburg, Loudoun County* PREHNITE: At Arlington Stone quarry reached by Hwy 659 S a mile from Hwy 7, and at Belmont Traprock quarry 4 miles SE on Goose Creek.
- *Luray, Page County* * UNAKITE: Go E on U.S. 211, then S on Hwy 689, cross stream just N of Ida; turn W several miles on dirt road; collect in stream bed and on hillside.

  BLOODSTONE, JASPER: In Naked Creek on Rockingham County line.
- *Lowesville, Amherst County* AMETHYST: NE 2½ miles.
- *Lynch Station, Campbell County* CRYPTOMELANE: In prospects E of the old Bishop mine.
- *Lynchburg, Campbell County* CRYPTOMELANE: At Bell mine 6 miles S and 1 mile W of Hwy 29. Also at the Piedmont mine 10 miles E.

  AMAZONSTONE: On T. Graves place 6 miles SE.

KYANITE: S 7½ miles.

• *Martinsville, Henry County* BERYL: Golden beryl on Williams prospect 3 miles SW and ⅓ mile S of U.S. 58.

STAUROLITE: SE 9 miles in road cut near S bank of Smith River.

EPIDOTE: S 2 miles along Hwy 229.

• *Moneta, Bedford County* AMAZONSTONE, GARNET: One mile SE at Young mine.

• *Mountsville, Loudoun County* SERPENTINE: E to Hwy 733, then to Highcamp road 1½ mile, at marble quarry.

• *Newport, Giles County* SMOKY QUARTZ CRYSTALS: SW 3½ miles on Spruce Run.

• *Oliver, Hanover County* MOONSTONE, GARNET: Take Hwy 738 from U.S. 1 for 7⅔ miles, hunt in stream N of house and left of barn at Harris Mica mine (fee).

• *Petersburg, Prince George County* PETRIFIED WOOD: In gravel pits to E.

• *Rice, Prince Edward County* AMETHYST: Take Hwy 619 N for 3 miles at Smith place. Amethyst is also found on H. D. Hodges farm; take Hwy 307 for less than a quarter mile, take first road left.

KYANITE: In old mica mines 1 mile N.

• *Rich Valley, Smyth County* QUARTZ: Loose in soil near Portersfield quarry.

• *Rileyville, Page County* SERPENTINE, EPIDOTE: In copper prospect on W side of Hwy 662, 2½ miles from Rileyville and 1 mile E of junction with Hwy 605.

• *Roseland, Nelson County* BLUE STAR QUARTZ: E ½ mile at American Rutile company quarry, with apatite.

• *Saltville, Smyth County* QUARTZ: At Worthy mine. Some is scepter quartz.

• *Schuyler, Nelson County* SOAPSTONE: In quarries here and in a belt trending NE 30 miles long.

• *Springfield, Page County* ORBICULAR JASPER: Go 2 miles E to collect in Jeremiah creek.

• *Stanley, Page County* UNAKITE: At Fisher's Gap S of Marksville on road from Hwy 680 to Bailey Mountain.

• *Stuart, Patrick County* STAUROLITE: In belt of schistose rocks extending from SW of Stuart for 20 miles NE.
Another similar belt runs from about 9 miles NE of Stuart across Henry County. Many of the stones are loose in the soil.

• *Syria, Madison County* * UNAKITE: Material from Fisher's Gap is found in the Rose River. Take the river road and collect in the stream. One place is at the Graves farm.

• *Troutsdale, Grayson County* UNAKITE: SE 2½ miles as outcrops along Rd. 16.

• *Vesuvius, Rockbridge County* * UNAKITE: Some of the best is found near here below the Blue Ridge Parkway. It is found along Hwy 56 in road cuts and in a quarry 2 miles W of the Tye River Gap.

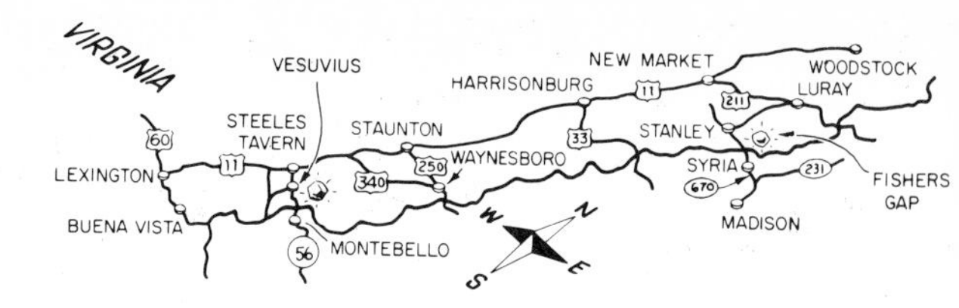

CHERT: At South River mine.

• *Willis, Floyd County* QUARTZ: At A. T. Moles farm 6 miles SW and a mile E of Buffalo Mountain Church.

• *Willkie, Nelson County* UNAKITE: E of Skyline drive at its intersection with Hwy 56.

Washington

The Cascade Mountains, containing a number of extinct volcanoes and ranging north from the Columbia River to Canada, divide the state into two regions. To the east of the mountains is a plain rising from the Columbia River, formed of lava beds and extending to the Okanogan highland to the north. West of the mountains is the great basin in which lies Puget Sound, cut off from the ocean by the rugged Coast range and Olympic Mountains. Washington's lavas are the matrix of rich petrified wood and agate materials.

• *Aberdeen, Grays Harbor County* FLOWER JASPER: On beaches and in stream banks all the way to Raymond.

• *Adna, Lewis County* CARNELIAN, PETRIFIED WOOD: Take Bunker Creek road N 4 miles, then W on Ceres Hill road 4 miles to McCoy farm (fee).

AGATE: In road cuts and ditches on Hwy 6 on way to PeEll, and along the Chehalis River.

• *Anacortes, Skagit County* JASPER PEBBLES: On beach.

• *Beverly, Grant County* OPALIZED LOGS: In volcanic ash on slopes of Saddle Mountains S of hwy from Beverly to Corfu. Go S to Mattawa, then E 3 miles and N to collecting area. (Fee).

PETRIFIED WOOD: Take Hwy 243 S 14 miles to Vernita ferry. Drive up bluffs on W side of river to cafe, ask way to Bennett claim (fee). Or go 6 miles upstream to wooden bridge over Crab Creek and collect on N bank of creek or in hills.

• *Bucoda, Thurston County* AGATE, CARNELIAN: Take road S to Tono, then 5 miles over hill to coal mine spoil piles. Dig by creek bed, or go to right to dig under clay stratum.

• *Castle Rock, Cowlitz County* CARNELIAN: Take Hwy 504 E to Kid Valley State Park, then E to Beaver Creek.

• *Centralia, Chehalis County* AGATE: On ground 4½ miles E.

• *Chehalis, Lewis County* CARNELIAN: Take Alpha road to Lucas Creek sign, go on to gate, then N to dig S of trail and N and S of creek. Then go on farther N and W to dig.

Also go 5 miles S on Hwy 99 and E 4 miles to bridge, and collect in gravels of N fork of Newaukum River.

• *Clay City, Pierce County* AMETHYST: E 1 mile on Siegmund ranch.

• *Clearwater, Jefferson County* AGATE, PETRIFIED WOOD: As pebbles on Kalaloch Beach.

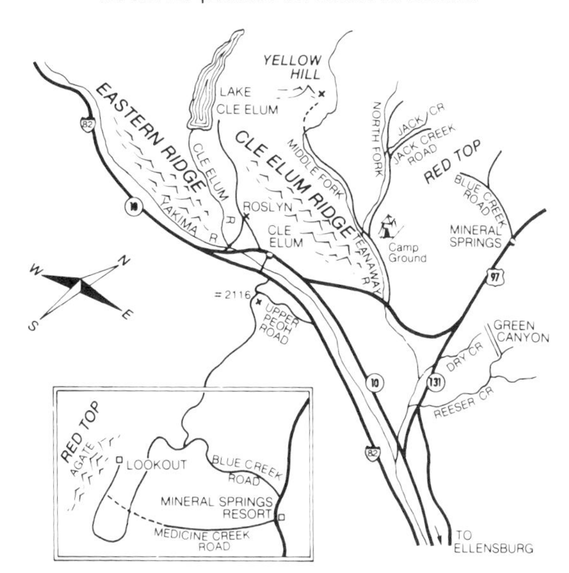

• *Cle Elum, Kittitas County* * BLUE AGATE: Widely distributed from Leavenworth along Hwy 97 S to Yakima. Some specific locations: Take Hwy 97 3 miles NE to steel bridge, cross, take road left 15 miles to Jack Creek sign. Turn right on this road and continue for 5 miles up mountain to a fork. Take left road almost 1 mile. Dig nodules in cliff up the bank or through woods on right.

Also take Hwy 97 NE turning off left on Blue Creek Road at Mineral Springs resort station for 9 miles. Park, take upper trail to Red Top Lookout, and dig beyond it.

Also take Hwy 97 N, turning right on Horse Canyon road beyond second bridge that crosses creek. Walk ¼ mile up road and to left up hill. Dig in red brown basalt cliffs along Dry Creek, Green Canyon, Reeser Creek, and Horse Canyon roads.

AGATE: Leave U.S. 10 at Roslyn interchange, take first logging road to left off overpass ramp and drive to crest of ridge. Dig S and E of beacon.

RED AGATE: Take Teanaway road from U.S. 97, turn left on first road beyond bridge. Turn onto Middle Fork of Teanaway road at Casland, go 4 miles, cross river on Hwy 2110, and take jeep road to Yellow Hill. Dig in bulldozed area and in canyons.

NODULES: At Roslyn interchange to W take first logging road to left off overpass ramp and go NW to crest of ridge. Dig S and E of beacon on side hill.

BLUE AGATE: Go S through South Cle Elum to Upper Peoh Point road, follow it to the second High Line Canal bridge, and walk S to base of steep ridge to S. Collect along ridge.

• *Colton, Whitman County* SMOKY QUARTZ: In sandpit.

• *Concrete, Skagit County* JADE, SERPENTINE: Take Dallas Bridge Road S 10 miles toward Darrington, keeping left at fork. Take Finney Creek Road right and follow creek on left 13 miles, using Gee Point Road to parking area. Collect in first creek.

Washington Gem and Mining company of Darrington has claim in this area.

• *Cumby, Kittitas County* JASPER-AGATE: On middle fork of Teanaway River.

• *Duvall, King County* BLACK PETRIFIED WOOD: Take Hwy 203 N, stay N at fork for 3 miles, cross Cherry Creek, and go 2½ miles more to road E up hill. Take it 1 mile to fork, then right to second fork, and stay right to locked gate. Hike 1 mile through woods to creek to collect.

• *Ellensburg, Kittitas County* PETRIFIED WOOD: Take Hwy 97 S for 13 miles to parking area on right where footbridge crosses river. Dig on hillsides across river.

• *Forks, Clallam County* ORBICULAR JASPER: Go N on Hwy 101 to Calawah and Soleduck rivers, collect in gravel and along banks.

• *Gilmore Corners, Cowlitz County* BLOODSTONE, CARNELIAN: Take Sightly Road S until it turns E, continue E to first road S, take it to Walter Swift farmhouse. Collect in area to E. (Fee.)

• *Goodnoe Hills, Klickitat County* CHERT: Go SW to small bridge, follow E bank upstream ½ mile to collecting spot.

• *Grays Harbor, Grays Harbor County* AGATE: N and S on beaches around Westport and Grayland.

• *Grays River, Wahkiakum County* AGATE: On Gorley ranch (fee).

• *Issaquah, Kings County* AMBER: Go S on Hobart road 3 miles, turn E on Tiger Mountain Road for 1½ miles and then N on dirt road. Go ½ mile to E side of Fifteen-Mile Creek, collect in place and on E side of road. Farther up road ½ mile is blue agate.

• *Kalaloch, Jefferson County* BEACH AGATE, PETRIFIED WOOD: N and S to Queets along beach.

• *Kalama, Cowlitz County* AGATE: In area E of Cowlitz River.

NODULES: Take cemetery road NE for 1½ miles and dig in cliff. Then go S on Green Mountain road 4 miles to Johnson road and turn N ¼ mile to dig geodes and agate.

• *La Push, Clallam County* SPHERULITIC JASPER: In gravels at mouth of Quillanute river, 6½ miles W of Lake Crescent in the rock, and 1 mile NW of the W end of Lake Crescent in gully as boulders.

• *Liberty, Kittikas County* JASPER-AGATE: Take Boulder Creek road to meadow, then jeep road to right up Robinson Gulch for 2 miles and take trail to top of ridge. Dig to left at top of Crystal Mountain.

FLUORESCENT QUARTZ: Take U.S. 97 to the summit, turn right on Lion Rock road No. 2107 and the Road 2101 to Lookout. Dig on either side of road about 2 miles beyond slide area on way to Lookout.

BLUE AGATE: For several miles to S along Hwy 97 in road cuts and hills.

NODULES: At heads of Williams and Boulder creeks and on Table Mountain.

• *Lyle, Klickitat County* AGATE, JASPER, PETRIFIED WOOD: To N 10 to 15 miles in gullies and on hillsides.
• *Mondovi, Lincoln County* OPAL: NW 1 mile and also 1 mile N in vesicular basalt.

AGATE: Take road toward Capps Talc Mine near Spokane River and dig 2 miles below mine for vein material in cliffs along river.

• *Mount Vernon, Skagit County* JADELIKE MATERIAL: In talc on SW side of Cultus Mountain. Take road from Clear Lake E 3½ miles to mine.

AGATE, GEODES: Take Hwy 538 S to Walker Valley road past Big Lake, then S 2 miles to diggings.

• *Newport, Pend Oreille County* AMETHYSTINE QUARTZ: On W bank of Pend Oreille River 2 miles NW.

AGATE: With jasper in beaches along Yaquina Bay park.

• *Okanogan, Okanogan County* AVENTURINE QUARTZ: Take road N along Salmon Creek, then turn right to Happy Hill (fee).
• *Olympia, Thurston County* AGATE, PETRIFIED WOOD: In sand to S at Tono.
• *Oso, Snohomish County* JADE: Along Deer creek upstream from bridge.
• *Palisades, Douglas County* OPALIZED WOOD: To W of road at Moses Coulee and S to Appledale.
• *Pasco, Franklin County* AGATE: In bluffs on E bank of Columbia River to NW.
• *Prosser, Benton County* OPALIZED WOOD: In volcanic ash in canyons of Horse Heaven Hills.
• *Pullman, Whitman County* AMETHYST: To NE on hill W of Ringo Station.

SMOKY QUARTZ: In sand pit with corundum at Bald Butte to S of Pullman and E of Hwy 195.

• *Riverside, Okanogan County* PINK THULITE: To NE at Tunk Creek.
• *Roosevelt, Klickitat County* PETRIFIED WOOD: Take Hwy 12 7 miles E to Pine Creek, turn N up road on left bank to canyon and 2 miles to Ford Creek. Dig in E bank of creek.
• *Sedro Woolley, Skagit County* SERPENTINE: NE 6 miles.
• *Silver Lake, Cowlitz County* AGATE, PETRIFIED WOOD: In nearby fields and stream beds.
• *Snoqualmie Pass, King County* QUARTZ: Go to Curtiss campground at Denny Mountain, then take Denny Creek trail 1½ miles to gorge, and collect in talus. There is also some amethyst.
• *Sunnyside, Yakima County* PETRIFIED WOOD: Take Hwy 12 SE to Vernita Ferry road, turn N on it for 9 miles to Anderson ranch cabin (formerly The Old Hard Rock Bennett) (fee) on right-hand side of road, dig on ranch. There are free diggings farther along road 13 miles to dig on left of road, and farther beyond it on road is another road on right. Take it 4 miles to collect.
The Silver Dollar diggings are near Sunnyside (fee).
• *Tenino, Thurston County* CARNELIAN, JASPER: Go to Johnson Creek Road, then 5½ miles E to Rocking B ranch. Collect above creek. Also take Hwy 507 S to Skookumchuck Road, go E for 7 miles to Johnson Creek Road, then N ⅓ mile to Anderson house (fee).
• *Toledo, Lewis County* CARNELIAN: Take any road E or N to Salmon Creek, collect in river bars.
• *Valley, Stevens County* RED MARBLE: Take Waits Lake Road W to Carr's Corner, go left 6 miles to quarry.
• *Vantage, Kittitas County* PETRIFIED WOOD: Take Wanapum Road 2 miles to Petrified Logs Trail sign, enter gate to right into Game Department land through stone pillars, go 2 miles to another gate and look for digging area.
• *Warwick, Klickitat County* CARNELIAN, GREEN JASPER: W 2 miles at bridge over wash in Hwy 8. Collect in fields and wash.
• *Whidbey Island, Island County* JADE, AGATE: On beaches.
• *Wiley, Yakima County* PETRIFIED WOOD: To S in Ahtanum canyon in L. T. Murray Wildlife Recreation Area. Collect on surface only. No digging.
• *Woodland, Cowlitz County* CARNELIAN: Go N on U.S. 99 5 miles to Cloverdale, then E on Todd Road to Cloverdale Road and N and E to Green Mountain Road. Collect in Cloverdale Creek.
• *Yakima, Yakima County* OPALIZED WOOD: In wash 33 miles E and mile N of Hwy 24 at Yakima Ridge.

West Virginia

The western two-thirds of West Virginia is a rough area of hills and valleys cut in sedimentary rocks and forming a part of the Allegheny plateau that extends from New York to Alabama. The eastern part lies in the Great Valley, in which mountain ridges and valleys have been the result of intense folding and erosion of the sedimentary rocks.

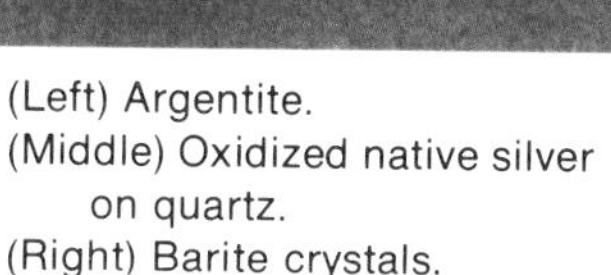
(Left) Argentite.
(Middle) Oxidized native silver on quartz.
(Right) Barite crystals.

- *Baker, Hardy County* QUARTZ: 5 miles NW on E slope of Branch Mountain.
- *Berkeley Springs, Morgan County* QUARTZ: NE along U.S. 522 for 4 miles; access to Pennsylvania Glass Sand Corp. mines is by road 1 mile NE of company offices. Also in quarry on U.S. 522 2 miles N of Cacapon Mountain State Park entrance.
- *Charlestown, Kanawha County* PETRIFIED WOOD: Take Hwy 14 W for 4 miles to bridge and hunt in creek banks along road to country club.
- *Huntersville, Pocahontas County* CHERT: SE 1½ miles and 1 mile from Hwy 89.
- *Marlington, Pocahontas County* AGATIZED CORAL: SW 8 miles on U.S. 219 to Mill Point quarry N of intersection of Hwy 219 and Hwy 39. Also 2 miles SW of Hillsboro to Locust Creek road, then left 1½ miles to stone bridge to collect in Locust creek.
- *Romney, Hampshire County* QUARTZ: S 3 miles on U.S. 220 at Tonoloway quarry.
- *Union, Monroe County* QUARTZ: Along Turkey Creek and on Fullen Brothers farm.
- *Willowtown, Mercer County* ONYX: In quarry.

Wisconsin

Wisconsin is a rolling plain laid down on sedimentary rocks and broken in places by upthrust igneous and metamorphic rocks, such as the Baraboo Hills in the south central region, the granite exposures in Waushara and Marathon counties, and the gneisses of the northeastern part of the state. Wisconsin's extensive glaciation is shown by its many lakes and the famous moraine district west of Milwaukee.

- * LAKE SUPERIOR TYPE AGATES (DERIVED FROM GLACIAL GRAVELS): Are found in a number of places in Wisconsin. Among them are: Along Hwy 64 E of New Richmond and generally from Hudson to New Richmond.

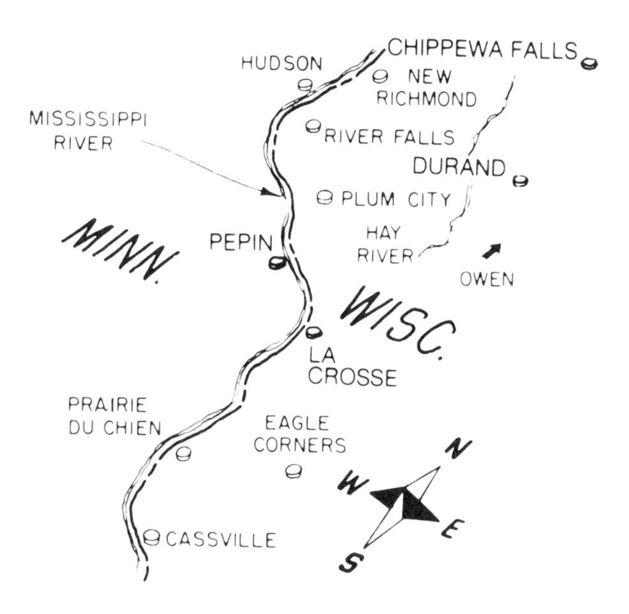

Just W of Hudson at gravel plant in Minnesota.
On gravel bars of the Hay River.
H. Turner and Son Plant at Cassville S on Hwy 133.
At Rush River Plant where Rush River crosses Hwy 10.
At Durand and Chippewa Falls in gravel pits.
At the River Falls Sand and Gravel Plant.
At Owen in gravels of Black River.
At Dillman Plant on Villa Louis Road in Prairie du Chien 3 blocks S of Hwy 18 and at Prairie City Gravel Co. pit ¼ mile N.
Bock Bros. Plant at Eagle Corners.
At Pepin on Deer Island and Lake Pepin beaches.
At LaCrosse in gravel dredging operations.

- *Afton, Rock County* AGATIZED CORAL: At gravel pit in village and at nearby quarries along road. Also at Shopiere to E in gravel pits.
- *Cascade, Sheboygan County* AGATE: S 2 miles at Bluhm Gravel pit.
- *Dickeyville, Grant County* ONYX: Take Hwy 151 for 4 miles, then dirt road right to pine tree on hill at quarry.
- *Hayward, Sawyer County* EPIDOTE, JASPER: N on Hwy 27 to Denver road, then W about 5 miles to mine road S and E across Ounce river to County mines and Skrupty mine for copper in epidote and jasper.
- *Janesville, Rock County* AGATIZED CORAL: Take Hwy 51 to junction with Hwy 14, then take first road left 1 mile to gravel pit.
- *Mosinee, Marathon County* UNAKITE: N 1 mile from where Hwy 153 and Hwy H meet.
- *Pittsville, Wood County* RED AND GREEN AVENTURINE QUARTZ: To S.
- *Powers Bluff, Wood County* QUARTZITE: Red, yellow, and black dendritic material SW of Arpin.
- *Spooner, Washburn County* AGATE: In lake area to NW and in roads and gravel pits, especially County Hwy C and P and at the Scott Township dump.
- *Redgranite, Waushara County* PINK GRANITE: In quarries to NW.
- *Waupaca, Waupaca County* RED AND GREEN GRANITE: N 5 miles in quarry.
- *Wausau, Marathon County* MOONSTONE: W on Hwy 29 to Hwy O, then N to Hwy U and W to collect in road fill banks.

  PERISTERITE: At Anderson Bros. & Johnson quarry.
- *Wisconsin Rapids, Wood County* SERPENTINE: N on Hwy 34 to Hwy C at Rudolph, then E to collect in outcrops along road.
- *Wittenburg, Shawano County* LABRADORITE: In boulders.

Wyoming

Much of Wyoming consists of rolling prairie more than a mile above sea level, broken by occasional buttes and erosion ridges. The northeastern part is a continuation of the Black Hills, while through the central part from east to west runs a long pass or valley below the Big Horn Mountains in north central Wyoming. Northwestern Wyoming is a complex region of igneous intrusions and upturned sedimentary rocks which holds the marvels of Yellowstone Park, the majesty of the Tetons, and the beautiful Wind River range to the south. Agate and petrified wood of many types exist in the gravels of all the regions, and jade in the eroded mountain ridges of the south central part.

- *Boslar, Albany County* JASPER: E 10 miles on Hwy 34. See Slim's Rock Shop in Boslar.
- *Buffalo, Johnson County* PETRIFIED WOOD: SE 12 miles along Crazy Woman Creek.
- *Casper, Natrona County* PETRIFIED WOOD: Along N bank of North Platte River E to Glenrock.

  CARNELIAN: To W in area between Poison Spider Creek and S fork of Casper Creek.
- *Cheyenne, Laramie County* CHALCEDONY: In gravels to W.

  QUARTZ CRYSTALS: In Cheyenne Pass.
- *Douglas, Converse County* * BLUE MOSS AGATE: Two collecting localities near graded road S to U.S. 30: first, Moss Agate Hill, about 30 miles SW of Douglas, a prominent hill W of road.

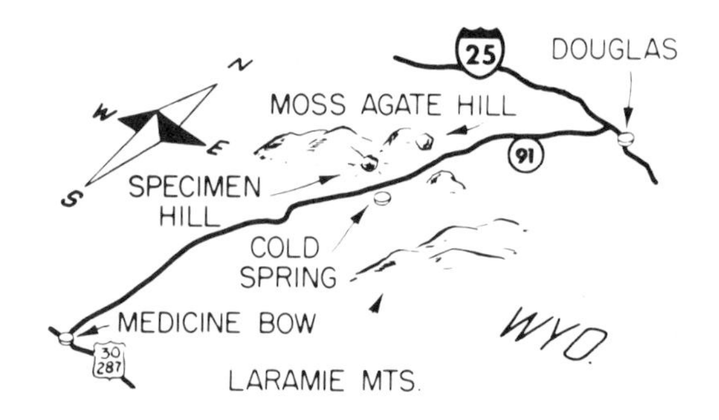

  Second, S of this locale about halfway to a place known as Coldspring lying in the Laramie Mountains—Specimen Hill, for dark blue moss agate in masses. E of road black agate is found on the ground.
- *Dubois, Fremont County* PETRIFIED WOOD: Drive 27 miles N to Wiggins Fork Creek, take road to forest service campground. Collecting is done by wading in Wiggins Fork and Frontier Creeks, searching flats along creek, and hiking up the mountain beyond the Wilderness Boundary. On the mountain is a petrified forest where collecting is not allowed.
- *Farson, Sweetwater County* * PETRIFIED WOOD: Farson is the center of a notable collecting area for limb casts and other petrified wood. N 9 miles on Hwy 187, turn E on dirt road 3 miles past end of Big Sandy reservoir, continue to fork, and take right hand one to collect near road for several miles. Also near Arandel reservoir No. 2.

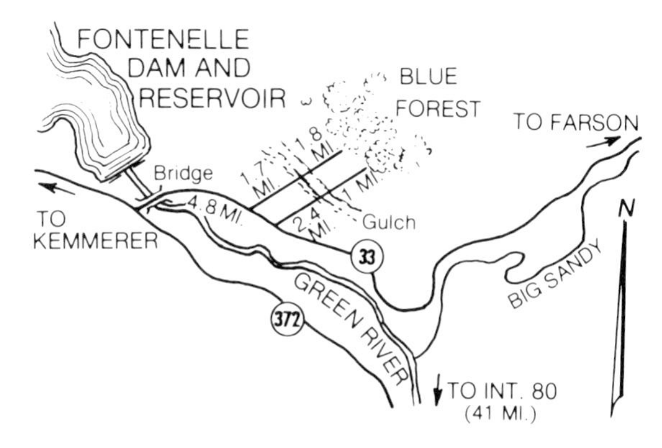

Take Hwy 28 NE 15 miles to Hay Ranch sign, take ranch road, then new road around ranch buildings and go E to collect in hills. Ranch is occasionally closed to visitors.

Take road SW 25 miles toward Fontenelle Dam, turn N to dig limb casts in Blue Forest area.

• *Glendo, Platte County* CHALCEDONY: NE in hills along North Platte River.

• *Guernsey, Platte County* QUARTZITE: Go 2 miles W on Hwy 26, then N, keeping right at fork for 8½ miles to W shore of Lake Guernsey, for youngite, a quartzite, as well as jasper and agate. The material is also reported from the NW shore of the lake near caves.

AGATE: Along W side of the road N to Hartville and farther N on left-hand fork. Also in quarry along road.

• *Jeffrey City, Fremont County* *MOSS AGATE: Go 3 miles E on Hwy 287 to ranch road leading N. Go through ranch gate and yard and beyond to collect the Sweetwater type fluorescent moss agates in flat. Or take Bureau of Land Management road 8 miles E. Recently a deposit of limb casts has been discovered N and E of this collecting area. The agates are covered with a white coating and lie along Sage Hen creek watershed.

AGATE, JADE: Ten miles farther W on U.S. 287, a road turns S to Crooks Gap, where agate and some jade have been found.

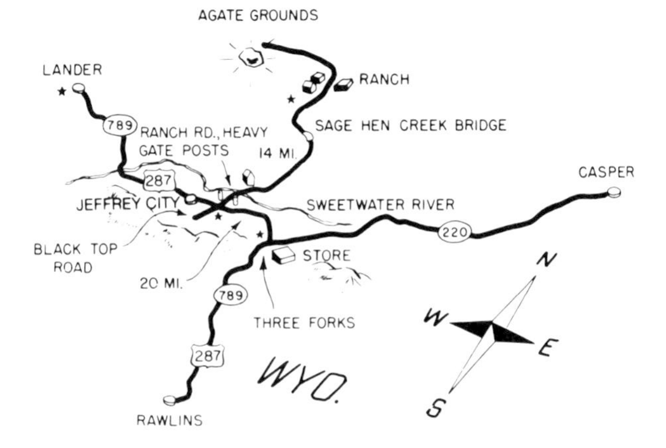

• *Kemmerer, Lincoln County* PETRIFIED ALGAE: E 10 miles on Hwy 30 near town of Opal.

• *Lander, Fremont County* NEPHRITE JADE: Over wide area in Wyoming in place or as boulders. Dark colored float jade is found along the course of the Sweetwater River between Crook's Creek on the E and the Wind River Mountains on the W.

BLACK JADE: Is found generally in the Granite Mountains and N of Split Rock.

LIGHT GREEN JADE: Has come from the Crook's Mountain area 65 miles SE of Lander and from the E side of Cottonwood Creek wherever black diorite boulders appear. To reach this area, take Hwy 287 12 miles past the Sweetwater River crossing and turn S for 8 miles.

NEPHRITE JADE: Abernathy claims, Fremont County, 40 miles SE of Lander, in diorite dike in granite, the material contains quartz crystals.

Curtis and Marion claims, Sec. 13, 18, T. 30, R. 92, 93 W; black, olive green outcrop ½ mile SW of this one.

Lucky Strike Claim, Secs. 19, 20, T. 30 N., R. 92 W., 61 miles from Lander, olive green pieces containing quartz crystals, at apex of a fold.

As float near Marston Lake, 40 miles from Lander, and at Moneta, Fremont County.

Copper Chief Gold Mine: 3 miles NE of Atlantic City, Fremont County.

Olive green, outcrop of East fork NE of Dubois and NE of Circle Ranch, Fremont County.

As float along Beaver Creek, 25 miles SE of Lander along Hwy 287, Fremont County.

In Green Mountains, 20 miles W of Bairoil, Fremont County.

Pathfinder Dam, Natrona County.

Along Dry Creek in Rattlesnake Mountains, Natrona County.

BLACK NEPHRITE JADE: As float over large area S of upper drainage of Sulfur Creek, 30 miles W of Bairoil, Fremont County.

PETRIFIED WOOD: Hwy 28 S for 35 miles to Bridger Wilderness sign, take dirt road left and stay on main road 9 miles toward two flat-topped buttes W of the road. At sharp turn in road, park and walk E and S for petrified wood, algae, and agate.

• *Medicine Bow, Carbon County* PETRIFIED WOOD, AGATE: N 18 miles and take right fork 13 miles to petrified forest to W of road.

PETRIFIED WOOD, BONE: To E at Como Bluff.

• *Moran, Teton County* JADE: Go S to Gros Ventre River, hike up bed 6 to 7 miles.

• *Riverton, Fremont County* MOSS AGATE NODULES: Take dirt road that runs W to Hwy 287; park where wires cross above road and collect in washes to NE.

PETRIFIED WOOD, AGATE: In gravels and streams in area between Hwy 287 N from Lander and Hwy 26 W from Riverton.

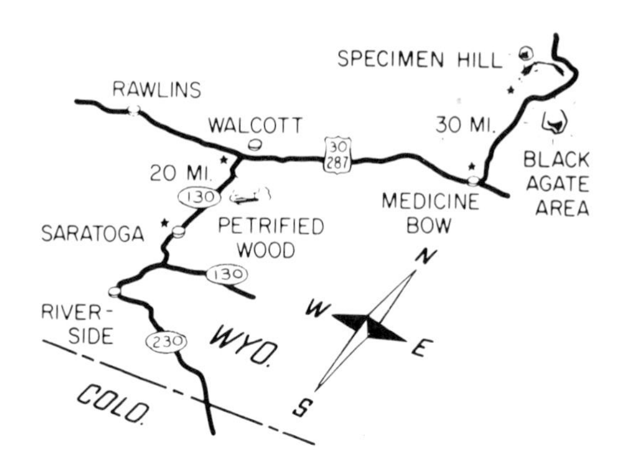

- *Saratoga, Carbon County* * PETRIFIED WOOD: On flats along Hwy 130 N to Walcott. The flats from Saratoga N to Walcott are strewn with petrified wood and chalcedony, especially on the E side just N of a road cut.
- *Shell, Big Horn County* PETRIFIED WOOD AND BONE: N 4 miles at Elkhorn ranch.
- *Sheridan, Sheridan County* GRANITE (LEOPARDITE): W 25 miles in dikes N of Burgess ranger station.
- *Shoshoni, Fremont County* AQUAMARINE: In dikes 15 miles NE in Bridger Mountains.
- *South Pass City, Fremont County* PETRIFIED WOOD: To N on divide between Hall and Twin creeks.
- *Split Rock, Fremont County* RUBY: In schist on Sweetwater divide.

  JADE: In place at American Jade Company claim N of junction of Longs Creek and Sweetwater River.
- *Tipton, Sweetwater County* * ALGAE AGATE, TURRITELLA AGATE: Drive S for less than 2 miles, take right-hand fork for 4 miles to within sight of Cathedral Bluffs on Delaneys Rim. Drive up the bluffs to top, turn left, and collect oolite, brown algae agate in outcrops on rim, as well as the silicified Oxytrema fossil shells known as turritella agate.

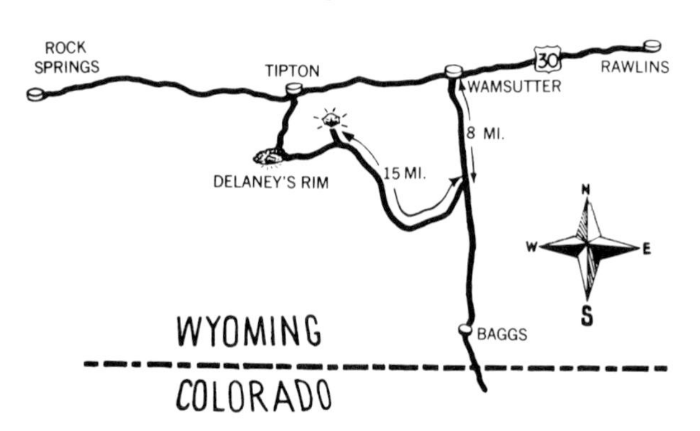

The area can also be approached from Wamsutter by going S 8 miles on the road to Baggs, then W on a ranch road 15 miles past barn and over ridge a mile to the Rim. There is black petrified wood in gullies and along the road.

- *Wheatland, Platte County* MOONSTONE: With labradorite to S and W along Hwy 34.

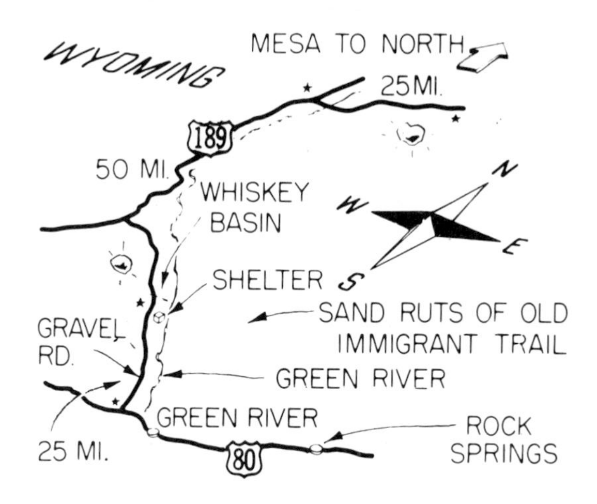

- *Whiskey Basin Area, Sweetwater and Sublette Counties* * AGATE: A gravel road that takes off N from Int. 80 a few miles W of Green River leads in 25 miles to the ruts of the old immigrant trail and to an area known as Whiskey Basin. To the W are hills where agate is found.
- *Worland, Washakie County* CHALCEDONY: To W of town.

Canada

Alberta

Most of the province is a part of the vast continental plain of Canada, but on the west its boundary is set by the Rocky Mountains, which rise in places to 10,000 feet. The southern part of the plain is prairie, while the northern part is rolling and wooded.

- *Calgary* PETRIFIED WOOD: E 90 miles in Red Deer River Valley. The wood is limb sections like Eden Valley wood.
- *Drumheller,* PETRIFIED WOOD, BONE: To NW in Valley of the Dinosaurs.

  AGATE: To E in seams in the Hand Hills.

  Note: Make a border declaration of any polished stone or jewelry taken into Canada or it may be dutiable on return to the United States.

British Columbia

Mountains cover almost all of British Columbia, from the Rockies to the Coast ranges. These were formed by giant granite masses forcing up the Coast and Selkirk ranges, and the overthrust toward the east that

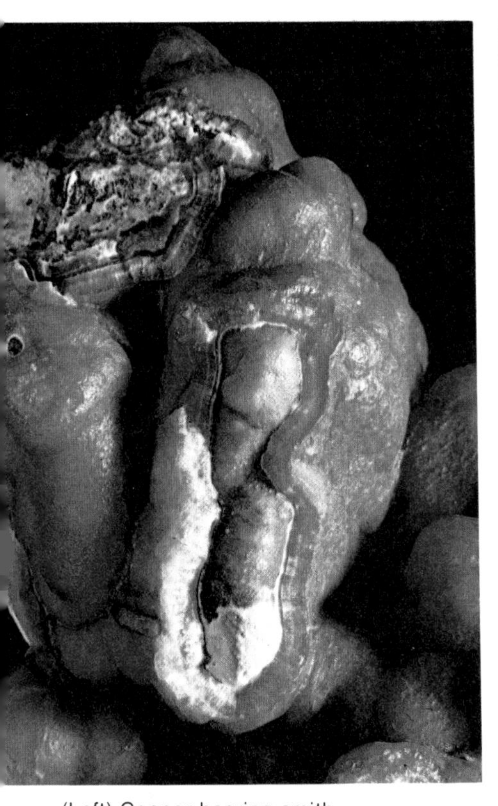

(Left) Copper-bearing smithsonite
(Right) Scalenohedral calcite.

created the Rockies. Later, lavas poured into the lower part of the province, as they did in the United States farther south, and the exposed rocks were carved into valleys by glaciers of the ice ages. Most of the mineralization has been in the western ranges, while vast quantities of quartz, jade, and petrified wood are contained in the enormous deposits of gravel along the rivers.

- *Agassiz* The bars in the Fraser River from Chilliwack on the south to above Lillooet in the north contain pebbles and boulders of nephrite jade, rhodonite, agate, and vesuvianite. Many are inaccessible except in times of low water in the late winter and early spring. Specific localities are described below under entries by cities.
  There are several collecting spots at Agassiz. To get to one, take the road to Seabird Island, turn at the sign, then right at the first fork and left at the crossroads. Go over the dike to a long narrow bar. Can be reached only by boat at other than low-water times.
  Take the road to Seabird Island and then the gravel road N to Waleach Station and turn on road to the river. Or continue past the station 3 miles to a construction camp, then right to the river.
- *Chilliwack* AGATE, JADE: In gravel bar by Fraser River bridge and downstream at sand bar at mouth of Ruby creek.
- *Clinton* AGATE NODULES: Take Hwy 97 N 11 miles to Gang Ranch turnoff, go NW for 55 miles to Fraser River, cross to Empire valley road, take it S for 20 miles to Bryson ranch and collect thundereggs and jasper 14 miles S at Freeze property (fee).

  AMETHYST: Continue 13½ miles S, then E through farm yard 4½ miles to Scottie Creek, follow along bank and dig in bluff on right bank.
- *Hope* JADE, AGATE, RHODONITE: Take road SW to Flood, then road to airport and on to Fraser River to search in several bars offshore. The same gem materials are found in the Coquihalla River E of Hope.

  RHYOLITE (WONDERSTONE): E 10 miles in slide debris.
- *Kamloops* AGATE: Take Hwy 97-1 E to Barnhart Vale road, then it to Robbin Range road; follow the latter a mile, then E on ranch road to collect seam agate in hills to N.
  Go back to Barnhart Vale road, take it 3 miles farther beyond Buse Lake, follow road S and path W around lake to collect blue agate in hills S of lake.

  AGATE: Take Hwy 97 SE 30 miles to Monte Lake, collect nodules and seam agate close to highway along lake.

  JASPER, AGATE: Take Hwy 1 W to Tunkwa Lake road S, follow it to Indian Garden ranch road and take it W for 5 miles; park, follow pipeline to third slope to collect.

- *Keremeos* RHODONITE, JASPER: In slide material along highway on W edge of village.
- *Lillooet* JADE, AGATE, ETC.: In rock piles on Lillooet side of bridge over Fraser River and in bar downstream. Also take road toward Seton River and hunt in Fraser River bar, as well as upstream in Bridge River and at its mouth. Upstream where the Yalakom River flows into the Bridge River is an excellent collecting spot for serpentine.

- *Lytton* * JADE, AGATE, ETC.: Cross Fraser River on ferry, go toward Stein River 1½ miles, turn right past corrals to road, take it ¼ mile and hike to Spences ranch bars. Then continue on Stein River road and down to Fraser River for more bars.

  AGATE: E on Hwy 1 to the Nicoamen river bridge, go 1 more mile, take dirt road right for 5 miles where there is a row of bluffs. Park and search below bluffs and in outcrops. Prase is reported here, too.
- *Paldi* RHODONITE: In old mine near Duncan on top of mountain.
- *Penticton* AMETHYST, GEODES: W 8 miles on Green Mountain Road.
- *Prince George* JASPER, AGATE: In gravels of delta of Nechako River within city limits, and 8 miles W at Miworth gravel pit on S side of river, and 7 miles W on N side of river.
- *Princeton* LIMB CASTS, AGATE: N across on Hwy 5, then Coalmont road left 2 miles, park and follow trail on N side of river 1¼ miles just past turn, collect in Vermilion Bluffs for limb casts and ½ to a mile farther N for agate on sides of bluffs.

  AGATE: Take Copper Mountain road S, turn left on dirt road on top of Wolfe Creek hill, cross Willis Creek and take logging road along the creek to sign "Jeep Road to Agate Mountain." Go 4 miles to top and collect agate and petrified wood in rock slides and bluffs on N side of mountain.
- *Quesnel* AGATE: In Fraser River to S opposite Macalister, as well as on E side.
- *Rosedale* AGATE, JADE, ETC.: Take Hope road 6 miles to Peters road and follow it to the Fraser River to collect on bars. A mile beyond this spot is another large bar. Yellow serpentine and rhodonite are also found here.
- *Shaw Springs* AGATE: N on Hwy 1, for a mile, take dirt road E for 5 miles to collect in small cliffs of mountain. On return go 2½ miles, take dirt road N to Soap Lake for agate on hill to left. Return to Shaw Springs, go a mile S to a culvert, walk E ⅓ mile along creek to collect agate in basalt cliffs.
- *Sidney* RHODONITE: Take ferry to Salt Spring Island and collect at Hallings farm near Fulford harbor.
- *Squilax* AMETHYST, AGATE: S to fork in road, take left fork to logging road and park after 1¾ miles. Look for agate and amethyst here. Walk 2 miles NE to collect in road cuts. Return to fork, go S to Turtle Valley road, at second junction take trail E and follow creek to top.
- *Takla Landing* JADE: E 16 miles in Vital Creek in Omenica mining district.
- *Trail* PREHNITE: In Le Roi mine 7 miles W at Rossland.
- *Vancouver* AGATE: On beach to W with jasper at Tsawwassen, where ferry docks.
- *Vancouver Island* BRECCIA: A rock known locally as dallasite is found at Qualicum Beach and at Horne Lake. Take road 8 miles N from Qualicum Beach to a store, then gravel road 4 miles to collect on surface and in creek.
- *Vanderhoof* JASPER, PETRIFIED WOOD: In dry bed of Nechako river 60 miles S and just N of Kenney dam.
- *Victoria* PORPHYRY: Pebbles known as chrysanthemum rock on beaches of southern Vancouver Island, specifically on beach at foot of Dallas road.

  JASPER: N 8 miles at Mill Bay.
- *Watson Lake* JADE: Take Alcan Highway to Milepost 644, then S to Cassiar for jade in asbestos mine dumps, then W to Dease Lake to hunt within 50-mile radius.
- *Westwold* AGATE: S on Douglas Lake road 7 miles to collect W of road. Go 8 miles farther and collect in long row of cliffs W of road.

Manitoba

Northeastern Manitoba is covered by rocks of the great shield that forms much of central Canada, but below Lake Winnipeg these dip below the limestones, which form a more fertile region. The southwest corner of the province is a plateau of younger sedimentary rocks.

- *Cedar Lake* AMBER: On beach on SW edge near mouth of Saskatchewan River.
- *Lac du Bonnet* BERYL, APATITE: At Bernic Lake mine. Take Hwy 11 to junction with Bird Lake road. Take it 25½ miles, then S to mine on N

shore of lake and another on E end of lake. S of Bernic Lake 1¾ miles is Shatford Lake, with beryl and topaz in pegmatite on N side.

- *Lamprey Falls* BERYL: Go 4¾ miles by boat along the Winnipeg river, then S 1¼ miles to Lake and Grace claims and at Silver Leaf property. About ⅓ mile E of Silver Lead property is the Huron claim with zoisite and black quartz as well as beryl, and ¼ mile NE are the Annie Claims. E of Lamprey Falls 6¼ miles a trail leads ¼ mile S of the Winnipeg River to Green Lake and beryl at its SE end at the Grace claims.
- *Souris* AGATE, PETRIFIED WOOD: In Janz brothers gravel pits along the Souris River. Look for Montana type agate and jasper in the oversize dumps (fee).

New Brunswick

Most of the province is a lowland of sedimentary rocks, but granite rocks are exposed in the western areas and the more rugged southern coast.

- *Cross Creek, York County* TOPAZ, BERYL: At Burnt Hill Tungsten mine. Take Hwy 25 for 3 miles, then W 5 miles on gravel road to Maple Grove Station. Register at the Miramichi Lumber company office, go 15½ miles on gravel road to a Department of Fisheries camp, then right on mine road ½ mile and right again to mine.
- *Dalhousie, Restigouche County* AGATE, JASPER: On beach between Peuplien Point and Pin Sec Point. Take Hwy 11 NW to CIL plant, turn E to beach on rough road. There are agates on the beach NW as far as Campbelltown and in seams in the cliffs, and on the beaches of Chaleur Bay.

  SERPENTINE, AGATE: On Belledune Point and as far SE as Nash Creek.
- *Grand Manan Island, Charlotte County* BLOODSTONE, AGATE: At Whale Cove and up the shore toward a cliff known as Seven Days Work. The island is reached by ferry from St. John.
- *Hillsborough, Albert County* ALABASTER: In gypsum quarry.
- *St. John, St. John County* AGATE: In basalt as far west along shore as Blacks Harbor.

  QUARTZ: On E side of Musquash.
- *St. Martins, St. John County* JASPER: In conglomerate on beach.
- *Woodstock, Carleton County* MANGANESE ROCK, RHODOCHROSITE: At Plymouth Iron mine. Take Hwy 5 W for 4¾ miles, turn N on Plymouth road 1½ miles to trail opposite farmhouse to collect at mine. The two materials are also found at Moody Hill and other pits. Take Hwy 275 N 3 miles to road left, go 1 mile to pits in clearing.
- *Upsalquitch, Restigouche County* AMETHYST: Above forks of Upsalquitch River 7 miles.

Newfoundland

Newfoundland is the northernmost extension of the Appalachian Mountain system which skirts the Atlantic Ocean in the United States. The province is a low plateau of ancient rocks rounded and scraped by extensive glacial action which has filled the valleys with drift. Labrador, which is administered as a part of Newfoundland, is the eastern tip of the great shield of ancient Laurentian crystalline rocks which are the source of most of Canada's mineral wealth.

- *Lawn, Placentia West County* AMETHYST: In dumps of LaManche mine.
- *Nain, Labrador* LABRADORITE: On Tabor's Island in Grenfell quarry, 20 miles SE. Also on Black and Paul islands and at Ford's Harbor.

Northwest Territories

The northeastern part of this large region is an arctic prairie of thin soil and almost entirely devoid of trees. Most of the rest of the territories is covered with forests, except the desolate Arctic Islands of which Baffin Island is the principal example.

- *Ellsmere Island* AMBER: In coal seams along Gilman River near Lake Hazen.
- *Fox Islands, Great Slave Lake* SAPPHIRE: At Philmore Mine.

Nova Scotia

Like southeastern Quebec and New Brunswick, Nova Scotia shows the Appalachian topography which dominates the eastern landscape of the United States. It is an ancient mountain land, much folded and intruded by granite, especially south of Halifax. Erosion has created the valleys that are the routes of communication, and sinking of the land has further left its mark in the harbors and offshore islands.

- *Digby, Digby County* * JASPER: Generally at beaches in area known as Digby Neck. Some specific localities are breccia jasper on shore of Long Island near Tiverton; lace agate less than a mile from the Tiverton ferry slip along dirt road; S on Hwy 217 toward Central Grove from Tiverton and right ½ mile toward Bear Cove beach; on beach at Centreville, and red chalcedony at St. Mary Bay.

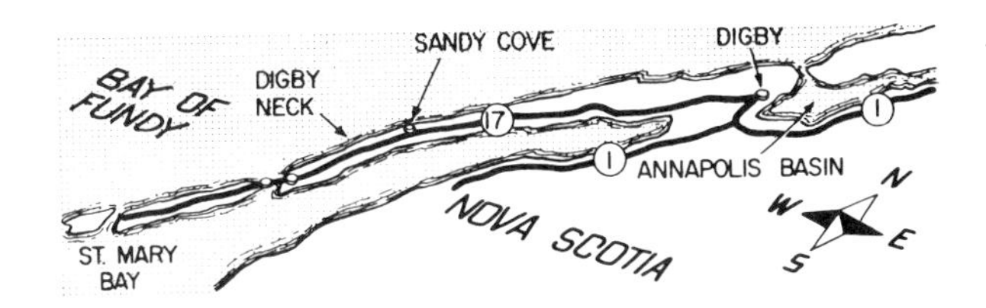

(Left) Phosgenite from Monteponi, Cagliari.
(Middle) Linarite in fibrous crystals.
(Right) Natural minium, red oxide of lead.

•*Halls Harbor, Kings County* AGATE, JASPER: Take road to Kentville, then road left to Glenmont and dirt road left for 3 miles to Ross Creek to collect on beach.

AMETHYST: Take road to Glenmont and N to Scott's Bay. Ask directions at farm to beach and Amethyst Cove. Another location is near Hall's Harbor. Turn right just before bottom of hill and take dirt road along shore, bearing right to road to beach. Collect at second rock fall. Ask directions of Everett Dunham to another location.

BLUE AGATE, AMETHYST: Take road to Lower Blomidon, collect on rocky beach. Start after peak of tide, get back before next tide.

•*Parrsboro, Cumberland County* * AGATE: Take Golf Course road 4½ miles to turnoff to right just beyond bridge. Go to cottage for permission, then take steep trail to beach, turn left and walk ¼ mile to Wasson's Bluff and farther on to collect. Return to road, go on to first right hand turn, park and walk to beach and go left past sandstone cliffs to McKay Head and beyond for agate and quartz. From here it is possible at low tide to wade to Two Islands to collect.

AMETHYST: Drive to Partridge Island, go right above marshy area to coves at beach to collect. Watch tides carefully. Return to the

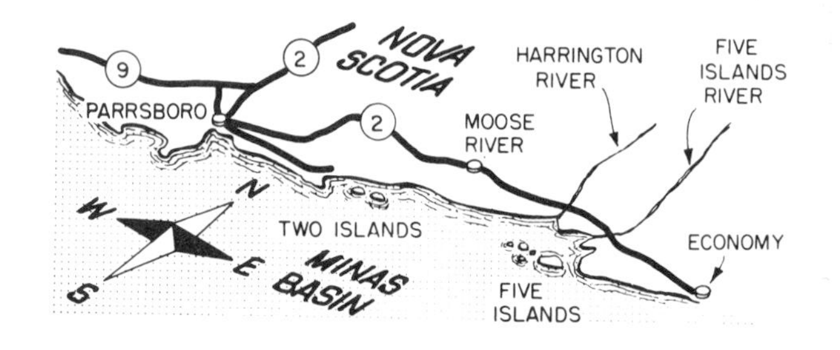

causeway, take path behind camp, turn right into woods and collect in stream.

BLUE AGATE, AMETHYST: Take Main Street W, go 7 miles to fork, take west fork to parking area and walk to West Bay beach to hunt on beach to right.

AGATE, AMETHYST: Moose Island is across the inlet from the Island View Motel at Lower Five Islands. Bruce Patterson of the motel will take collectors to the island by boat.

Ontario

Southeastern Ontario is a fertile area of glacial soils bordering the Great Lakes. To the northeast lies more rolling country set off by a great ridge known as the Niagara escarpment. North and west of Lake Superior, however, Ontario is part of the vast Laurentian shield of granite and other crystalline rocks containing gold and industrial minerals.

- *Atikokan, Rainy River County* QUARTZ: In limestone to N at Steep Rock iron mines at Steep Rock lake.
- *Bancroft, Hastings County* SODALITE: At Cancrinite Hill. E on Hwy 500 for 2⅓ miles, then right for ⅓ mile to vacant house, walk across stream to clearing and follow trail ⅓ mile to outcrop. Nearby is another outcrop at Davis Hill. At Princess quarry (fee). Take Hwy 100 2½ miles E and turn N from highway to mine store. At the Golding-Keene quarry, which is on the W bank of the York River just N of Hwy 500, and at the Morrison quarry on the E bank and 1½ miles N of the highway.

  AMETHYST: In dumps along the York river to the N.

  PERISTERITE: At the Faraday mine. Take Hwy 28 SW for 4½ miles, then ½ mile N.

  MARBLE: At the Stewart quarry. Take Hwy 62 S for 2¾ miles, then E a mile.
- *Batchawana, Thunder Bay County* EPIDOTE: Pebbles at mouth of the Montreal River and the Agawa River on the Lake Superior shore.
- *Bird Creek, Hastings County* DIOPSIDE: Drive W ¼ mile to first road N, cross creek, go to end and hike along E side of McFalls Lake to N end to collect on side of cliff.
- *Bruce Mines, Algoma County* CONGLOMERATE: E 2½ miles of the intersection of Hwys 17 and 561, and also W and N of Bruce Mines. The conglomerate contains jasper pebbles.
- *Craigmont, Renfrew County* CORUNDUM: In quarries on Craigmont Mountain, 7 miles S of Combermere and just E of Hwy 517.
- *Dryden, Kenora County* SOAPSTONE: On hill on W side of Barritt Bay on Wabigoon Lake, just W of Wabigoon. Also on SE and NW shore of Miles Lake and on islands in Trap Lake, reached by boat.

  BERYL: In pegmatite on E shore of Medicine Lake on the property of E. Zabeski of Kenora. Reached by taking Hwy 17 to Gordon Lake road for 1½ miles to cabin on property.
- *Eganville, Renfrew County* AMAZONSTONE: On A. Berger farm on road to Germanicus 2 miles N of intersection of Hwys 41 and 60. Also at the Smart mine. Take Lake Clear road toward Foymount; at first dirt road past bridge turn left to end, and right 2½ miles to mine.
- *Foymount, Renfrew County* APATITE: At Turner's Island. Take Lake Clear road left for 3¼ miles to road to Goulet's cabins. Rent boat. After landing, go to left of boat landing at NW end of island. Dig in pits.
- *Gananoque, Leeds County* QUARTZ: At Marble Rock quarry. Go N on Hwy 32 to side road marked Marble Rock. Cross iron bridge, keep right to first farm gate on left, enter and go to gravel bed, park and take path to quarry.
- *Gooderham, Haliburton County* SODALITE, APATITE: Take Hwy 500 from Tory Hill for ¾ mile, then S 2½ miles to barn; dig in pits ½ mile SW of barn.
- *Griffith, Renfrew County* SCAPOLITE: At Spain mine. Take Hwy 41 for 6 miles NE. Mine is on S side of highway.
- *Hybla, Hastings County* AMAZONITE: In pit in pegmatite on R. McCormack farm E of the railroad and a mile S of Hybla. Also at the Woodcox farm 2¼ miles E and S of the road to Monteagle Valley.
- *Kaladar, Lennox and Addington Counties* DIOPSIDE, KYANITE, STAUROLITE: On S side of road W from Hwy 41 just S of railroad crossing S of Kaladar. Also take Hwy 41 N for 11 miles, then right on Hwy 506 for 12 miles and left on access road E of Fernleigh. Go ¼ mile to rocky slope on left to collect.
- *Ludgate, Parry Sound County* SUNSTONE: In gneiss on N shore of Lake Huron 20 miles E of the French River.
- *Lyndhurst, Leeds County* QUARTZ: At Black Rapids (Steele) mine. Take road to Lansdowne 5½ miles to bridge, cross and take road to La Rosa bay on E side of the bridge at Black Rapids for 1½ miles to Steele house, where J. A. Steele will sell specimens but no longer allows collecting. There are other pits S and E of Black Rapids.
- *Madoc, Hastings County* MARBLE: Go S on Durham Street ½ mile, right on Seymour Street for 1⅓ miles and keep right to Jones quarry for black marble. There are six other Jones quarries in the area.
- *Marathon, Thunder Bay County* LAURVIKITE (SYENITE): A rock that has a schiller like labradorite. Found in road cuts along Hwy 17 from a mile W to the bridge over the Little Pic River, and in road cuts from 2 to 4 miles W of the Marathon turnoff and to E of the turnoff.
- *Matachewan, Timiskaming County* PORPHYRY: Found 19 miles W and just N of Rahn Lake.
- *Michipicoten Island, Thunder Bay County* AGATE, AMETHYST: Reached by plane or boat from Wawa. Land at Quebec harbor. Agates are found on extreme SW end but the best collecting is on the islets offshore, for which a boat is needed. Agate Islet in Quebec Harbor, the W end of Schafer Bay and along Channel Lake are favored spots.
- *Nipigon, Thunder Bay County* AGATE: On beaches of West Bay on Lake Nipigon, just W of Kelvin Island.

  AMETHYST: E 9 miles where Hwy 17 crosses the Jackfish River and on E bank of river 1½ miles above Canadian Pacific bridge. Best reached by boat.
- *Nolalu, Thunder Bay County* * JASPER: Material that often is bloodstone is found on Arrow Lake 28 miles W, in Whitefish River 1¾ miles

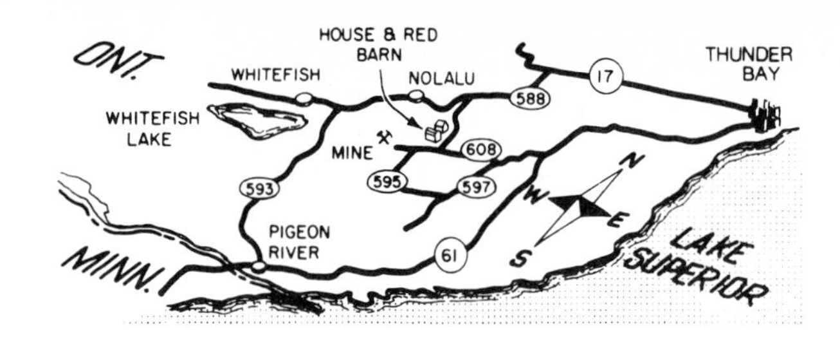

W and 2 miles E, and in Peerless Creek at the Hwy 588 bridge.

AMETHYST: Take road E to Aleck Teukula house, get permission to collect at mine.

- *Ouimet, Thunder Bay County* AMETHYST: Go 6 miles S on Hwy 17 and left on Hwy 69-13 to railroad tracks and walk 1/5 mile along tracks to mine dump.
- *Perth, Lanark County* PERTHITE: To S in pegmatites between Otty and Adam Lake. Also take Hwy 7 W for ½ mile to Lanark road, turn right to Balderson and then left to crossroad and drive 1½ miles to Bell Corners, turn right 1 mile and then left ⅔ mile to school, where right turn for ¼ mile will reach mine. Other mines are nearby.
- *Quadeville, Renfrew County* BERYL, ROSE QUARTZ: At Canadian Beryllium and Alloys mine, 2 miles W on Hwy 515 and then N 1¼ miles (fee).
- *Rossport, Thunder Bay County* AGATE, PREHNITE, PUMPELLYITE: Along S shore of Copper Island, at E end of S shore of Wilson island and at Greenstone Beach, at Salter Island just W of Old Man's Pocket Harbor, at Harry Island in cove on W end, along S shore of Simpson Island and W of McKay Cove, and on Bowman and Agate islands and at Agate Point on E shore of Black Bay Peninsula.
  Agates are also found in basic lavas on the islands E of Sibley Peninsula and S of Rossport.

  AMETHYST: In road cuts on Hwy 17 1½ miles W of turnoff and also just W of Billy Lake 9 miles E on N side of the highway. Also 8 miles W in road cuts at Rossport Provincial park.
- *Sault Ste. Marie, Algoma County* CONGLOMERATE: In boulders on Lake Superior shore N of Goulais Bay, in the St. Mary's river 4 miles W of Campment d'Ours, and at quarry near E end of Echo Lake.
- *Spragge, Algoma County* STAUROLITE: E 4½ miles on Hwy 17 and S of highway.
- *Stanley, Thunder Bay County* AMETHYST, ROSE QUARTZ: Take Silver Mountain road SW to Victoria mine N of road. Nearby are the Beaver Jr., West Beaver, Climax, and Badger mines, all S of the road.
- *Superior Junction, Kenora County* JASPER (JASPALITE): With magnetite on S side of Minnitaki Lake, 12 miles S.
- *Sydenham, Frontenac County* APATITE, DATOLITE: At Lacey mine 7 miles NE on E side of Eel Bay in Sydenham Lake.
- *Terrace Bay, Thunder Bay County* JASPER: Pebbles on W shore of the largest, Slate Island, which is 8 miles S.
- *Thunder Bay, Thunder Bay County* * AMETHYST: There are many locations for digging amethyst in the area once known as Port Arthur and Fort William and now as Thunder Bay. The most publicized location is a fee mine reached by taking Hwy 17 N, then right at the first intersection for 8 miles, and right 2 miles following signs to the Thunder Bay mine near Loon Lake.
  Other locations include amethyst at the mouth of the McKenzie river 10 miles NE of Thunder Bay, in the Current River, and on the outskirts of Thunder Bay between Boulevard Lake and Trowbridge Falls Park.
  Another is 13 miles N on Hwy 17 to Silver Harbor road, cross railroad tracks, then drive left and walk along tracks ½ mile to pits E of tracks.
  At Jarvis River, take Hwy 61 S 3¼ miles to Jarvis Bay road, go 5½ miles to Jarvis Bay resort, and follow shore to headland of Prince Bay and mine on hill.
  There are prospect hole and mine dumps 4 miles NE of Little Gull Lake, on the N side of Sunset Lake, ½ mile S of the E end of Whitefish Lake, 1½ miles SE of Silver Mountain railroad station, and E of Ancliff. Some of these locations also yield agates, and oolitic jasper is found in taconite in the bed of the McIntyre River.
- *Vermilion Bay, Kenora County* GARNET: On shore of Garnet Bay at N end of Eagle Lake, reached by boat. Soapstone deposit on W shore of the lake.
- *Verona, Frontenac County* PERISTERITE, QUARTZ: N on Hwy 38 1 mile and then right on Desert Lake road for 4⅔ miles, go left at church to Richardson Feldspar quarry. Also nearby on Abrams farm.
- *Wawa, Algoma County* EPIDOTE, QUARTZ: As pebbles on beaches of Coldwater River at park 40 miles S. Also in the Agawa River.
- *Wilberforce, Haliburton County* APATITE: At Cardiff Uranium mines 1¾ miles S on Hwy 500 to gravel road E for 1 mile. Also in calcite in dumps on ridge ¾ mile SW, and at Fission and Liscombe mines.
  PERISTERITE: E 4 miles at Richardson mine.

Quebec

Most of Quebec lies within the Canadian or Laurentian shield, a vast area of ancient granites and gneisses, covered with thin glacial deposits and dotted with typical glacial lakes. A part of this region near Lake

Abitibi, near the Ontario border, is rich in minerals. Most of the population of the province lives in the sedimentary St. Lawrence River basin which was the bed of the former Champlain Sea. Eastern Quebec is Appalachian, like much of eastern Canada, formed of sedimentary rocks broken by granite hills.

- *Asbestos, Richmond County* GARNET: At Jeffrey mine of Johns Manville company. Also at same company's Union mine near Thetford. Also collect serpentine and vesuvianite in dumps.
- *Black Lake, Megantic County* SERPENTINE: In Megantic mine.
- *Coleraine, Megantic County* SERPENTINE: Gem quality serpentine at Continental mine. Take road W toward Vimy Ridge 1½ miles to sign to Demerco mines, turn right to mine. Also at nearby Windsor mine. Take Rue Martel E to Av. St. Joseph, then left ⅓ mile and left on gravel road 1 mile to road junction, then left ⅓ mile to junction and right a mile to the mine.
  Also at Montreal Chrome pit. Take Hwy 1 for 2¼ miles N, then E on Petit Lac St. François road for 3¾ miles. Take right fork ½ mile, then left at gravel pit 1½ miles to mine.
- *East Broughton, Beauce County* SERPENTINE: At Quebec Asbestos Corp. pits. Take road NW from Hwy 1 for 1½ miles. Also at Fraser mine near Broughton Station.
- *Chandler, Gaspé East County* CRINOIDAL LIMESTONE: In road cuts SW to Port Daniel and in bay shore rocks, in quarry and beach pebbles.
- *Gaspé East County* JASPER, AGATE: In beach pebbles here and to N and W, and especially to S at Pointe St. Pierre, Belle Anse, and Cap-d'Espoir.
- *Hull, Hull County* SCAPOLITE, APATITE: At Headley mine. Take mine road $4\frac{4}{5}$ miles, then trail ¾ mile to flooded pit.
- *Kilmar, Argenteuil County* SERPENTINE, MARBLE: At Canadian Refractories mine.
- *Kipawa, Temiscamingue County* AMAZONSTONE: E of Kipawa on S side of island in N end of Lac Sairs. It is accessible by plane or canoe. Get permission from Tasso Komossa in Toronto.
- *Labelle Station, Labelle County* GARNET: In quarry 2 miles S on Canadian Pacific Railroad right-of-way.
- *Laurel, Argenteuil County* DIOPSIDE, VESUVIANITE: W 2 miles on S side of road to Lost River.
- *Maniwaki, Gatineau County* QUARTZ: On Britt farm. Take Hwy 11E to E side of Gatineau River, turn N for 4½ miles, take right fork and go ½ mile to farmhouse.
- *Matane, Matane County* EPIDOTE: Pebbles with flint on St. Lawrence beaches.
- *Mont St. Hilaire, Rouville County* SODALITE: In Desourdy quarry with albite on NE slope of mountain.

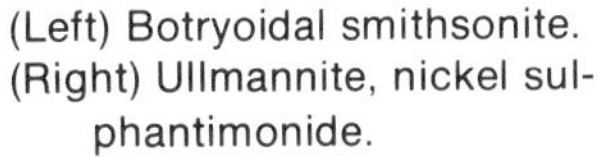
(Left) Botryoidal smithsonite.
(Right) Ullmannite, nickel sulphantimonide.

• *Notre Dame de la Salette, Papineau County* STAR QUARTZ: N on Hwy 35 to sharp bend in road just beyond Mine de Mica, hike NW to hill to collect in Villeneuve mine.

• *Ottawa, Federal District* APATITE: At Forsyth mine 10 miles N, also at Laurentide mine, and the Scott mine N of the latter, and the McConnel mine a mile N of the Scott mine.

• *Otter Lake Village, Pontiac County* CORDIERITE, APATITE: W on the A. Richards farm. See Richards in the village. Also apatite and diopside at Yates Uranium mine 9 miles N, then W for 2½ miles.

• *Phillipsburg, Missisquoi County* MARBLE: At Phillipsburg marble quarries. Take St. Armand road E, turn left at church and drive ⅔ mile to quarries. Also at Missisquoi-Lautz quarries ¾ mile N. There are other quarries at South Stukey.

• *Pointe au Chene, Argenteuil County* SCAPOLITE, DIOPSIDE: At McGill farm N 3 miles.

• *Ste. Anne des Monts, Gaspé West County* PORPHYRY: Red material 40 miles S on Hwy 299 in Berry Mountain Brook.

• *St. Denis de-Brompton, Shefford County* SERPENTINE: At Webster Lake mines. Go S to trail around N end of Lac Montjoie (Webster). The pits and dumps are on the NW side.

• *St. Ludger de Milot, Lake St. John West County* MOONSTONE: In outcrops of gneiss near No. 4 bridge 70 miles N on W side of road to Passe Dangereuse.

• *St. Pierre de Wakefield, Gatineau County* AMAZONSTONE, TOURMALINE: In Le Duc quarry.

• *Scotstown, Compton County* NORDMARKITE (AUGITE SYENITE): A dark rock with a schiller like labradorite in Scotstown Granite company quarry.

• *Sheldrake, Saguenay County* LABRADORITE: On N shore of St. Lawrence River. Also to NE around La Garnier and N to Lac Rougemont.

• *Sherbrooke, Sherbrooke County* JASPER-MAGNETITE: In pits behind lighted cross on De La Breiere street.

• *Wakefield, Gatineau County* TOURMALINE: At Le Duc mine on ridge 2½ miles W.

SERPENTINE: SE 2 miles at Canadian Aluminium Company quarry.

Mexico

Most of Mexico is a high plateau, underlain by folded sedimentary rocks and extensively altered by thick layers of volcanic rocks. Mountains linked with American ranges border both coasts. Baja California, for instance, is a continuation of the California Coast range. Between the mountains and the sea on both coasts are narrow lowlands. Southeastern Mexico belongs to the mountainous Central American plateau. Yucatán is a low limestone plain. In many respects Mexico resembles the Great Basin area of the United States.

Baja California

• *El Marmol* ONYX: In quarry 5 miles away at Volcan Springs.

• *El Rosario* TURQUOISE: E 2 miles at El Aquajito.

• *Ensenada* PREHNITE: S 50 miles at Punta China.

• *Puertocitos* ONYX: Go to Oakie's Landing 29 miles away, then 4 miles to mine W of Route 5.

• *Rancho Viejo* TOURMALINE: In pegmatite 2 miles S at Socorro mine.

SPHENE, TOURMALINATED QUARTZ, EPIDOTE: At Pino Solo near Rancho Viejo in pegmatite pits 100 yards N of landmark tree and 300 yards W.

ALABASTER: Take Hwy 1 SE to San Agustin, then 10 miles E to quarry for alabaster (onyx).

TURQUOISE: S 23 miles in dumps of La Turquesa mine.

• *Tecate* PETRIFIED WOOD: On S side of red hill just S of Pinto Wash near U.S. border.

RHYOLITE: In Cerro Pinto Ridge in Pinto Basin, E of Tecate.

TOPAZ, QUARTZ: In pegmatites 25 miles E on Route 2.

AXINITE: Take Route 2 to El Condor, then S 40 miles, staying right at forks to El Topo road, then stay left to La Olivia mine.

Chiapas

• *San Cristobal las Casas* AMBER: Around Simojovel.

Chihuahua

AGATE: On privately owned ranches crossed by the highway from Juárez to Chihuahua City. These begin S of Villa Ahumada, especially at Gallego, Oja Laguna, and Moctezuma. Other areas are SW of Parral, NE of Alameda, W of Camargo, SW of Zaragoza, W of Rosario, and SE of Reforma. Collecting is rarely permitted.

• *Naica* MOSS AGATE: In nearby diggings.

• *Santa Eulalia* QUARTZ: At San Antonio mine, 4 miles away.

Durango

• *Durango* AGATE, JASPER: In creek beds to N along Hwy 45, especially near Rodeo.

AGATE NODULES: Take Mazatlán Highway 17 miles to first bridge, then 1¾ miles more, collect in road cut to right.

Guanajuato

Miners at the Valenciana mine will sell quartz crystals and amethyst. Cherry opal and fire opal are found nearby in rhyolite.

• *Apaseo* OBSIDIAN: A green variety to N.

Guerrero

- *Real del Monte* CAT'S-EYE OBSIDIAN: At Aztec obsidian mine.

Hidalgo

- *Hidalgo* FIRE OPAL: In rhyolite, at Barranca de Tepezala in Atotonilco district.
- *Huichapan District* PETRIFIED WOOD: At Salitera mine.

  GARNET: Near Laguna Haso Cherhuahan and Zimapan-Canhardo.
- *Pachuca* OBSIDIAN: S 30 miles at Huasca. Also at Cerro de la Navajas, 10 miles S. Also 3 miles N of San Miguel Regla in cornfields at N end of lake.

  RHODONITE: On dumps of Real del Monte mine, 6 miles S.
- *Rosarito* AGATE: On beach one mile N of hotel.

Jalisco

- *Guadalajara* OBSIDIAN: Take Tepic-Mazatlán Highway 16 miles, collect before reaching Tequila.
- *Tequila* OPAL: Go on Route 15 to La Magdalena area, then 4 miles W and 3 miles N to San Simeon mine near village of the same name. Also at the Cinco mine near Hosta.

Morelos

GARNET: Pink grossularite at Rancho San Juan, near Xalostoc, Sierra Tlayacac.

Nueva Leon

- *Guerrero* AGATE, JASPER: The road from the U.S. border customs office winds through the hills. Collect along the road and also on the road to the Uribe ranch.

Puebla

- *Tecali* ONYX: Turn off Route 150 at Tepeaca to La Pedrara quarry in mountains to S.

Queretaro

- *San Juan del Rio* OPAL: Several mines are near Trinidad, reached from San Juan del Rio by taking Morelos Oriente avenue NE, then at 7½ miles crossing bridge, and going ½ mile farther left to Trinidad. Two miles W is La Carbonera mine, and nearby are La Guadalupana and Bernal mines. The Simpatica mine is at Esperanza. 30 miles NW and nearby is the Rosario mine. For entry to the La Guadalupana mine, see Senor Cabrera at La Guadalupana lapidary shop, 16th of Sept. st, in San Juan del Rio.

  CHALCEDONY: At Granadas.

  OBSIDIAN: Along highway from Queretero to San Juan del Rio.

San Luis Potosí

- *San Luis Potosí* FIRE AGATE: S 45 miles on Route 57 at Tula Hill. Take Route 57 to kilopost 359, and turn off road to the hill on E side of highway as far as kilopost 361.

  AGATE NODULES: Take Hwy 80 SW 12 miles to dam, then backtrack ½ mile and collect on N side of road.

  TOPAZ: S 30 miles at Tepetate.

Sinaloa

- *Culiacan* AMETHYST: In nearby diggings.

Sonora

- *Magdalena* OPAL: At La Unica, San Simeon, and La Estancia mines. Opal is also mined at Tequila, Etzatlán, San Marco, and Hostotipaquillo.
- *Cananea* SPHALERITE: Transparent crystals at the Manzanal and Chivera mines.

Vera Cruz

GARNET: At Las Vagas and Escobar.

Zacatecas

- *Concepcion del Oro* CHRYSOCOLLA, TURQUOISE: On dumps of San Elijio mine N of Salaverna, and Socovan mine between Salaverna and Bonanza.
- *Zacatecas* AMETHYST: N 6 miles in dumps of El Bote mine gem material is found.

  Note: Visitors to Mexico should get a permit at any Mexican consulate and should have a birth certificate, car title if driving, and evidence of smallpox vaccination. Tetanus shots are also advisable, as well as halazone tablets to purify water. Car insurance should be obtained in Mexico for the duration of the visit. It is wise to keep the gas tank full, to carry small-denomination traveler's checks, and make payments in Mexican money. A permit to collect should be obtained at the site and should be shown when leaving Mexico. Collecting of ancient carvings and artifacts is forbidden and even possession of them is illegal. In Mexico the people should be treated with every courtesy, and ability to speak some Spanish and to show a friendly attitude is very helpful. Use of guides whenever possible is invaluable in making contacts and avoiding trouble. Cigarettes and candy (for children) are much appreciated small gifts.

Bibliography

BOOKS

Arem, Joel. *Rocks and Minerals.* Bantam Books, New York, 1973.
Attractive paperback with excellent illustrations by Lee Boltin, and a readable text by a former Smithsonian staff member.

Dana, Edward S. and W. E. Ford. *A Textbook of Mineralogy,* 4th ed. John Wiley and Sons, New York, 1932.
Although it lacks information about many newly described minerals, this is still the most commonly used reference work of its kind in English.

Fay, Gordon S. *The Rockhound's Manual.* Barnes and Noble, New York, 1972.
Hardback and paperback editions of a readable general book for amateurs, strong in guidance to governmental organizations.

Fenton, C. L. and M. A. *The Rock Book.* Doubleday, New York, 1940.
Handsomely illustrated and readable except that its locality and descriptive material is badly out of date.

MacFall, Russell P. *Collecting Rocks, Minerals, Gems and Fossils.* Hawthorn Books, New York, 1963.
A general book suitable for the beginner because of its how-to-do-it instruction, its identification information, and its illustrations.

——— *Gem Hunter's Guide,* 5th ed. Thomas Y. Crowell, New York, 1975.
The most widely used guide to American and North American gem locations, completely rewritten and revised for the fifth edition.

Putnam, William C. *Geology,* 2nd ed. Oxford, New York, 1971.
Exceptionally well organized and up-to-date textbook, revised by Ann B. Bassett.

Pough, Frederick H. *A Field Guide to Rocks and Minerals,* 3rd ed. Houghton Mifflin, Boston, Mass., 1960.
Useful for identification of minerals and locations for American specimens. The color illustrations vary in quality.

Roberts, Willard L., George R. Rapp, Jr., and Julius Weber. *Encyclopedia of Minerals.* Van Nostrand-Reinhold, New York, 1974.
Comprehensive treatment in tabular form of all known minerals by an authority with excellent photographs. Brings all other authorities up to date.

Sinkankas, John. *Prospecting for Gem Stones and Minerals.* Van Nostrand-Reinhold, New York, 1969.
A how-to-do-it book, well written, and well illustrated, by an advanced amateur.

Strunz, H. *Mineralogische Tabellen.* Geest & Portig, Leipzig, Academische Verlag, 1970.
Frequently revised standard reference book in German designed for the professional or advanced amateur. The latest revision is in 1970. Despite the language difference it is readily useable by a person unacquainted with German.

MAGAZINES

Earth Science, P. O. Box 1815, Colorado Springs, Colorado 80901.
Bimonthly strong on educational material, edited by Professor Raymond Pearl.

Gems and Gemology, Gemological Institute of America, 11940 San Vicente Boulevard, Los Angeles, California 90049.
Quarterly published by an organization that offers courses in gemology and a research service.

Gems and Minerals, Box 687, Mentone, California 92359.
Popular hobby magazine emphasizing lapidary work and prospecting.

Lapidary Journal, P. O. Box 80937, San Diego, California 92138.
Monthly for jewelers and amateurs. Its April issue is a comprehensive listing of dealers, mineral clubs, etc. Good color illustrations.

Mineral Digest, 155 E. 34 Street, New York, New York 10016.
Notable for its magnificent color illustrations and the irregularity of its publication, presumably quarterly.

Mineralogical Record, P. O. Box 783, Bowie, Maryland 20715.
Excellent bimonthly with articles keyed to the advanced amateur collector.

Photo Credits

City Museum of Natural History, Milan: 22 (2–5), 25 (bottom right), 35 (1–3), 42 (all), 45 (all), 53 (bottom), 79 (top), 133 (right), 136 (middle), 137, 143 (left and right), 145 (right), 148 (right), 149 (left), 153 (left and middle), 154, 157 (all), 163 (all), 166 (all), 168 (all), 169 (all), 171 (all), 175 (left and middle), 179 (all), 198 (left and right), 205 (left and right), 209, 211 (right), 212 (left and right), 224 (left), 227 (left)
Collection of Dr. Ratto, Milan: 19, 23, 61 (2), 64, 69 (all), 92 (6), 107 (1–2), 108, 110, 111
Collection of Professor Bressoni; S. Pellegrino, Bergamo: 92 (9), 149 (middle)
Collection of Professor Gramaccioli, Milan: 92 (5), 107 (4), 149 (right), 205 (bottom)
Enrico Robba: 22 (1)
Galileo Offices of Mariani, Milan: 120
Kennecott Copper Corporation, documentation Cisar, 15
"La Miniera" of Pio Mariani, Desio Milan: 20, 21, 24, 25 (top and bottom left), 39 (bottom right), 41 (bottom right), 46, 49 (right), 68, 75 (bottom), 79 (2), 85 (all), 86 (top), 87 (all), 92 (1–3), 93, 98, 100, 101, 102 (all), 133 (left and middle), 141 (right), 143 (middle), 145 (left and middle), 148 (left), 153 (right), 159 (middle and right), 175 (right), 183 (right), 195 (right), 196 (middle and right), 198 (middle), 211 (middle), 212 (middle), 213 (all), 217 (middle and right), 221 (all), 224 (right)
Museum of Natural History G. Doria, Genoa: 183 (left)
Museum of Natural Sciences, Genoa: 217 (left), 224 (middle), 227 (right)
Private collection; Milan: 72, 73
Professor Moro, Rapallo: 33 (all), 41 (top), 43, 44, 60, 61 (4), 80 (2)
The "sassi" of Alfredo Ferri, Milan: 26 (top), 36, 38 (top and bottom), 39 (bottom left), 57, 92 (4, 7, 8), 94, 107 (3), 136 (left and right), 159 (left), 195 (left and middle), 196 (left), 211 (left)
Selo, Milan: 105
Servizi Editoriali Fotografici: 11

Index

3 1221 01509 7665